CAROLUS WALLIÆ
PRINCEPS &c. &c. &c.

1745   1746
Eriskay to   Derby –
Derby –   Culloden
Red Route   Yellow Route

MALCOLM MSON

Irish Sea

DUMFRIES ⟡

CARLISLE
DEC. 1745

NOV. 20 1745
Penrith
CLIFTON
Kendal
LANCASTER
DEC. 1745

PRESTON
NOV. 1745
Wigan
NOV. 28 1745
NOV. 29 1745

Congleton
MANCHESTER

DEC. 4 1745
DERBY

SUTHERLAND
EDUCATION COMMITTEE.

HELMSDALE
HIGHER GRADE PUBLIC SCHOOL.

1ST. (Eq.)

◁◁ PRIZE ▷▷

PRESENTED BY

Miss Matheson

TO

Bruce Gordon

FOR

Geography

Class Pr. V. Session *1946-47*

JOHN COOK, ▬▬▬▬▬ M.A.,
HEADMASTER.

Uniform with:

THE
YOUNG CHEVALIER

by

WILSON MACARTHUR

Illustrated by STEVEN SPURRIER, A.R.A.

COLLINS
LONDON AND GLASGOW

PRINTED AND MADE IN GREAT BRITAIN
BY
WM. COLLINS SONS AND CO. LTD.
LONDON AND GLASGOW

CONTENTS

ILLUSTRATIONS

CHAPTER ONE

A PRINCESS ELOPES

Princess Clementina Sobieski went early to bed.

She had bade her mother a dutiful good-night. Their eyes had been, perhaps, a little brighter than usual, their manner a little more subdued ; but if the Governor of Innsbruck or any of his guards noticed that they suspected nothing.

But the moment she was alone in her room—a spacious room, befitting a princess even in captivity—Clementina undressed and went to bed, just in case anyone should come ; but her heart sang with excitement, and there was no danger that she would fall asleep.

To-night she was going to elope. She was going to be rescued from her prison, to marry a king. She would become a queen. What if the king was in exile, with his throne still to win ? That only added to the spice of adventure. The future was bright ; and her rescue was to be as daring and romantic as the heart of any young girl could wish.

So she lay in bed, closing her eyes and pretending to compose herself to sleep ; but her thoughts were a whirl of excitement and happiness and eager anticipation of the moment that was to come, when the adventure should begin.

Lying there, she recalled the stirring events of the past few months. They had started with the arrival of the young Chevalier, Charles Wogan, at her father's court in Silesia. He came as a suitor for her hand, and he was the prince of suitors—tall, handsome, persuasive and reckless. His reputation had gone before him. Of all the Irish Jacobites in exile on the Continent none was so daredevil and gallant as Charles Wogan. He had been " out," as they put it, with the Pretender, James Stuart, in the rebellion of 1715, and had been taken prisoner at the Battle of Preston. The Hanoverians had shut him up in Newgate Gaol, to cool his heels until the processes of law should allow them to put a rope round his neck. But while they were busy getting the rope ready Wogan's wits were not idle, and when they came to fetch him he could not be found. He had broken out of gaol and was in hiding in London. When the hue and cry died down he slipped across to France to join the Pretender's service again.

So when he turned up at the court of Prince and Princess Sobieski in Silesia it was not for himself that he sought the hand of their charming daughter Clementina. His was a much more momentous errand; he came on behalf of his master, James.

His Irish blarney charmed the court, and Clementina's bright eyes lit up as much at his flattery as at the prospect he held out before her. To be Queen of England ! What a future for a Polish princess ! Her parents gave their consent, soon everything was arranged, and she and her mother set out for Italy, where the marriage was to take place.

They got as far as Innsbruck. Then the blow fell. Rumour travels far and fast—and the government in London, with " German Geordie " still feeling very insecure on his unaccustomed throne, had its spies everywhere, watching every move the Pretender made. Word reached England of the intended marriage. London protested to the Emperor. The Emperor, mindful of the

value of his alliance with England against France, ordered
the Princess Sobieski and her daughter to be detained.
So here they were, treated with every politeness yet
strictly guarded in the Governor's palace.

Day after day had dragged past with no word from the
future bridegroom ; and then had come a whisper.
Monsieur Chateaudoux, gentleman usher to Clementina's
mother, had heard something. The magic name of
Wogan had been mentioned ; and Clementina's heart
had leapt at the sound of it.

Suddenly the guards at the palace were doubled. A
new rumour had got about. James Stuart himself was
on his way to rescue his princess ! For a few days there
was great excitement, soldiers at every door and gate ;
and then the rumour died, the excitement faded away.
Fresh news leaked out. James had gone to Spain. He
had himself started the rumour of a rescue, to throw the
spies off his track.

The Governor breathed freely again, allowed himself
to relax. He reduced the guards, and the palace settled
down to its ordinary humdrum existence, with the two
princesses still captive but no longer watched day and
night. They too could relax.

And then Monsieur Chateaudoux sprang his surprise.
Wogan was in Innsbruck. The rescue was planned.
To-night, the 2nd of May in the year 1719, it was to be
carried out.

Clementina tried to contain her excitement a little
longer. There was always the risk someone might come
into the room—some servant who would rush off at
once to betray her. But the Governor had already made
his usual evening round of inspection, and presently
Clementina rose. She could bear the suspense no longer.
She must be up and doing.

She packed her baggage, and having something to do
helped to calm her a little. She packed her jewel-case,
then she sat down to write a letter.

§

Rain drummed on the window panes.

Outside the night was black and hideous, the little town dark and silent. There had been heavy snow early in the day ; later it had turned to sleet and rain, and the gutters that ran down the middle of the narrow cobbled streets were filthy torrents of water. Not a night for a dog to be out of doors ! But so much the better, Clementina thought, for their desperate adventure.

She shivered a little, with cold as well as excitement. But she did not shrink. She had only one fear—what might happen to her mother. So the letter had to be written, and written carefully. The quill scratched busily over the thick paper, tracing the lines on which her mother's very life might depend. A short letter, of course—the shorter the better ; but it must contain everything. A humble apology for eloping like this, for upsetting her mother so ; and the wording quite clear, making it seem that her mother had known nothing about it. Then, when her flight was discovered and an angry Governor confronted her mother, the letter could be produced. Faced with that evidence of the elder lady's innocence, he could not harm her.

Clementina added her signature with a characteristic flourish, and sealed the letter and placed it where it would be found at once. Then, with all her preparations made, she sat down to wait.

She did not have to wait long. A soft discreet knock, and Clementina, rising swiftly, stood facing the door, her hand on her heart.

" Come in," she whispered, and the door opened gently. Chateaudoux peered round it, his eyes glowing with excitement. He tiptoed into the room, surveying Clementina and her luggage with satisfaction. At his heels came a startling figure—a tall bedraggled girl whose stormy eyes and scowling face made Clementina's heart sink.

" This is Jenny," Chateaudoux explained. " She will change places with you."

He bowed and withdrew.

The two girls looked at each other for a long moment —Clementina lovely, beautifully dressed, sparkling with excitement yet stricken with dismay at the expression on the strange girl's face ; Jenny soaked, plastered with mud, and in a raging temper.

Jenny was half French, half Irish. From her Irish father she had learned to think for herself, and from the French *vivandiere* who had been her mother she had learned to say what she thought—in forceful language. She left nobody in doubt about what she thought of this escapade. She had been promised fine clothes, plenty of money and a dash of adventure thrown in if only she would come to Innsbruck and play the part they wanted her for ; and instead of being flattered and made a fuss of and treated like a real heroine she had been forced into these drab travelling clothes and made to trudge to the palace through the dark, rain-swept streets in the middle of the night. No wonder Jenny was annoyed !

In a surly silence she began stripping off the hateful clothes. In equal silence Clementina too undressed. But her pent-up emotions were too much for her. At this moment, when all her spirit was keyed up for the great adventure, the sight of that scowling unfriendly Irish face was more than she could bear. Tears started to her eyes and she began to cry, quietly but uncontrollably.

Jenny was abashed. After all, she was a serving maid, used to waiting on fine ladies, and the sight of a pretty young princess in tears was enough. She rushed over to Clementina and whispered consoling words.

" Sure and if my lady only knew all the fine gentlemen who are dying for a sight of her pretty face it is not crying she would be at this minute ! "

Clementina bit back her sobs, dried her eyes, and began changing clothes in a sudden fever of impatience. After all, it was only over-wrought nerves that had made her cry. Underneath, her heart was singing with excitement and joy and triumph.

Jenny climbed into the great, luxurious bed—the bed of a real princess ! That was something to think about : The princess, in the serving girl's clothes, stood ready to go. Chateaudoux crept back into the room. A last quick glance round to see that everything was in order, then a deep breath, and they sallied out into the long, dimly-lit corridor. They crept downstairs.

The gentleman usher knew precisely what to do. He was a friendly soul who liked company—easier company than the Princess Sobieski and her daughter ; so he had often had lady friends in to visit him in the evenings. The guards were quite used to that ; it would never occur to them to stop him when he was seeing a lady off the premises.

Nobody noticed them as they left the palace and crossed the dark courtyard. They came to the gate. For a moment they hesitated. This was the critical point, and Celementina tried to breathe calmly as they listened for the sentry's challenge. It did not come. The sentry, wise man, was warming himself at the guardroom fire. Chateaudoux opened the gate. Then he raised his voice. It was not the quiet, respectful voice Clementina was used to hearing, but a loud, hearty, familiar voice, for the sentry's benefit.

" Well, my dear, here we are. A filthy night, too. Hope you enjoyed yourself. Come again some time. Good-night ! "

Clementina pulled her cloak tightly around her and stepped out into the darkness and the pouring rain. The gate clanged shut behind her. She had escaped from her prison.

§

A tall figure emerged from the shelter of a doorway

and confronted her. She stumbled towards him, her heart in her mouth, but when his hand touched her arm she knew who he was, even in the darkness, and a cry of relief escaped her lips. Charles Wogan !

They were old friends, for in Silesia Wogan had not only talked of his master James. He had talked a lot about Charles Wogan, and Clementina had listened with a girlish eagerness, that delighted in all the tales of wild adventure he had to tell.

They wasted no time in greeting. He tucked her hand under his arm and immediately led her away from the palace gate. They put their heads down against the blinding rain and set out through the empty streets of Innsbruck, stumbling on the wet uneven cobbles, picking their way over the wide filthy gutters and open drains, sheltering as best they could close to the houses.

Suddenly they fetched up short at a gutter broader than usual, far too wide to step across. A torrent of dirty water poured down it, for in those days, with no proper system of drains, it was the custom to throw all your rubbish and slops into the middle of the street— generally without bothering to see if there was anybody passing under the window at the time.

Wogan, peering down, caught sight of something white in the swirling water, which he took to be a stepping-stone.

" Put your foot here," he urged the princess, and she obeyed. Her foot went right through and she floundered in the filthy torrent. The stone was, after all, only a bundle of sodden straw. Wogan, leaping over and helping her out on to the cobbles, was overcome with shame. He stood there muttering apologies. But Clementina laughed in his face, clung to his arm again and urged him to go on. What were wet feet and mud-spattered clothes compared with the throne that awaited her ? Such a mishap was all part of the great adventure.

There was no one about. They trudged on against the storm ; and at last Wogan guided her towards an old building whose windows shone with welcoming lights—the Black Eagle Inn. This was the rescue party's rendezvous, and he led her swiftly to a private room, whose occupants jumped up at their entry.

Clementina looked with lively curiosity at the people who had come to rescue her. There were two men and one woman. She was grateful for that. When Chateaudoux had first whispered to her about the scheme she had insisted there must be another woman, so that no scandalmongering tongues could clack. But it was the men who first engaged her attention.

Under their mud-spattered and soaking cloaks they wore the uniform of Dillon's Irish Regiment, most famous of the exiled Jacobite regiments in the service of Louis XV of France. While they waited at the Inn for Wogan to fetch the princess they had straightened their wigs and dried their boots at the fire after the long hard ride to Innsbruck ; but even so they still looked more like a pair of brigands than the entourage of a princess.

Wogan introduced them.

" Major Richard Gaydon, of Dillon's Regiment," he said, indicating the elder of the two, fat and short of breath and more than middle-aged. As he bowed and kissed her hand Clementina caught the sparkle of fun in his eyes and knew that for all his unromantic appearance here was a man who enjoyed such ploys as this, as much as if he had still been a boy.

" Ensign Lucius O'Toole," said Wogan, and the younger officer, tall, finely built, and blue-eyed, squared his great shoulders, bowed low and vowed himself her most faithful servant.

Clementina turned to her companion for the journey ahead—Mrs. Misset, whose husband had gone on with a servant to arrange for fresh horses down the route. Mrs. Misset's clever Irish face had puckered in dismay at sight of the little princess, bedraggled and soaking, shivering with cold, yet with eyes dancing with excite-

ment and the thrill of happiness at being free and among friends. They came forward to lead her to the fire; but Clementina laughed merrily at the look of horror on their faces.

" What does it matter if I am wet and cold? " she cried. " All that matters is to drive on—to get to Italy."

But she could not go like that. Mrs. Misset took charge of her, led her upstairs to a bedroom to change her stockings. The poor girl's legs were frozen, for the water in the gutter had been icy cold.

" You cannot start out on an all-night journey in that state ! " cried Mrs. Misset, in great consternation ; but the men downstairs solved the difficulty. It was the fashion then for gentlemen to carry muffs—a sensible idea, since it meant that they could bare their hands instantly to reach for sword or pistol.

" The princess," Major Gaydon declared, " shall wear our muffs—not on her hands but on her legs ! "

So they carried her out to the carriage that stood waiting in the yard, and placed her inside, then made her thrust her legs into the muffs and so keep herself warm.

The coach was a berlin which Wogan had bought for the journey, complete with horses and two sets of harness and a large supply of rope. It was a four-wheeled carriage with a hooded seat behind, and was as comfortable a means of travel as could be found in those days when any travel was supremely uncomfortable.

The coachman mounted to his seat, the postillion hopped up behind. The horses, standing shivering and streaming wet in the yard, were whipped up, the berlin clattered out of the yard into the street and went rattling along on the road to the south. O'Toole, who knew the language better than any of the others, watched them go then went back into the Black Eagle to pay the landlord's reckoning.

The berlin, swaying and jolting, left the last houses of the little town behind. The night was pitch dark, the pouring rain had an icy touch of sleet in it, but it was warm and cosy inside, and Clementina sat back against the cushions and prepared to settle down for the journey. She and Wogan sat side by side, with the other two—Mrs. Misset and Gaydon—facing them.

Almost at once Gaydon, for all his zest for adventure, began to nod, and Mrs. Misset, who was far from well, also grew sleepy. But Clementina was wide awake and longing to hear all the news.

Wogan laughed suddenly, pointing to the sleeping major.

" I wonder what His Majesty King Louis would say to that ! " he whispered. " Here are two of my uncle's best officers gallivanting about Germany when they should be attending to their duties in Strasbourg ! "

Clementina, interested at once, demanded details.

" They have taken French leave," he told her, chuckling. " His Majesty knows his Irishmen. He gave strict orders only the other day. Any officer of Dillon's Regiment who went off on an exploit without authority would be cashiered on the spot. And here they are, on a jaunt that will set the Emperor by the ears ! They'll be lucky if they escape with merely being cashiered when they get back to Strasbourg ! I wonder does my uncle Colonel Dillon know what's in the wind ? "

He laughed again.

" At any rate the Governor of Strasbourg knows," he added, " for Gaydon told me. When they were leaving the town to cross the frontier the Governor had a word with them. 'You are not crossing the Rhine for nothing,' he said. 'You seem to be going to try to make a hole in the moon !' Maybe they'll only make a hole in the ground when King Louis hears about it ! But they never think of that. Here's an exploit after their hearts, and that's all that matters to an Irishman."

Clementina, peering across at the large fat officer slumbering there, with his head lolling back, breathed a prayer of thankfulness that there were such men, willing to risk everything for the sake of an old loyalty. Then, in the next breath, she let out a cry of consternation.

" My jewel-case ! I have left it behind ! "

Wogan sat up with a jerk. The jewel-case ! It contained the greater part of Clementina's wealth.

" The devil ! " he thought. " We dare not go back to Innsbruck. Now what is to be done? "

At that moment the patter of hooves came to them along the wild road, and Ensign O'Toole, galloping up, reined in his mount beside the coach. Wogan put his head out and explained the situation. O'Toole grinned.

" All right ! " he cried. " Go on. I'll go back."

He wheeled his horse's head, dug his heels into its flanks and in a moment was thundering back along the way he had come. The coach rattled on ; and now there was silence inside—a silence deep with anxiety. It was not just of the jewel-case they thought, but of young O'Toole, gallantly racing back into the enemy citadel without a thought for his own danger.

Mile after mile unrolled beneath the carriage wheels ; and then at last Clementina's sharp ears detected a faint sound. The thud of hooves again, and O'Toole was back, the precious jewel-case in his arms.

" I got back to the inn," he reported. " There was no one about, so I went up to the bedroom. But the door was locked. I could not risk fetching the landlord, so I leaned my weight on it till the latch gave way, and

there was the case—on the table where Her Highness
had left it."

He handed it over with a smile, and Wogan took charge
of it, holding it tightly against his chest.

They jogged on ; and suddenly the coachman drew
rein. They looked out, to find houses on each side of
them and a little cobbled street, and a coaching inn
beside them. It was the village of Brenner, a posting
station high on the top of the Brenner Pass.

Two men strode out of the inn—Captain Misset and
the servant, Michel. They had refreshments and fresh
horses waiting ; but the runaways dared not linger.
A switched egg was all that Clementina would take, and
as the sun was rising in the valley below, the fresh horses
were harnessed and whipped up, and the berlin rumbled
on again, bumping and jolting down the difficult winding
mountain road.

O'Toole, soaked to the skin, plastered with mud and
grime, swung himself on to his horse and fell in behind
with Misset and Michel, shivering a little in the cold
unfriendly dawn.

The brief halt had been enough for Clementina.
Refreshed, she was wide awake again, and she made
Wogan talk while the other two slept.

He told her about England, taught her a few words
of English. She must learn the language of the country
of which she was to be queen ! But now fatigue was
growing stronger than excitement. Clementina's eyes
grew heavy, Wogan's voice trailed off into silence.
She slept. Gradually she toppled over until she was
lying on Wogan's knee. But Wogan did not know that,
for he too had fallen asleep, with his head back against
the cushions ; and as he slept the precious jewel-case
slipped from his arms—and fell smack on Clementina's
head.

Clementina woke up.

§

The rain had ceased, the biting chill had gone out of the air. This was no longer the cold unfriendly north, for the Italian frontier was not so very far away now, and as they clattered along the mountain side high above the River Adige coachman and postillion livened up to their work. Wogan had refreshed them handsomely at Brenner and given them something to encourage them on their way. They had swallowed plenty of encouragement.

O'Toole, riding wearily behind, began to realise that something had gone wrong—dangerously wrong. The coachman was plying his whip, shouting to his beasts, sending them faster and faster down the steep and difficult road. The coach rocked and swayed and jolted, and suddenly O'Toole gave a cry of horror. The horses had swerved—not in towards the steep mountain side but out to the very edge of the road, where a sheer precipice fell to the river below. A country cart had suddenly appeared, on a bend of the road.

The coach tilted on two wheels with the violent swerve —tilted right out into space. O'Toole and his companions, galloping behind, held their breath in an agony of terror. But at the last moment, just as it seemed that the coach must plunge over the verge into the gorge below, a wheel struck an old tree stump. The jolt threw the coach back with a sickening crash towards the road, the struggling horses dragged it clear as it righted, and it went careering on down the road.

O'Toole dug his heels in and overtook it, in a blaze of fury. Coachman and postillion were roaring drunk! He laid into them both with his whip and sobered them in short order. The coachman reined in his horses to a safer pace. But the damage had already been done.

§

"Someone must stay behind," Wogan declared, "and act as rearguard."

Young O'Toole grinned cheerfully. He was ready for anything ; and Captain Misset nodded grimly. He too was ready. What these two men could achieve against all the resources of an outraged Emperor they did not stop to think.

"We'll put up at the next inn," Misset volunteered, "and intercept any couriers who come."

They were in the Austrian Tyrol now, and growing more cheerful with every mile ; for the sun was shining, the day was warm and pleasant—and Italy was not far away. But luck was about to desert them.

At Innsbruck, before the rescue of the princess, they had been worried by the arrival in the town of a dangerous personage, none other than the Princess of Baden, a violent supporter of the Emperor and an inveterate enemy of the Stuarts. Had she heard even a whisper of the exploit that was planned she would have betrayed it immediately—and betrayal would have meant death for all the conspirators, And now she had turned up again.

They came to a village. There were no horses. The Princess of Baden, they were told, had taken them all. She was travelling with a large suite and everywhere she went she emptied all the stables for fresh mounts and carriage horses.

Wogan cursed their ill fortune. At any moment they might overtake the Princess and her entourage ; and if that happened discovery would be immediate. But even more pressing than this danger was the difficulty over the horses. Whatever happened, they must find fresh horses.

They pushed on, and at last, weary, travel-stained and

anxious, they came into Trent—ninety miles, Wogan remembered, from Innsbruck. They had travelled far and fast ; but Clementina was feverishly anxious to get on. She kicked off the muffs, which had kept her legs warm throughout the journey, and she threw aside the furred hood she had been wearing. While the men searched for horses she yielded to Mrs. Misset's pleadings and had some food—biscuits and wine.

The men reappeared. They had found a coachman and horses at last, and they wasted no further time but drove out of Trent at once. They passed through Roveredo without stopping ; and now Wogan and Gaydon drew deep breaths and turned to the princess with broad smiles.

" Allow me to congratulate your Highness," Wogan cried. " We have safely passed the last town in the Emperor's dominions where a military garrison is maintained. The frontier is before us—with nothing to stop us now."

Clementina laughed happily, all her fatigue gone, her spirits high ; but while she laughed she shook her head at him.

" We must not rejoice too soon, Wogan," she said. " We have not yet *crossed* the frontier."

A minute later there was a loud crash, and they were thrown in a heap on the carriage floor. Startled, they scrambled up and looked at each other ; then the men leapt out and stood staring in dismay. What they saw was a broken axle tree.

Clementina was helped to the ground, and surveyed the catastrophe calmly. She seemed quite unperturbed, and turned at once to assist Mrs. Misset, who was really ill now after all the severe jolting of the coach.

A short distance away across some fields lay a pretty Tyrolese village. Wogan escorted the ladies to a cottage, where the good people listened sympathetically to their plight and offered them refreshments. Then two villagers were found who were willing to lend a hand.

The axle tree was patched up, and the villagers agreed to walk on either side of the coach and hold it up. It meant that hereafter their pace would be little more than a crawl; but at least they would be moving on towards safety.

Wogan reckoned the distance. Forty miles yet to go. At any moment the thunder of hooves might proclaim pursuit and the Emperor's men would be upon them. What hope that Misset and O'Toole could hold them up?

They went back to the coach and clambered gingerly in. Clementina, smiling serenely upon them all, lay back against the cushions—and fell sound asleep.

Another violent jolt and another crash; but Clementina did not wake up. What woke her was the sudden shock of cold water, for the axle tree had snapped again and Wogan, lifting her gently out of the coach, had splashed her feet in a roadside pool.

She blinked, looked round, and burst out laughing.

" What say you to this, Wogan? " she cried, " you who always find stepping stones to wet me! "

The unhappy Irishman hung his head.

Her high spirits and the calm way she accepted this fresh disaster had their effect. The men set to work with a will, patched the axle tree again, and they staggered on. But they must have fresh horses.

Michel came forward. He would see what could be done, if they would give him permission; so they sent him off. While he was gone, Wogan told Clementina all about him.

" This isn't a new experience for Michel," he said. " He is a specialist in escapes. You have heard of my Lord Nithsdale? He was imprisoned in Newgate with me, after the rebellion. His wife saved him. She managed to get permission to visit him, then changed clothes with him so that he could be smuggled out of gaol. Everybody knows the story. He went into hiding at the Venetian Embassy—a servant hid him in his room for several days. Then the Ambassador's coach-and-six was going down to Dover to meet His Excellency's brother. The servant dressed Nithsdale up in a livery and took him down to Dover in the Ambassador's retinue— and nobody noticed him. At Dover the servant chartered a small vessel and took my lord safely across to France. When they got there, the servant entered King James's service. His name is Michel."

As he finished the story Michel reappeared, leading a pair of aged nags that had been pulling a plough a few minutes before. As horse-flesh they had little to boast of ; but they saved the situation, and the coach went on.

But presently it was clear that it could go no farther. Michel slipped away, and came back with an old farm cart.

Clementina regarded her new conveyance with merry eyes, and promptly jumped up into it. The men assisted Mrs. Misset to clamber up, and they started on the last stage of the long wild journey.

Wogan looked back. Only a few miles still to go. Would they manage it in time ? Would the Emperor's soldiers reach the frontier before them and hold them up? He looked into the cart. Clementina, with as much sangfroid as any seasoned campaigner, had fallen soundly asleep. While she slept the wretched farm cart rumbled out of Austria and into Italy.

Wogan drew a long deep breath, then looked up sharply at the thud of hooves in the distance. Two horsemen appeared. They came galloping down the road and overtook the cart with a shout of triumph. It was the precious rearguard, and O'Toole, jumping from his saddle, had a story to tell.

He and Misset had been sitting at dinner in the inn when a man had ridden into the courtyard. O'Toole had noticed him—and at once guessed his business. So presently they went into the parlour and started to chat to the stranger. O'Toole ordered wine. When it came, Misset, sitting at his elbow, tipped brandy into the stranger's glass without his noticing, and as glass after glass went down O'Toole and Misset exchanged broader and broader grins.

" Come ! " cried O'Toole. " Your health again, sir ! "

One last glass. The stranger lolled in his chair, toppled over, and slipped under the table. O'Toole and Misset bent down swiftly, ransacked him, and brought to light the despatches he was carrying. They were orders from the Emperor to the frontier post to intercept the fugitives at all costs. The pair looked at each other with pleased grins ; then, remembering their manners, they picked up the unfortunate courier, carried him upstairs and put him to bed. They left him snoring blissfully while they rode on to overtake the rest.

The cart drew up. Clementina awoke. Gathered around her she saw the faces of her friends, beaming and triumphant, and her heart leapt as she realised the truth —she was in Italy. She was safe. She was free.

Now at last she could marry James, whom she had never seen. The only trouble was—there was no sign of James. . . .

CHAPTER TWO

A PRINCE IS BORN

JAMES STUART, Chevalier de St. George and rightful King of Scotland, England and Ireland, travelled post-haste to Corunna.

In December, 1718, the government in London had declared war on Spain, and James, forever seeking some new opportunity to regain the throne, had sent his agent, the Duke of Ormond, to Madrid to put matters in train there. The Spanish court received this emissary with delight. He came at an opportune moment, providing a cast-iron excuse for vigorous action, and soon a plan for the invasion of Britain was in readiness.

When word arrived of this, James wasted no time in following Ormond. He had failed utterly in the well-planned rising of 1715 and, shrewd and forthright as he was, he must have realised that he had himself largely to blame for that. Now he meant to see to it that there should not be another failure. With the might of Spain to back his cause it should not be long now before he had something more to offer his future bride than the empty pomp of exile in Rome.

In Madrid he was received with royal honours as King of Britain. He was also told of the preparations that had been made. A fleet of ten warships and twenty-one transports was collected at Cadiz ; another fleet had been assembled at Corunna and was about to sail in consort. Here was invasion on a scale almost comparable to the plan of the Great Armada itself—but with this vital difference, that in England now there would be many who would welcome the invaders and be ready to help them when they came ashore. It was, in fact, this assurance of Jacobite help that made the project feasible.

The moment was almost ripe. Ormond was sailing, with a commission as Regent for James, with the fleet ; James was to follow immediately. So he set off for Corunna, full of hope and buoyed up by the seeming certainty of success at last.

He arrived on the 17th of April, 1719, and was at once greeted with staggering news.

Off Finisterre the great fleet had run into a violent storm.

" The entire fleet is dispersed, Your Majesty," he was bluntly told. " Many ships have been lost, with their crews and soldiers. Nearly all the others are heavily damaged and in no condition to proceed. Only two remain unaccounted for. They were last seen steering a course north, and they may reach their destination, for they signalled their intention to proceed. But if they do reach Scotland, if they do land their men, there can only be one result. So paltry a force will not be able to support itself for long, nor even to defend itself, far less to attack. The expedition, Your Majesty, has failed utterly. We have been defeated at the very outset by the weather."

Stunned, James listened to these fatal words. But even now he refused to accept defeat tamely. He was obstinate. He had been brought up in misfortune, and misfortune had taught him patience, and courage, and a single-minded determination. He remained in Corunna, writing urgent letters to Madrid, making urgent plans.

The blow had been severe ; but Spain was powerful, the war was still to be fought, surely another fleet could be got together ! But he faced an obstacle far more formidable than the loss of the fleet. The war, not just in England but in Spain as well, was far from popular. At best it could only be a war at sea—and neither nation's seafaring men liked the prospect. After all, what they all wanted was trade and freedom to trade—and war killed trade.

So back in Madrid, where even personal appeals to the Court brought no better results, James faced the bitter truth. He had long ago learnt to accept a situation when he could not better it ; and now he accepted this new defeat—and made up his mind to wait, with what patience he could muster, for a more favourable opportunity.

He thought suddenly of Clementina. After all, he was now a married man, albeit he had never seen his bride. It was of the highest importance that the royal race of Stuart should not die out ; there must be an heir to succeed him in his claim to the British throne. So James packed up and set off for Italy again.

His bride meanwhile had reached Bologna with her rescue party on May 2nd and had found rooms at the Pilgrim's Inn. It was not an ideal lodging for a princess —especially as a party of English tourists arrived and, after the time-honoured manner of English tourists, took complete possession of the place.

So Wogan went off to pay his respects to Cardinal Origo in Bologna and solicit his aid. The Cardinal, when he heard the story, was delighted. Here was romance after a man's heart ! Of course he would help. He sent messengers off to Rome to acquaint the Pope with the news, and he lent the Princess a palace in the town where she could enjoy at least privacy and comfort.

On the 8th of May came news from the missing bride-groom. It was brought by his secretary, James Murray, and Murray's sister, Mrs. Hay, whose husband, Colonel John Hay, was employed in the royal household. James was still in Spain, the marriage would have to be by proxy. So the ceremony took place next day, and the Princess and her supporters set out for Rome.

Clementina, after her wild adventure and the vexations that had followed, savoured her new condition with delight. No longer was she a hunted fugutive. Now she was a royal personage ; and, with a heart full of joy and pride, she made her royal progress to Rome, received all along the route with the honours due to the bride of the rightful King of Britain.

She reached Rome on the 15th of the month and was immediately received by the Pope ; for James was His Holiness's pensioner, and Clementina was a good Catholic. Everywhere she went she was accorded royal honours, and the Pope lent her a palace in Rome to live in while waiting for her husband. Roman society flocked to pay their respects to the young bride, and to entertain her, and for three happy months Clementina savoured all the delights of royalty and the status of bride without having to adjust herself in any way to the presence of a husband. Then word came from James. He had at last given up hope of Madrid. He was on his way to Rome.

He had been a failure in so many directions ; but at least his marriage had gone through with spectacular success and he was determined that as a husband he should not fail. Clementina, for her part, was eager to see the man whom she had married, and on whom all her hopes of future greatness depended. So she set off to meet him.

On the road near Montefiascone their carriages met, on August 28th. James sprang down to the road and came forward with a reassuring eagerness, greeting his lovely young bride with the greatest affection and delight. He had not been deceived in the accounts he had heard of her beauty and charm, and at the prospect of a happy married life he threw off his gloom and

became, for the time at least, the devoted lover, with all the natural gallantry and charm of his Stuart blood.

Then at Montifiascone another wedding ceremony took place, this time in person, and the royal couple travelled together to Rome, where the Pope gave them the Muti Palace to live in and a handsome pension as well. He was, for the moment, pleased with James, for the Pretender's tolerant attitude towards Protestants had been a thorn in the papal flesh. With a devout Catholic for his wife he might be expected to mend his ways.

It was a peculiar household that Clementina found herself mistress of. She had few friends of her own, chief of them being a Mrs. Sheldon, who became a great favourite ; on the other hand she took an immediate and intense dislike to her husband's secretary and still more to his sister, Mrs. Hay, both of them Protestants and apt to be more familiar in their manner than the Princess liked.

However, all went well for a while, and presently Walton, the English government's agent in Rome, heard a rumour which alarmed him mightily. The Princess was about to have a baby.

The rumour was soon confirmed ; and in due course an announcement came from the Muti Palace, on New Year's Eve, December 31st, 1720. The Princess had been safely delivered of a boy. Walton sat down in great excitement and nibbled the end of his quill while he tried to think what he ought to say in his report to London.

A boy. . . . That meant an heir. An heir to the throne, a future claimant for the throne, rival of the Hanoverian George, Walton's master. . . .

The whole of Europe buzzed with the news. And the boy himself—they christened him Charles Edward Louis Philip Casimir. Charles Edward Stuart, destined to be known to history as the Young Pretender and to be idolised by a whole nation as Bonnie Prince Charlie.

§

There was rejoicing in Rome, in Paris, in Madrid. But there was consternation in London.

Couriers hurried back and forth. Walton was badgered with demands for fuller information and he set about supplying it.

He had his own theory about the duties of an agent in such a case. What his masters wanted was reassurance ; he would send them reassurances. So he sat down and penned the kind of report that they would like to read, and London learned with relief and delight that the infant prince was a complete weakling, that " his legs are so turned in and distorted that it is very much in doubt if he will ever be able to walk."

In spite of this, the gentlemen in London were still uneasy. The news of James's romantic marriage had been alarming enough : the existence of an heir was positively menacing. So Walton went even farther. He declared the young prince's health to be so bad that " every day reveals new imperfections in it, and consequently he will not live very long."

That was some consolation to the Hanoverians ; but it did not last long, for another staunch English whig, the Marquis of Blandford, who had not trace of sympathy with the Stuart cause, wrote home to a friend in a very different vein. He described Charles as " a fine, promising child," and even Walton's fabrications could not blind the government to the simple truth. There was nothing whatever wrong with the infant. Indeed, Mrs. Hay's husband was soon reporting : " The Prince is the finest child in the world, healthy and strong, and runs about from morning till night."

Consternation grew in London—and Charles grew, in Rome.

§

Mrs. Sheldon had charge of the infant at first ; but it was not long before young Charlie made it clear that he needed a man to look after him. He was never still, and his boundless energy exhausted the unfortunate lady ; so James Murray was appointed tutor.

It was not a happy choice. The small boy began by disliking him, and very soon despised him ; but Murray did his best and Charlie, who had had a high sense of duty dinned into him from his earliest conscious moments, learnt his lessons docilely enough.

When he was four another momentous event occurred in the Muti Palace. On the 6th of March, 1725, Clementina presented her husband with a second son, christened Henry Benedict, and London suffered another shock of alarm. But by this time Walton was finding plenty of reassurance to send home to England ; for gossip was busy about the household in the Muti Palace.

James had been a courteous, attentive and devoted husband. He remained courteous, but soon ceased to be devoted. He was by nature cautious, reserved, and dignified ; he did not have it in him to unbend, to forget his dignity and be gay.

Clementina was young, ambitious, witty, and eager for society. Her husband was none of these things. He had a fine command of the English language and a scholarly interest in using it ; he had inherited the studious nature of his ancestor, James VI, and he had always preferred a good book or his own correspondence to society. The empty pomp of his life in Rome riled him, the flattery of Roman society left him cold and he remained obsessed, day and night, with his plans for the return to the throne of Britain. Clementina found herself more and more neglected in favour of the company of men who might help him with these schemes ; and unhappily this company too often included the not unattractive wife of Colonel Hay.

Clementina began by growing bored and restless and resentful ; then she grew disillusioned, and the household split into two factions—those who supported James and those who supported Clementina.

She had always been bitterly jealous of James's chosen confidantes—and more particularly of Mrs. Hay. Soon she hated them. She resented their influence with her husband, she resented what she considered their familiar attitude towards herself, above all she resented their religion. They were Protestants ; and Clementina, a zealous Catholic, abhorred all Protestants.

When she discovered a Church of England chaplain installed in the Palace she was shocked and outraged, and it was no consolation when English visitors in Rome flocked to the services he daily held. But James was adamant. A Catholic himself, he had the sense to realise that the only hope for the Stuarts lay in sinking religious prejudice and declaring for complete religious toleration. He applied that principle, in spite of his wife's protests, to the upbringing of his son, so that young Charlie grew up half a Catholic, half a Protestant and with no very great interest in either denomination. The boy was much more concerned with learning to ride and shoot and with studying the arts of government and war. In fact, he would often stay out long after dark with his shotgun, trying to hit bats on the wing.

So Walton, who had his informants planted every-where, was able to report a growing rift in the Stuart household. Quarrels were becoming more and more frequent and a real break seemed imminent. James's pension from the Pope might be enough to support the household ; but James was not content with a life of idleness. | He worked ceaselessly, at scheme after scheme for a restoration—and such schemes cost money. The endless drain on his limited resources soon had repercussions on the Palace. He was often at his wits' end to meet his bills, and he came to resent the costly society functions that were almost the only diversion left to his unhappy wife. Still young, still lovely, Clementina found her life growing more and more dull as her high hopes faded ; she was bound to admit to herself how slender her chances were of realising those girlish dreams she had once cherished. Queen of England ! She was the wife of a morose and embittered pensioner of the Pope.

Her only remaining hope was Charles—and Charles was rapidly growing away from her. He was an affectionate child, quick to understand and sympathise ; but he was also a stirring child, with a passion for every sort of outdoor sport and a ready adaptability to any company. Completely at his ease among the highest dignitaries in Rome, he could be equally at ease among the humblest, the servants and common soldiers. He charmed them all alike—and delighted alike in their company. So what with his lessons and his music and his dancing and his riding and shooting and racing, a small boy had no time left on his hands to sit with his mother and take sides against his father. He was much too busy being just a healthy small boy.

The perpetual clash of two strong and very different characters could only lead, in the end, to an open breach. Inevitably it came ; and because Clementina had always been a woman of spirit it came dramatically, publicly, in a manner calculated to delight all James's enemies.

§

On the morning of November 15th, 1725, Clementina went out for an airing in her carriage. But she did not simply enjoy a short drive through the streets of Rome.

She gave the coachman a sharp order, and he turned the horses' heads away from their accustomed route, and made for the Convent of St. Cecilia. Clementina had been in communication with the Mother Superior for some days, in preparation for the dramatic step she was about to take.

She was received into the Convent—and there she stayed.

All Rome was electrified. Tongues clacked busily, and soon the whole world heard the story—or versions of the story.

Clementina issued an ultimatum to her husband. She would not return to the Palace unless he dismissed the Hays, and Murray, and others of his household to whom she objected.

James, for once, flew into a towering passion. This was the last straw. He had put up with so much, for the sake of preserving appearances before the world. Clementina threw discretion to the winds and brought their quarrels out before the public gaze. Not only that, but she startled the unhappy James by blunt accusations that must have seemed to him monstrous.

She wrote to the Pope accusing her husband of having an affair with Mrs. Hay. The Pope believed every word of it. So, too, did every other good Catholic—for James was not a good Catholic. The scandal spread. It reached Britain; and Lockhart, James's agent in Scotland, believed the story and furiously accused his master of throwing away his last chances of a restoration. True or not, the story was bound to do infinite harm to the Stuart cause.

Clementina may even have believed it herself, carried away as she was by her jealousy of Mrs. Hay; certainly she acted as if she was convinced of the truth of every accusation she made.

The fact of the matter was that James had one sole obsession—the throne of Britain. Solemn, dignified, and for ever preoccupied with his affairs of state and with the upbringing of his promising young heir, he was the most unlikely person to indulge in a clandestine love affair. He had never shown any interest in women. But at this time, when he was surrounded by enemies eager to discredit him and when even his best friends had grown weary of repeated failures and had secretly begun to lose all hope, no one was likely to sit back calmly and review the charges made against him and dismiss them for what they were—preposterous nonsense. And James himself, still in a royal rage, promptly did a thing which added fuel to the flames of calumny although, oddly enough, it provided the best possible proof, to unbiassed eyes, of his innocence. He took Mrs. Hay to the Opera.

The Pope wrote a strong letter to him protesting about his alleged misconduct. Cardinal Alberoni, former dictator of Spain and hitherto a good friend of the Pretender, came in person to remonstrate with him. He began by speaking to James as if he had been a naughty boy in need of a scolding, and James, always a Stuart, lost his temper and told him roundly to mend his manners and mind his own business.

The angry Cardinal leapt out of his chair in such a fury that he caught his robes on the arms and ripped them as he rose.

" I have never failed to speak the truth in the presence of powerful sovereigns who could have executed me on the spot," he stormed, " and much less am I to be intimidated by a king without a country ! "

Wherewith he marched out of the Muti Palace and went home to write a long letter to James in which he told him, in precise terms, what he thought of him and his conduct.

James, still furious, found himself frustrated at every turn. Nobody would believe a good word of him. Nobody gave him the benefit of the doubt. The whole world sided with poor Clementina and poor Clementina made the most of the situation. She wrote to the Pope and others accusing James not only of committing adultery but of bringing up his children as heretics, which in the eyes of Rome was a far more heinous crime. The Pope, accepting everything she said literally, sent for young Charlie, and that bright and charming youth went through his Catechism (at the age of five !) with such complete assurance that His Holiness was mollified and thought a little more kindly of the erring father. But Clementina was determined to see this quarrel through to the bitter end.

Her ultimatum remained.

James was baffled. The wretched stubborn woman was, in point of fact, deliberately wrecking what chances remained of her ever ascending the throne of Britain. She was cutting off her nose to spite her face with a vengeance ; but once having set out to do that she would not be turned from her purpose.

James tried to save his own face. He made no objection to the young princes visiting their mother in her lonely convent cell. She retaliated by having their portraits painted and hung up in her cell—a charming pathetic touch that won her fresh sympathy.

A rumour went round that young Charlie was being forced to recite a simple but subversive lesson : "A fig for the priests, all monks are rascals, the Mass cost my grandfather three kingdoms." If there was any truth in the rumour it only does credit to James's common-sense ; for there was no manner of doubt that the biggest stumbling block to a Stuart restoration was this question of religion. And in any case young Charlie, who preferred action to theory and never showed any patience with dogma, was far too eager even at the age of five, to grow up into a fine soldier to bother his head with the quarrels of priests and prelates.

If he ever had to recite those lines, he probably did so with gusto.

But affairs could not be allowed to continue as they were. The Stuart cause had suffered sufficient setbacks already, and since the Stuart cause was the mainspring of all James's actions he swallowed his anger, overcame his own obstinacy, and agreed to capitulate. He promised to dismiss the Hays and Murray, and, on those terms, Clementina consented to return to the Palace.

She came with not even the ghost of the gay vivacious girl of the Innsbruck adventure lingering about her. A soured and embittered woman, she presided once more with what graciousness she could muster, at her husband's dinner table and, in private, considered herself a martyr to her religion—a willing martyr, since she believed that the world was well lost for the true faith.

Young Charlie was not sorry to be rid of Murray. He had never liked him, generally despised him, and kept all his admiration for the occasional visitors to the Palace who matched more perfectly his own ideas of what a man should be. In due course one of these visitors was to carry the boy off and introduce him to the life he longed for—the tented field, the gorgeous panoply of war and the clatter and clash of battle, the dream of any small boy of spirit in a martial age.

CHAPTER THREE

A STIRRING LADDIE

YOUNG CHARLIE, finished with lessons for the moment, went out on his small sturdy legs into the grounds of the palace. He was just six ; but already he had shown the kind of man he was going to be. Lessons he would learn dutifully, because a sense of duty had been dinned into him from the earliest moments ; but lessons held his interest only briefly. What he enjoyed was action, and now he meant to have some action.

He took his crossbow with him, and a lackey followed at his heels to do whatever the young gentleman commanded.

" Throw the ball," said young Charlie, and the lackey hurled a small ball across the lawn.

The crossbow swung up. The boy took swift aim, pulled the trigger. There was a sharp *whang*, and next moment the crossbow bolt hit the ball fair and square.

" Throw another one ! " commanded Charlie. Again the lackey threw, and again the crossbow twanged and scored another hit.

" Again ! "

A third ball went spinning across the smooth lawn ; and a third time the unerring aim of a six-year-old sent a bolt to split it clean in mid career. Even the impassive face of the lackey broke into a smile, for such a performance by a grown man would have been sufficiently impressive. In a child of six it was amazing. But Charlie thought nothing of it. He was simply learning to be a man.

The lackey slipped away. Here was a story to tell! It ought to be worth a drink or two. So he scribbled his report and took his earliest opportunity of passing it to Walton ; for nearly half the royal household was in the pay of the English agent. But what Walton did with that report or others like it the lackey never knew ; the agent had his own ideas on that point and kept his pay-masters in good humour by suppressing anything they might not like to hear.

Meanwhile young Charlie, abandoning the crossbow, was busy practising with a more modern weapon—his shotgun. At six, he could not only clean and load it, he could lift it to his shoulder, aim, and fire—and he was already almost as expert a shot with it as with his beloved crossbow.

He had grown amazingly.

There were two sorts of Stuarts, and oddly enough their names distinguished them. James VI was a solemn, cautious man totally unlike his brilliant mother, Mary Queen of Scots. James VII was sober, morose, and filled with an intolerable sense of duty. Charles I was dashing, bold, imperious and witty. Charles II gay and reckless and lovable and astute. " He never said a foolish thing— and never did a wise one," his enemies declared ; to which Charles retorted promptly : " My words are my own, my actions are those of my ministers," and so neatly turned the tables on his detractors.

Prince Charles Edward was aptly named ; for it was the Charles's that he took after ; but perhaps because of his solemn conscientious father's influence, perhaps because of his upbringing in exile, perhaps simply because he had qualities his predecessors lacked, he was to prove himself incomparably the greatest of the Stuarts—even although that greatness was only to show itself in one brief and glorious burst.

Meantime, he had to grow up, he had to learn his lessons and dream his dreams—and school himself for the part that lay ahead.

Like most small boys he soon quarrelled with his tutors, and on one occasion there was a violent scene with the unfortunate James Murray. Charlie, losing his temper as very small boys will, threatened to kick him, even to kill him. It was a display of sudden fury any child of six might make, and he was treated accordingly. They locked him in his room to cool his heels and get over it ; but first they took away all the firearms, for they remembered his achievements in the grounds of the Palace and there was no saying what might happen !

He cooled his heels and got over it ; and afterwards he was charmingly contrite and dutiful. This was indeed almost the only occasion when he let his temper get the better of him ; as he grew up he showed a very different side to his character, for the thing that most impressed the people he met was his unfailing courtesy and his constant consideration for other people's feelings and welfare. Dreaming his boyish dreams, he saw himself not just a brilliant soldier and a splendid leader of men ; he pictured himself with all the princely virtues— courage and patience and understanding and gentleness and compassion—and as he dreamed so he grew up.

The next tutor they found for him was the Chevalier Ramsay. He took an instant liking for his young pupil and might have done a lot with him ; but the atmosphere of the Muti Palace, a house divided against itself, distressed him deeply. However much he might delight in his small charge, and especially in the boy's passion for manly sports, he could not stomach the constant bickerings and intrigues indoors. Charlie's parents seemed for ever scheming against each other to win and hold the boy's affection, and in such an atmosphere

Ramsay found his own position intolerable. He did not stay long.

But he gave up his charge with real reluctance.

" He is continually in motion," he declared of the Prince. " No porter's child in the country has stronger legs and arms."

It was a conclusion that was gradually being borne in upon the authorities in London, who had listened only too eagerly to the reassuring falsehoods so assiduously sent them by their agent in Rome.

Charlie kept all his admiration for men who could do things that, to a stirring small boy, seemed really important—riding, shooting, fencing, racing. He had tremendous energy and vitality and a passion for outdoor exercise of every kind.

He also had a passion for music which he learnt with a natural flair. Mary Queen of Scots had played the clarsach exquisitely ; her descendants had all had a keen ear for music ; and Charlie was not content just to sing prettily in his boyish treble, and to play a little. He studied hard. He loved his music, and his small agile fingers soon mastered the intricacies of the violin just as an unerring taste taught him to appreciate good music when he heard it. But he did not like women.

They could do none of the things he admired. They could not shoot, or ride, or run, they knew nothing about soldiering, and they interfered with his liberty. Even his mother worried him a little, because when he was with her he had to try hard to restrain his natural impulses and behave quietly and sedately and not make a noise. So he wrote his first letter to his father, who had gone off on one of his interminable journeys connected with schemes for the restoration of the Stuart fortunes :

DEAR PAPA,
        I thank you mightily for your kind letter. I shall strive to obey you in all things. I will be very

dutifull to Mama, and not jump too near her. I
shall be much obliged to the Cardinal for his animals.
I long to see you soon and in good health.

I am, dear Papa,

Your most dutifull and affectionate son,
CHARLES P.

Any father could be proud of a letter like that from a
seven-year-old son ; young Charlie, for all his outdoor
sporting proclivities, was evidently learning his lessons
as well, and James, solemn, studious and ineffectual,
must have been delighted with his elder boy ; but he
had reason also to be pleased with his younger son.

The boys had a remarkable family resemblance ; but
there the similarity ceased ; for Henry had inherited all
his father's scholarly tastes and soon showed himself a
grave, serious-minded little boy, and a great student.
So they made a charming contrast, each of them
delightful in his way yet so very different.

Charlie was tall, finely built, strong. From his Scots
tutor he acquired a passion for golf—and, apparently, a
Scots accent. His boyish errors in spelling are
characteristic. Humour he spelt " umer," and even his
own father's name appeared startlingly from his pen as
" Gems," which was exactly the Scots pronunciation of it.

There was one point on which their father's mind was
firmly made up.

" We may have to live in exile in Rome," he declared,
" and my sons may have to be brought up in Rome, but
we are British to the core. There will be nothing foreign
about my sons."

Charlie might be a " pretty, brown-eyed boy," as one
visitor called him, but he was strong and sturdy and full
of the spirit of adventure and independence.

Even at table James insisted on bringing him up in the
British tradition. There were guests at dinner each day,
men and women of many nationalities, and the meal was
all that any in that cosmopolitan gathering could desire.

"I will have no foreign fripperies about me or my sons."

There was French as well as English cookery, French and Italian wines as well as English beer. But James ate only the English dishes, drank only beer with his roast-beef—and saw to it that his sons copied his example.

" I will have no foreign fripperies about me or my sons," he declared roundly ; and young Charlie, who could talk to any of the guests with complete ease in their own languages, never thought of himself as anything but British. In his boyish dreams he saw himself one day a great soldier ; but he also remembered that he was by descent the future chief of a Highland clan, and the Highlands early captured his imagination. That fact was yet to prove the turning point in his whole career.

There was one thing that James, for all his sternness and dislike of society functions, did consent to do. It went against the grain ; but the Cause was paramount, and it would help the Cause. He was the father of two very delightful small boys, and he had the acumen to realise what an asset they could be. So he steeled himself to the ordeal and showed them off in Roman society, giving parties for them (parties which he personally disliked intensely) and even allowed them to display their talents like other small boys. Charlie would dance and Henry would sing to delight the guests, and indeed everyone who saw them was enchanted with them. Anything athletic was the breath of life to Charlie, and he took to dancing with the same flair he had shown for music. Indeed it was his wonderful dancing that was so to charm the hearts of the ladies of Edinburgh in a later year.

Walton, still assiduously earning his bread and butter with his reports to the Secretary of State in England, became more and more alarmed as the years passed and Charles, far from fulfilling the prophecies he had made, displayed more and more of the very qualities needed for a claimant to the British throne. He saw, with dismay, that scores of English visitors to Rome—good

Hanoverians and Whigs though they were—went to James's parties, and came away with glowing accounts of the small Prince's charm. Lies were of no avail now, and gradually Walton was forced to hint at the bitter truth in his reports—it had become the regular thing for English visitors to go to the Muti Palace and pay homage to the delightful young Prince and his gentle, studious little brother.

" This custom of doing homage to the two little boys," wrote Walton, " gains ground every day among the young people travelling here, and is degenerating into a kind of tenderness and compassion for the two boys."

§

To the boy Charles the thing that mattered most in life, next to his shooting and riding and fishing and military studies, was the situation in Europe. He had been brought up to look forward eagerly to the day when the family would return in triumph to Britain ; and he had the good sense to realise from the start that this return was not likely to come about in a peaceable manner. He saw himself entering London at the head of an army, driving out the Hanoverians by force of arms while loyal men from all over the country flocked to his standard.

To become a king he had first to become a soldier ; and one summer's day in the year 1734 his great chance came.

A visitor arrived at the Muti Palace, and Charles met for the first time a kinsman of his own—the young Duke of Liria, who was soon to inherit the title of Duke of Berwick. He was a son of James's natural brother, James Fitzjames, whose mother was Arabella Churchill. Liria, a keen soldier, was on his way to join the Spanish forces under Don Carlos, campaigning in southern Italy.

Charlie listened eagerly to his talk. The Emperor was having a bad time of it, assailed by enemies on all sides,

and his Italian dominions were threatened now by the
Spaniards, who aimed at winning Naples for the
Bourbons. The Imperial garrison had retired into the
town of Gaeta and was prepared to defend itself
desperately ; but it had little hope of succour and the
upshot was clear.

Here was action after a boy's heart. The Emperor,
clinging to his alliance with Hanoverian England, was
an enemy of the Stuarts ; and a Stuart was going to
share in the struggle against the Emperor. Here was not
just talk, and intrigue, and the weariness of diplomacy ;
here were deeds, not words, and Charlie hung on his
kinsman's words, his eyes glowing with excitement as
Liria described the situation with a soldier's graphic
terseness. It would be a hard fight.

" They're good soldiers, these Austrians," Liria
declared. " And they have a strong position. They are
vastly outnumbered, but they'll fight hard. It will be a
campaign worth any soldier's while."

He kept glancing at the boy, conscious of his tense
admiration, of his excitement—and of his charm. He
talked to him, and the more they talked the more he
liked this splendid youngster who listened so eagerly
and with such deep respect.

He tackled James about the matter.

" The boy is itching to go," he declared. " I will
look after him. It will do him a world of good. And—
it won't do our cause any harm."

James thought it over. His son was precious to him
in many ways—and war had its dangers. But Liria's
arguments were sound. It was high time Charles had
his baptism of fire—after all, he was fourteen, and he
ought to show his mettle. If he stood the test well, then
prospects would be bright ; and if he won a good report
it would surely have some effect on the waverers and
doubters at home, who hesitated to declare themselves
for the Stuarts.

He gave his consent.

"I'll get him a commission in the army," Liria promised, "and I'll take care of him."

Charles, wild with excitement, made his hasty preparations. His father gave him some pocket money. The Pope, hearing of the decision, sent for him and, wishing him God speed, made him a handsome present. A prince should not go to war with an empty purse.

They set out on their journey southwards. To an impatient youngster these seventy-five miles seemed interminable; but at last they came down out of the Volscian mountains and caught sight of the gleaming array of tents where the besieging army lay encamped opposite the town. Looking down, they could trace the line of earthworks in a semicircle facing the walls and spires of the old town, with the blue of the Mediterranean beyond.

It was on the 6th of August that they reached Don Carlos's headquarters. They went into action straight away, for Liria was ordered immmediately to the front-line trenches. Charles went with him, and as they made their way forward his ears became attuned to the thunder of the siege guns and to the rattle and crackle of musketry. They came under fire at once.

The bullets hissed about his ears, as Liria reported afterwards, but the youngster displayed not the least concern.

He had used a shotgun often enough. Now he was at the other end of it, with men sniping at him—and he enjoyed every moment of it. The excitement, the movement, the din, the danger were balm to his spirit; he felt that now he was really living at last; and the strange indescribable orderliness of it all was impressive. Out of this seeming chaos, this bedlam of smoke and flame and thunder and shouting, his keen young eyes could trace the clear, carefully thought-out pattern, and he welcomed the fact that he had a job to do.

He was no mere onlooker. He held a commission in the army, and he was quick to grasp his duties.

Liria, seeing the flush of excitement on the fresh young
face, seeing the glow in the clear boyish eyes, felt himself
amply rewarded. But he was not too happy about it all.
He had hoped they might be employed some distance
from the actual firing line, where the danger would
not be so great, for it was no light responsibility to have
charge of the person of a prince ; but it did not occur
to him to demur at the orders he had received or to make
a special plea for the boy. Let him take his chance with
the rest !

He had some anxious moments. Young Charlie was
far too intent on his job to notice the danger, or give it
a thought. He took some appalling risks ; but he
survived, and next day fresh orders came. Liria was
relieved of trench duty and was sent back.

They made for the house that had been allotted to
them as billets. When they reached it, one glance was
enough for Liria, an experienced soldier. The Austrians
had got it accurately within range and had already
pounded it several times.

Liria promptly ordered his men to move to other
quarters. But the boy hung back.

" I want to look," he announced, and went calmly into
the house to examine the shot-holes in the walls. The
mere fact that five Austrian pieces were busy trying to
demolish it did not bother him at all. This was the
first chance he had had to see the effect of cannon
balls at close quarters, and he meant to make the most
of it.

When he came out, still unharmed, his anxious kinsman
led him out of range of the guns and heaved a sigh of
relief when at last his young charge was installed in
comparative safety.

The next six days were glorious. Wherever the boy
went he won golden opinions from everyone, officers
and soldiers alike. He seemed to be without fear, and
he talked to everyone as man to man without the slightest
diffidence. As often as he could, he mixed with the

ordinary soldiers, asking questions, chatting with them completely at his ease—and in their own language. French, Spanish, Italian—he spoke them all with equal fluency. Whatever they might say against him, he had certainly not neglected his studies, for even in those days few boys of fourteen could have boasted of complete command of four languages.

His father, at any rate, must have been proud of him, for in all the reports from Gaeta there was a general chorus of approval.

" The prince exceeds anything I was capable of fancying about him, and meets here with as many admirers as he has spectators."

" A young prince so affable and of so charming behaviour cannot fail of being adored by both officers and men."

At Gaeta he had begun by displaying his courage, his contempt of danger, and his keenness on his job. At Gaeta he displayed also all the qualities of a born leader of men, winning affection and deep respect from all manner of men. At Gaeta he displayed, unmistakably, the promise of future greatness.

" Everybody," wrote Walton to his masters in London, scared into a burst of candour, " says that he will be in time a far more dangerous enemy to the present establishment of the Government of England than ever his father was."

But Charlie's adventures at Gaeta were brief. After those six days the town capitulated, and if Charlie shared in the rejoicings and also regretted the abrupt end of his first military escapade, his kinsman Liria heaved a sigh of relief and prepared to send his young charge back intact and triumphant to an anxious father.

First, the boy drew his pay as an officer in the army—and he had earned it to the full. Next he had a meeting with the King of Naples, who had formed a deep attachment to the lad and presented him with a gift of jewellery and a pair of fine horses. Then Charlie set off for home, his pockets full of valuables and his heart full of boyish pride.

He was back in Rome by September, and if before crowds had flocked to admire the young prince and his little brother they came now to acclaim a gallant youngster who had proved his mettle and won his spurs. But while he was thus making a reputation for himself for his manly qualities he was by no means neglecting the social graces, and with his charming manners and superb dancing he might soon have become the spoiled darling of Roman society. Only his passion for an outdoor life and a feeling of urgency in training himself for the soldier's task ahead saved him from this fate.

But the happiness of this glorious return from the wars and of the winter that followed was soon to be clouded.

Early in January, 1735, there were lowered voices and soft footsteps and a hush of apprehension in the Muti Palace. Princess Clementina was ill. On the 18th Charlie, so recently turned fourteen, faced the first sharp tragedy of his life. His mother was dead.

In spite of everything, it must have been a deep shock to a sensitive youngster, for he had managed to preserve a balance in his affections between his parents in spite of their quarrels and disagreements. But these last few years of poor Clementina's broken romance cannot have been easy for any of the household. Her obsession with a formal and ritualistic religion must often have been wearisome to a boy who had been deliberately brought up to preserve an open mind on religious matters. Even the cold graciousness with which she received her husband's guests must have had a dampening effect. But perhaps in the privacy of her own rooms she had shown to her sons some of that gay vivacity and wit and warm affection that had been so large a part of her girlish charm, and Charlie may have known that with her death something that could never be replaced had gone out of his life, and that henceforth there was to be no softening influence to temper the rigour of a masculine household.

§

For over two years Charles continued his education quietly in the Muti Palace while his father immersed himself more and more completely in the abortive plans, the intrigues, the constant comings and goings and writing of letters that occupied all his thoughts. Then he remembered an essential part of any young gentleman's education which had still to be attended to—the grand tour. Charles must set out on his travels.

There were difficulties. First of all, an itinerary had to be drawn up with considerable care. It must include only those places in Europe where a Stuart prince would be received with royal honours as the rightful heir to the British throne, and this excluded as a matter of course most of the Austrian Emperor's domains. But the arrangements were finally made, and in May, 1737, Charles set out.

He travelled as the Duke of Albano, taking the name of the little mountain town which had been the family's favourite summer resort. He was accompanied by three of his tutors—the unhappy James Murray, and Henry Goring, both of whom he cordially disliked, and Francis Strickland, for whom the boy had a real affection.

He had a farewell interview with the Pope, who made him a handsome present of money for his journey, and then he set off to see the world.

The world was delighted to see him. Wherever he went he was acclaimed by enthusiastic crowds, and in Bologna and Parma military displays were held in honour of a young man who had already proved himself a gallant soldier. Venice, anticipating a visit, set eagerly about preparing a great carnival for the occasion, and Walton, trotting after the prince like a disgruntled dog, wrote long despairing letters home to England, describing in

detail the wonderful reception Charles received everywhere. " The fashionable idol of the moment," he called
him enviously, and had only one consoling piece of news
to offer. The Court of Tuscany held aloof from all these
celebrations.

But the people of Florence ignored the timid aloofness
of the Court and drove out in their carriages to meet
the Prince and his entourage as they approached the lovely
old town. Charles was showered with invitations to
balls and dinner parties held in his honour and Florence
defied officialdom and went *en fete*.

Pisa, Leghorn and Siena were included in the Prince's
triumphal progress, and young Charlie enjoyed himself
so much that he entirely neglected his anxious and
worried father, sitting in Rome longing for news of it
all. But however much he may have enjoyed his tour,
which lasted until the end of the summer, he was not
long back in Rome before his restless spirit showed itself
and he insisted on discussing his future with his father.

He was determined to be a soldier. It was the only
profession that interested him, and in any case it seemed
the only one that would fit in with his own plans and the
chances that lay ahead. James agreed readily. He
himself, for all his personal bravery, had shown little
aptitude for the life and no great grasp of strategy and
tactics ; but the trend of events in England had made
it abundantly clear that only a gifted soldier would have
any chance of winning the throne for the Stuarts. It
was idle to hope now that Britain would tire of her
German masters and daily the numbers of those at
home willing to risk their lives and their fortunes for
the Pretender's sake was dwindling.

So James set about finding a suitable opening for a
likely young man. He failed. The courts of France
and Spain both refused to have the Prince. For the
moment there was peace, and neither country had any
desire to offer Britain a direct affront by giving the
Pretender's son a commission.

The Emperor was preparing a campaign against the Turks. James decided to forget old differences and apply in that quarter. Surely there could be no political objection to employing his son against the Turks ! But apparently there was. The Emperor would have none of him.

It seemed, indeed, that the only friends the Stuarts had were here in Italy ; and even in Italy that friendship was becoming a little strained. Walton's reports of the carnivals in the Prince's honour at Venice had had an immediate and unfortunate effect—the Venetian Ambassador at the Court of St. James's was peremptorily dismissed ; and Venice, however indignant, was naturally inclined to blame this development—which might have serious effects on Venetian trade—upon the Stuarts.

So Charlie, thwarted at every turn, sought action in the only sphere left open to him. He went back to the shooting expeditions in the mountains that had always absorbed so much of his restless energy. A poor substitute for soldiering ; but they kept him fit, they took up his time and gave him the needed outlet for all that boundless physical energy he was storing up, and they fitted his mood of impatience and the need for action.

He grew tall, strikingly graceful in every movement, and as the years passed he became a splendid, virile young animal keyed up for the most desperate adventure. As a boy he had been lovable ; as a young man he showed himself possessed of a quite extraordinary personal charm.

But he still did not like women. They had no part in his scheme of things, and although such a handsome young prince was bound to be much sought after, with impassioned young ladies vying for a kind word or a smiling glance, he remained indifferent. He was, as always, the soul of charm ; but there it stopped. He had other things to think of, and preferred his shotgun or his fishing rod.

But . . . to waste the precious days of young

manhood, shooting and fishing ! He longed for action. He was not allowed to be a soldier ; but he could make a soldier of himself. There were old campaigns to be studied, books to read, battles to fight over again, on paper, for at all costs he meant, when the time came, to be capable of assuming command, to have the technical knowledge and ability to grapple with immediate problems on the field as well as to plan campaigns and carry out his plans.

" What a pleasure it would be," declared his father's secretary, Edgar, in a letter to the old Earl Marischal in Paris, " to see better game than the shooting of quails ! "

The better game was to come ; and young Charlie, athletic and in many ways Spartan, a splendid shot, a magnificent horseman, a soldier of proved gallantry and coolness, was ready for the long awaited moment.

CHAPTER FOUR

ALARMS AND EXCURSIONS

I hae seen the guid auld day,
  The day o' pride and chieftain glory,
When Royal Stuarts bore the sway,
  And ne'er heard tell o' Whig nor Tory.
Though lyart be my locks and grey,
  And eild has crook'd me down, what matter?
I'll dance and sing ae ither day—
  That day our king comes o'er the water!

CHARLES paced restlessly up and down. His tremendous energy allowed him no peace and he was growing exasperated by the continued delays, the inaction, the feeling of frustration.

He had been out since long before dawn, shooting. His father, worried a little still, had grown used to the restless behaviour of his elder son, who could not bear to be idle. He knew that Charles had not been to bed the night before—he had simply thrown himself into a chair, wrapped his riding coat round him, and slept for a few hours fully dressed and booted, ready to be up and away before the first daylight.

When he came back he showed no sign of fatigue. The two servants who had gone with him—men picked specially for their stamina and endurance—were utterly exhausted keeping up with the young Prince; but

Charles was still fresh and sleepless. Instead of resting he sat down in the music room and played his beloved violin, hour after hour. Then, after a hasty meal, he had come badgering his father for the news that never arrived, and now was walking up and down like a caged animal, tireless and impatient.

If only something could be done ! He was ready for the test—ready for the great moment in his life, when he should land in Britain and raise his standard and make the valiant attempt to regain the throne of his ancestors.

From the moment in 1740 when word had come of the death of the old Emperor of Austria, Charles VI, the Prince had been ready. Now surely the moment must be near ! All Europe was being dragged into the quarrels over the Austrian succession. Young Queen Maria Teresa of Hungary was surrounded by enemies and had appealed to England for help. Surely the government in London must make some move ? But, as nation after nation was involved in the European war, London remained aloof.

Charles knew of the scheme which had been worked out. It was Cardinal Fleury, Prime Minister of France, who had proposed it—an offer of 13,000 men for the invasion of Britain. Fifteen hundred were to land in the West Highlands, where Charles had always insisted that loyalty to the Stuarts was strongest ; fifteen hundred more were to land near Inverness, and the remaining ten thousand in the Thames, as near London as possible. The famous Marshal Saxe was to be put in command, and Charles was to accompany him.

But nothing had happened. Day after day, month after month passed, and still London did not declare war ; and Fleury would not move until London was involved. He cared not a fig for the Stuart cause ; all he cared about was France. Charles, on tenterhooks, had waited in vain for a summons to Paris. He had had to try to burn up his boundless energy in hunting and shooting, for physical fitness was a fetish with him and he meant to be ready at any moment for the most arduous campaign.

So on October 1st, 1742, his father had written of him : " Charles is quite wearied of this country (Italy). I don't wonder at it, for his sole amusement here is to go out shooting, to which he has gone every other day all this season before daybreak, whether fair or foul."

James proudly informed a friend that after these excursions Charles " sits down and diverts himself with music for an hour or two, as if he had not been abroad." Indeed the young man had music in his soul, and although his brother Henry could sing more sweetly it was Charles who had inherited all the Stuart passion for music.

But music was only a brief solace ; for he was eating his heart out in enforced inaction ; and all the while he knew that every moment was precious, that there was no time to waste.

Occasionally there had been heartening news. The Scots Jacobites had formed an association in Edinburgh which included the Duke of Perth, Lord John Drummond, Lord Lovat, the chief of the Frasers, Lord Linton, his brother the Hon. John Stuart, Donald Cameron the younger of Lochiel (whose aged father was in exile), and his father-in-law, Sir John Campbell of Auchenbreck. As secretary, they had William Drummond of Bochaldy, and as their travelling agent John Murray of Broughton, who was sent over to Paris in January, 1743 to see how the land lay.

Murray had had a disappointing visit. Fleury died suddenly, and the French minister in charge of foreign affairs, Amelot, told him bluntly that the French King would do nothing without definite assurances that the English Jacobites would take up arms to support the proposed invasion. In Paris, too, the aged Earl Marischal, one of the leading Jacobite supporters there, was inclined to be over cautious, and discredited the high-spirited optimism of men like Bochaldy and Lord Sempil and other Jacobites.

This had all happened a year ago. A whole year ! Charles, fretting in Rome, had controlled his impatience as best he could, with only one piece of encouragement. His father had promised him definitely that he should go to Britain as Regent.

Then suddenly fresh news had come—news that sent Charles's spirits soaring, and raised his hopes to fever pitch. England had moved at last. There had been a clash between English and French troops at Dettingen. True, the French had been soundly trounced, and George II, who had been present at the battle, had displayed a certain amount of clumsy courage ; but the very fact that the French had been defeated was likely to help the Stuart cause. It infuriated King Louis, who promptly ordered troops to be assembled at Dunkirk.

Something was bound to happen soon ; and as Charles paced up and down he heard a commotion in the Palace, and strode out to discover what was happening.

A courier had arrived from Paris. The despatches he brought were torn open by eager hands, and a shout of joy escaped from the Prince's lips. The moment had come. The despatches contained an urgent summons for the Prince to repair to Paris forthwith.

His eyes glowing with excitement, his face transformed, Charles looked triumphantly at his father.

§

He summoned his brother Henry, that gentle, studious youth who adored him. He summoned his servants. He summoned the old secretary and tutor, James Murray. He needed them now. " We leave at once," he announced, crisply. " I am going—hunting."

They were used to that, to the sudden decision, the sudden departure. By late evening they were ready to leave. In the darkness horses were saddled and the little party rode out from the Palace and took the road for Albano, that pleasant little village where the family was accustomed to spending the summer months and where Charles made his headquarters on his hunting trips.

No sooner out of Rome than Charles set the pace, galloping along the dark familiar road. Mile after mile passed under the thundering hooves, and towards dawn they were still travelling, pressing forward at full speed. Then Charles, turning, gave a slight signal to the elderly tutor.

A few minutes later Murray's horse shied and threw him into the ditch beside the road. Charles drew rein. " Go on ! " he cried to the rest. " I'll attend to Murray. I'll overtake you later."

They galloped on, only one personal servant staying behind with the Prince. Charles dismounted and ran across to the ditch where Murray lay. He bent over him solicitously ; but there was a smile on his face, and as he slipped an arm under the tutor's shoulders he said, quietly :

" Well done, Murray. You contrived that neatly."

The tutor, sitting up stiffly, returned a glum smile. Charles had never liked him ; for that matter Murray had never particularly liked Charles. But he was ready to perform a service for him at a moment of crisis— the very last service he had the chance of performing. He got slowly to his feet.

They changed clothes. Charles beckoned his servant, and they mounted again. A last handshake, and they wheeled and galloped off, leaving Murray to swing himself back into his own saddle and follow the shooting party.

Now Charles felt he really could travel. He took a side road he knew well, and the pair went thundering away on a wide detour that would put any pursuit off their track.

Back at the Muti Palace it was being given out that Charles and Henry had left in the middle of the night on one of the Prince's mad hunting trips.

But Charles was headed for Genoa. The long ride had been gruelling, and the servant was worn out ; but Charles was tireless. A night or so without sleep—what mattered that to a splendid young athlete of twenty-three ?

He did not linger in Genoa. Travelling in the guise of a Spanish courier, with passports furnished by Cardinal Aquaviva, he hastened on to Savona, where he found a felucca to take him to Antibes, on the coast of France beyond Monte Carlo. They sailed at once.

One factor he could not reckon with in his planning—the weather ; and from the outset the weather was against him. They ran into a storm. For himself, Charles did not care. His restless energetic spirit welcomed the buffeting of the storm, the discomfort and exposure and danger. He gloried in the sense of personal combat against the sea ; but precious time was passing. The ship was delayed, and the passage to Antibes seemed interminable.

At last they saw the coast of France, and the ship headed for the little harbour. Charles was first ashore, consumed with impatience to be on his way. At Antibes he found horses and a chaise and servants, and headed for Paris.

But at Antibes he had been recognised, and word was already on its way to England. The Prince was in France ! It would not take genius to put two and two together and guess that Prince Charles in France meant danger to the Hanoverians.

In Paris Charles met the Earl Marischal, and Sempil, and Bochaldy and the rest ; and he also had secret meetings with the men on whom he had to rely for military assistance—King Louis, and Amelot, and Marshal Saxe. It was dangerous to remain in Paris, which was alive with spies and secret agents of the Hanoverian Government ; so he went on to Gravelines to await the signal.

Here he was able to keep an eye on the preparations

going ahead for the great day. The French fleet, with fifteen ships of the line and five frigates, sailed from Brest, and, coming up the Channel, made a great show of force. Its commander, de Roquefeuille, set a course which brought the fleet within sight of Spithead, and he discovered to his delight that not a single English ship was to be seen. That could only mean, he argued, that they had all retired within their harbours and were not prepared to risk an action ; so he sent five ships in haste to Dunkirk, with orders to speed up the embarkation of the troops and get the transports to sea at once.

The transports were awkwardly placed, and embarkation was slow, but Marshal Saxe was on his way to Dunkirk, and Charles joined him there.

On the very day they arrived at Dunkirk, de Roquefeuille discovered that he had been too optimistic. A powerful English fleet appeared in the Channel, and he had to withdraw rather than risk an engagement just when he was expecting the transports.

Charles worked with a will, helping to direct the embarkation. Here was a job after his own heart, the job he had prepared himself for, and in that first day no fewer than 7,000 men were put on board, and proceeded to sea.

Ashore, they still worked feverishly ; but by evening anxious faces were lifted to the sky, anxious eyes stared out to sea ; for the wind had changed. Within an hour it was blowing a gale, and the work of embarkation came to a standstill.

Charles and the Marshal looked on helplessly. The sailors did what they could ; but the transports that had already left the anchorage were fighting a losing battle with the gale, which was driving them steadily on the rocks. By dark, the terrible truth was forced upon them. Several of the transports had been wrecked, hundreds of soldiers had been drowned, vast quantities of stores had been lost and all the other ships still in harbour had been severely damaged. Many of them had

dragged their anchors and gone ashore. The great invasion fleet was smashed. It would take weeks, months to repair the damage and make the ships fit for sea again.

§

It was a bitter blow. Charles, trying desperately to weigh up the situation, to find some way of saving it, faced the grim facts with a grimmer courage.

It had all been so well planned, so carefully worked out, so wonderfully well carried out ! But for this terrible accident of the storm the landing would have already been made, a well-trained army would already be marching on London, sweeping aside all opposition and securing thousands of recruits among the English Jacobites. And now. . . .

Now all was lost. All hope of surprise was gone, and as news arrived of a powerful English squadron out patrolling the Channel Charles steeled himself for the interview which he knew to be inevitable.

It came very soon. Marshal Saxe desired an audience.

The Marshal came in with a glum face, his tight-lipped mouth betraying the bitterness of his disappointment. " I have instructions from Paris," he said abruptly. " I am to inform Your Highness that the plan of invasion has been abandoned."

Charles looked at him with quick sympathy. He understood the feelings of a soldier whose plans had gone awry—and who was in the hands of the politicians.

" I expected no other decision," he replied quietly. " But I am resolved not to give up the attempt. It is not invasion of England that concerns me, sir. It is my father's throne. We can no longer invade England, but may I entreat you, sir, to carry out at least one part of the plan? May I entreat you to send off the expeditions to Scotland?"

The Marshal listened to the young and ardent voice, looked with a seasoned soldier's eye at this tall, slim youth who confronted him so passionately. Admiration kindled in his eyes, for he recognised the Prince's mettle, he knew that here was a man born to be a leader of men, a man whom men would follow blindly to victory— or to death. But he shook his head. He would try; he had little hope that he would succeed.

He tried. But the Court was adamant. The whole plan had been abandoned; the King was not prepared to throw away even so small a force on a wildcat scheme that must come to naught.

Charles did not give up hope. He refused to leave Gravelines. The aged Earl Mareschal, that staunch Jacobite who when it came to the bit was always urging caution, pleaded with him. In turn the Prince pleaded.

" I have never placed much faith in these English Jacobites. They drink the health of the king over the water, they drink my health each New Year's Eve, they talk of their ancient loyalty and how they long for the restoration of the rightful king. But I have not heard that it ever went beyond talking. In Scotland it is different. There the Stuart cause still lives. There my loyal Highlanders will rise to a man to fight for a just cause. That is why I urge you to persuade France to send troops to Scotland. With fifteen hundred men landed at Inverness and other fifteen hundred in the West Highlands, and arms and supplies for the recruits that will pour in, I can yet win the throne for my father. I beg you will use all your influence to persuade the

Court to carry out the project. You have but to persuade
the French, and I will sail. With only these three
thousand men I will land in Scotland—and chase the
Elector of Hanover out of Britain."

The Earl, sighing over lost opportunities, listened,
admired—and privately decided that the time was not ripe.

Charles argued. He pleaded passionately, he fought to
win his own way ; for he knew better than anyone what
it meant. They did not realise, these exiled Jacobites,
that time was passing—and time was precious. In the
solitude of his own room Charles brooded, seeing the
situation with clear young eyes.

It was thirty years since a Stuart had sat on the throne
of Britain. Thirty years since Queen Anne died. Thirty
years of foreign rule. There might be discontent,
there might be popular dissatisfaction—particularly in
Scotland, where the Union of Parliaments had been so
bitterly resented—with these foreign usurpers, these
awkward, boorish German nonentities who had come
from their miserable little castles to fill the English
Court, bringing their fat and ugly *fraus* to waddle around
the gracious gardens of Hampton Court and to banish
all elegance and good breeding from English society.
What was it the song said :

> Wha the deil hae we gotten for a king
> But a wee, wee German lairdie?
> And when they sent to bring him hame
> He was delving in his kail-yairdie,
> Sheughing kail and laying leeks,
> Without the hose and but the breeks,
> When up his beggar duds he cleeks,
>   The wee, wee German lairdie !

Ridicule—yes ; there was plenty of that. Plenty of
people who despised these fat illiterate foreigners, with
their crude habits and their unpleasant ways. But—
what more than that ? That was the question. The
people might sing :

The very dogs at England's court
They bark and howl in German !

But . . . did discontent amount to more than
discontent ? In thirty years the country had changed.
Ways of life had changed. The royal prerogative was
gone, the king was but a cipher now. He no longer
interfered directly in the government of the country.
If he dared to do an unpopular thing he would soon be
called to heel. And England was getting used to this
state of affairs. What chance the ordinary people, who
were growing prosperous under the new regime, and the
aristocracy, who had accepted it and were turning it to
good use for their own purposes, would be prepared to
rise against it and throw it out—in favour of the Stuarts?

So Charles, pacing his room in Gravelines, realised
the blunt and wretched truth. Every moment counted.
Every day he delayed meant less support for his cause.
The Earl Marischal might counsel caution and inaction,
a policy of waiting ; Charles saw how fatal that would
be. He wrote to his father in a tone of humorous despair,
describing the letters, " rather books," he called them,
that came from his supporters, all advising caution and
patience. But he could not be patient. Too much was
at stake.

Again the French Court returned a definite " No."
Even the 3,000 men Charles asked for were denied him.
The opportunity was past, the cause was lost ; he must
look elsewhere.

He knew where to look—where, all his life, he had
believed he would find his real support—Scotland. For
years he had talked of Scotland, of his " loyal Highlanders " whom he had never seen, whose language he
could not speak. He had picked up a few words from
men he had met—Drummond (or MacGregor) of
Bochaldy and others ; he had learnt all he could about
the Highlands ; but still they were only a dream, the
final hope of his cause.

§

He tackled the old Earl again.

"I cannot be idle," he declared passionately. "I must be up and doing. If nothing can be done immediately for my father's cause at least I can be doing for myself. I am a soldier. You know that I am well trained, and have had experience of war. At least allow me to serve France, since I may not serve my own country."

The old Earl, gazing at this impulsive youth whose high spirits could not be quenched by any disaster, may have felt his heart swell with pride and admiration ; but his cautious old brain registered alarm. He was genuinely worried. Charles was just the type to go and get himself killed in some reckless action—and so ruin all. He must be dissuaded.

Of course his request had to be passed on ; but the Earl could breathe a sigh of relief very soon, for the French turned it down immediately. They had no wish for the services of His Royal Highness in the French army.

Charles, frustrated wherever he turned, agreed at last to move from Gravelines. But he did not move far. He went to Montmartre, near Paris, and there he was joined by Sir Thomas Sheridan, one of his former tutors, who had been with him at Gaeta. He was one of the few tutors to whom Charles, as a boy, had taken a real liking, and now Charles welcomed his company. He brought with him two other Irishmen, George Kelly and a Father Kelly, and had they but known it this association was, in the end, to prove fatal for the cause.

There were others of consequence in Paris at the time —those enthusiastic and optimistic Jacobites, Sempil and Bochaldy ; and inevitably Scots and Irish quarrelled. The young Prince, fretting his heart out in idleness, was annoyed by these quarrels—and inevitably sided with the man whom he had known and liked for years.

Writing to his father he several times made rash remarks, siding with the Irish against the Scots, and James, who had never lost his sense of values, wrote back sharply, reprimanding him for his lack of discretion. But in reality Charles had never lost sight of the one thing of moment—the cause ; and now he showed that his brain was hard and clear and completely logical, just as he was soon to show that in action he could be resolute and decisive. He knew that his greatest hope lay in the Highlands.

So Charles patched up the quarrels as best he could, and went on quietly with his plans. His mind was made up. He spoke to the Earl Marischal.

" We cannot depend upon France for help," he reminded him. " But time is short. I am ready to go alone, to raise the standard in Scotland and rely upon the loyalty of my own people to come to my help."

The Earl was deeply shocked. Such a course was utterly out of the question ; it could only lead to disaster. He reported the matter to James, and James, eager as he was to see his son land in Britain, agreed wholeheartedly with the Earl. To go alone, without the support of a powerful army, would be utter folly.

Charles listened to the Earl, politely thanked his father for his advice—and kept his own counsel thereafter. Whatever plans he made now he was determined not to let his father know. He had had enough of interference and disappointment, he had suffered enough as a pawn in the hands of the politicians. He would go his own way henceforth—and tell no one.

His mind made up, he could be patient now, until the moment arrived. He would choose that himself.

§

A servant came to announce the arrival of visitors to see the Prince. Charles, who was now staying with Æneas MacDonald, the Jacobite banker in Paris, was immersed in correspondence, but he threw down his pen gladly and received his visitors. They were Drummond of Bochaldy and Lord Sempil, the Old Pretender's agents in Paris, and they brought with them the agent of the Edinburgh Association, John Murray of Broughton, newly arrived from Scotland.

Here was a new and welcome contact with his Scots supporters, and Charles, eager for any sort of news of the home he had never seen, invited Murray to a private interview next day.

Murray was deeply worried. The abject failure of the French expedition had had a serious effect on Jacobite prospects, and the long months that has passed since then—for this was now July—without any further plan being made had cast the Scots Jacobites deep in gloom.

" Your Highness," he said bluntly, " we of the Association in Edinburgh are greatly perturbed. That is why I have come to Paris—first, to discover and report on the situation here, and secondly to explain to you the situation at home."

Charles was impressed with his earnestness. He knew that Murray would not have undertaken so dangerous a journey lightly, and he replied with equal frankness.

" I do not doubt at all that King Louis intends to invade Britain next spring. Preparations are already being made, and I am convinced it will take place as soon as the campaign in Flanders is over. But whether King Louis undertakes the expedition or not, sir, I am determined to delay no further, but to go to Scotland myself."

Murray gave a start of surprise. He had more sense than to imagine this was mere bravado.

" That would indeed be a desperate enterprise," he declared ; but the Prince smiled gently and merely nodded. Plainly, he had no illusions about that.

" Your Highness must understand," Murray went on earnestly, " that you could not hope to raise more than four or five thousand men in the Highlands. The clans are wary. They have suffered deeply. Roads have been built and bridges thrown across the rivers, and forts erected and garrisoned at many points. The Highlanders have been disarmed—— "

" There are muskets and claymores in every thatch ! "

" And danger too," Murray pointed out. " Danger to all our people. They need expect no mercy, no justice, no compassion. Their chiefs will think long before they ask their people to risk such a fate."

Charles listened attentively ; but when Murray had finished he smiled slightly again, and replied :

" Nevertheless my mind is made up. I shall go to Scotland next year—even if I have only one footman with me."

Murray shook an anxious head ; but there was admiration in his eyes, and his own enthusiasm kindled. Out of a sense of caution he tried again to persuade the Prince to abandon the mad idea ; but his arguments now had lost their conviction. He was beginning to believe himself that if the Prince once showed himself in Scotland thousands would flock to his standard. Who could resist the appeal of that magnetic personality, the fascination of a Prince who was every inch a prince ? The level-headed, clear-sighted Scot had fallen under the spell—and, being an ambitious man, saw new possibilities in the Prince.

All the same, Murray was still against the plan. After the interview he sought out Sir Thomas Sheridan, who was reputed to have great influence with the Prince, and begged him to do everything in his power to dissuade Charles from the rash step he contemplated. The Irishman promised to do what he could ; but there was a deep gulf between Irish and Scots.

The Irish Jacobites had nothing to lose. They had no estates, no people dependent upon them, no fortunes to place in pawn. They could see no reason for holding back. If the gamble succeeded, what rewards would be theirs ! If it failed, and they escaped with their lives

and got back to France, then they would be no worse off than before. They failed to understand the position in Scotland. Failure meant, for the Highlands, not just a return to idleness in exile but the end of all things, the destruction of their homes, the massacre of their women and children, all the horrors of occupation by a brutal and merciless foe.

Murray went home to Scotland, to report to the Association, and his reception was what he had expected. All but the Duke of Perth condemned the Prince's determination and insisted that he must not set foot in Scotland except at the head of a strong and well-trained force. Murray wrote a long letter to Charles, setting out all the arguments in detail ; but the letter was never delivered. It went astray, found its way back to Murray the following April, and, sent off again on its wanderings, reached France too late.

§

Charles went on with his preparations. His mind made up, he never once wavered in his determination— or in his optimism. But he knew the terrible risk that lay ahead, and so he kept his agents busy at the French court, trying to pin King Louis down to a definite promise and a definite plan. They failed. The French, who had found the Stuarts useful pawns to play in the

game of international politics, would not give a definite
refusal ; instead they renewed their assurances of support
—conditional assurances that seemed important but
meant little.

James, fretting in Rome, engaged in his endless correspondence, realised the blunt truth. The promises of the
French court were worthless ; no help would be forthcoming from that quarter—unless it suited King Louis'
own schemes. Then a new worry came to plague the
Old Pretender. Somehow a rumour of Charles's intention
got about in Paris, and Sempil picked it up. He passed it
on, at once, and in a letter of February 23rd, 1745, James
who had thought the mad scheme long ago forgotten,
replied :

" I am noways surprised that some French people
should have a notion of the Prince's going to Scotland
without troops, tho' nobody surely can enter into such
an idea except out of ignorance, and from not knowing
the true state of things. But I am always alarmed at it,
because I think it impossible that the King of France
should approve of such a project, and that it is well
known how much I should myself be averse to it."

But the rumour soon died ; Charles accepted invitations
from the Duke of Fitzjames and other friends of the
Stuart family to visit their country houses near Paris,
and in a round of pleasant visits among these people,
and in the country sports he always had delighted in,
Charles spent the next few months without betraying
a hint of what was in his mind. It seemed, in fact, that
he had entirely forgotten why he had come to France,
and was no longer interested in anything but the pleasures
of society. His father forgot his alarm, the family friends
accepted the change in the Prince without suspicion, and
Charles went on, in the privacy of his own room, with
his quiet patient planning.

§

Charles opened the letter from Paris with a sudden quickening of the pulse. He had the feeling that momentous news was contained in it, and a glance at the signature made him eager to read without delay ; for the letter was from Colonel O'Bryan, one of his father's agents, and it contained news of the war—vital news. On the 11th of May a costly battle had been fought between the French army under Marshal Saxe and the British army, at Fontenoy. The Marshal had won a decisive victory.

Charles read the letter several times, studied it carefully, then sat back to think. He was twenty-four ; but his upbringing in exile had given him a grasp of hard facts far firmer than that of many a man of twice his age. He was not to be deceived by news, good or bad. He thought it over quietly and calmly.

When, eventually, he wrote his reply to O'Bryan he pointed out that it was not easy to form an opinion whether the news would prove good or bad for his cause. Others might rejoice eagerly in the French victory ; not so Charles. For by this time he was not deceived about the value of French promises.

The war was practically over. Why should it be prolonged indefinitely, and at great cost, merely in order to put a different king on the British throne ? Louis, in his moment of victory, would sit back and breathe easily once more—and almost · certainly make up his mind to take no further risks.

But there were other things to be borne in mind over this Battle of Fontenoy. The British army had been overwhelmed by superior numbers ; it had, however, retired from the field in good order and without confusion. Its reputation as a fighting force remained intact. But its casualties had been enormous. A large part of the flower of the British army had been destroyed ; and Charles was quick to seize upon that fact. Britain was depleted of her soldiers, the government at home could, at best, raise only a small and ill-trained force in case of need.

Charles came to his feet, drawing a deep breath. His eyes lit up, and he stood for a long moment, staring into the future. The hour had struck.

CHAPTER FIVE

THE SEVEN MEN OF MOIDART

The news frae Moidart cam' yestreen
Will soon gar money ferlie,
For ships o' war hae just come in
And landed royal Charlie !

CHARLES sat silent, fingering the long stem of his glass.
His face was impassive, but the two Irishmen opposite
him, glancing at him now and again, caught the intent-
ness with which he was watching them and read the
eagerness that burned in his eyes. They noted, too, that
he did not empty his glass. He drank little, for he had
always been abstemious.

They listened in silence while the fourth man talked.
He wore the uniform of a lieutenant-general in the
French service ; but his accent proclaimed his nationality
—that, and the eagerness with which he spoke. He was
Lord Clare, afterwards Marshal Thomond, and he
carried a definite commission from the French Government. He had been authorised to negotiate certain
urgent matters.

" His Royal Highness," he explained bluntly, " intends
to land in Scotland. The French Government will not

officially sanction this step, but I can assure you, gentlemen, that there will be no difficulty about that. Otherwise I, an officer in His French Majesty's forces, would not be here. The Prince means to land in the West Highlands, where his best hope of support lies, and he wishes to take with him as many men as can be raised, and whatever arms and equipment are available. He himself has purchased a thousand muskets and eighteen hundred broadswords and some small field pieces, out of his own pocket—and he will forgive me for telling you plainly, gentlemen, that it has not been easy. He has had to scrimp and save every penny piece to do that. Now he requires transport, and that is why I have sent for you two gentlemen."

The two gentlemen nodded understandingly. They were merchants, both Irish, and they had made a fair amount of money trading in the West Indies. During the war they had found a more lucrative trade, for they had fitted out privateers and, in partnership, had recently managed to persuade the French Government to make them a grant of a fine ship for their purpose, the *Elizabeth*, an old man-of-war of sixty guns. They had also bought a frigate, the *Doutelle*, of sixteen guns, and both ships were even now being fitted out for their first cruise.

" I offer you the chance of a far more momentous cruise than you had dreamed of, gentlemen," Lord Clare told them, and Ruttledge and Walsh looked at each other, looked at the Prince, and nodded immediately.

" The ships are yours," they said, and held a brief conference together. The Prince and Clare waited quietly, only the glow in the Prince's eyes betraying his excitement ; then the Irish merchants made a new offer.

" We will supply Your Highness with whatever money and arms we can procure."

They rose to take their leave ; and Charles went back to Navarre where he was now staying as the guest of the Duke of Bouillon.

His spirits were high. Arrangements were going

smoothly, he had contrived to save enough money at least for the small supply of arms he had bought, and to keep a reserve of four thousand louis d'or in cash, since gold was essential to any enterprise ; and now at Navarre he occupied his days hunting, shooting and fishing, kept his own counsel and was determined to cheat not only the English spies but his own father's agents. He was not going to have his plans wrecked by his father's interference.

The great day drew nearer, and still he hunted, shot, and fished ; still such news of him as came from Navarre was entirely reassuring. By no outward sign could anyone guess what was in his mind.

He sent out secret instructions to the picked band of men who alone were in the secret. They were to assemble at Nantes, near the mouth of the Loire, and they were to go there separately, find lodgings in different parts of the town, and give no sign of recognition when they passed each other in the streets. Even walls had eyes and ears, and France swarmed with spies and secret agents.

He wrote again to Colonel O'Bryan, to inform him that he was about to pay a visit to the monastery of La Trappe near Rouen, and would be back in Paris in a few days' time. O'Bryan dutifully reported this move to the Old Pretender, as Charles hoped he would do ; and so, unsuspected, he prepared for his fateful journey.

§

Nobody noticed the tall young man, so plainly dressed and so quiet mannered, who journeyed to Nantes a few days later, and who, at Nantes, persuaded some fishermen to take him on board and drop down the Loire. Nobody paid any attention to the same young man when he went quietly out to a little frigate that lay at anchor in the roads. That was on the 21st of June, and it excited no comment whatever when the little frigate raised anchor next day and shifted down to Belleisle, where she anchored again. But on board the frigate was a small party, some young, some middle-aged or more, who spoke together in quiet tones and looked often at the tall youth who had come so unobtrusively among them.

There were six men in the party—six men in whom the Hanoverian Government was more than interested. There was first the Marquis of Tullibardine, elder brother of the Duke of Athole. He had himself been Duke of Athole, but had been " out " in the Fifteen and had been attainted and stripped of the title and estates, which had gone to his younger brother. There was Sir John MacDonald, an Irish captain in the Spanish Carabineers ; there were the banker Æneas MacDonald, who had several times been Prince Charles's host in Paris and was a brother of MacDonald of Kinlochmoidart ; the clergyman, George Kelly ; Colonel John William O'Sullivan, of the French army ; Sir Thomas Sheridan, the Prince's old tutor and friend ; and lastly, Francis Strickland, the only Englishman among them.

Besides the six there were two others, the Jacobite Buchanan who had lived with Æneas MacDonald in Paris and had served as a messenger not only for the Jacobites but for Cardinal Tencin, and a man from Barra, Duncan Cameron, who had gone into exile with old Lochiel and had been his servant at Boulogne. He had been sent with the party for the express purpose of acting as pilot when the ships should reach the West Highlands, for he alone of them all would be able to recognise the Long Isle when he saw it—that string of islands which, like a broken barrier reef, protect the West Highlands from the broad Atlantic.

For several days the little *Doutelle* lay idly at anchor, while adverse winds delayed her consort ; then at last, on July 4th, a shout went up, and presently into the anchorage came the fine old man-of-war, *Elizabeth*, with a handful of sailors at the ropes and nothing to give away her purpose. But below deck lay a hundred marines, recruited by Lord Clare, and in the hold were two

thousand muskets and several hundred French broadswords.

The *Elizabeth* came to her anchor near the frigate and
snugged down for the night. The wind had dropped,
the anchorage was tranquil, the two ships lay idle, silent,
insignificant. But in his cabin on board the *Doutelle*
the tall young man sat all alone, conscious of a great
sense of relief and calm.

The decision had been irrevocably made. The die
was about to be cast. At last the long months and years
of weary waiting, of hope deferred and plans frustrated,
of maddening inaction and doubt and deceit, were over.
Ahead lay action—brisk, decisive action, perhaps a forlorn
hope but at least the action for which his whole soul
had longed since the days when a boy first dreamed of
recovering a throne.

Charles went quietly to bed, with a serene, clear mind,
to await the morrow.

§

The day dawned fine and clear. A fair wind blew
from the south, and Charles, coming early on deck,
spoke quietly to Walsh, who was sailing in command
of the *Doutelle*. The Irishman greeted him with a smile,
then turned to give his orders. Both ships hove their
cables short, the sails were broken out along the yards,

and as they bellied in the wind a feeling of excitement and anticipation spread through the ships.

Charles paced the frigate's quarterdeck, gazing at the shores of France, turning to gaze ahead into the far distance. Anchors were aweigh, the *Doutelle* began slipping through the calm water, and her bigger, heavier consort followed. They came out into the open, heading West, until Charles could look northward at last. Beyond that horizon lay England. Beyond England lay Scotland, that remote country from which came these ardent, opinionated and moody men upon whom he had come to rely completely.

The fair wind held all day, the two ships, keeping close company, made excellent progress, and when Charles retired to bed that night it was with the knowledge that very soon they would be approaching dangerous waters —waters in which they might expect to meet at least some units of the British fleet. For the next two days the wind held fair, and then Charles, coming on deck on the 8th, realised that a change had come over the scene. The sea, which before had been dancing with white caps, lay heaving in long slow oily undulations ; the sun blazed out of a cloudless sky that soon hazed over, and not a breath of wind stirred the heavy white folds of canvas above his head. The two ships, idle, lay rolling gently on the swell.

These shifts of fortune had but to be endured. Charles had been too used to winds that blew hot and cold, the winds of politics and intrigue, too accustomed to setbacks and delays to show his impatience now. Calmly he paced the quarterdeck, taking his daily exercise, or sat in his cabin reading, writing, or making plans. The long day passed, and during the night, as he lay in his bunk, he heard the creaking of blocks and tackle taking the strain again, and the ripple of broken water slipping along the ship's side. The wind had revived, the two ships were moving once more. But the wind remained light, and his first sight of the sea and sky in the morning gave him no promise of a stronger breeze. They were travelling —but travelling slowly.

Walsh, making his reckoning, gave their position as latitude 47° 57′ North, and just a hundred and eleven miles west of the Lizard. England would soon be abeam.

Suddenly a lookout hailed.

" Sail-ho ! Sail to windward ! "

All eyes turned to gaze over the starboard quarter, and presently they made out the towering snowy canvas of a ship rising above the horizon.

" What ship is she, do you think, Master Walsh ? " the Prince enquired. The Irishman, experienced privateer that he was, had no need to look long.

" An English ship," he replied promptly, " and on our heels."

Helplessly they watched, as the stranger gradually overhauled them, and suddenly Walsh nodded his head and declared :

" She is the *Lion*, an English ship of sixty guns. She will give us a bad time if she proves inquisitive."

There was no doubt that she was inquisitive, and Charles, who had been on the point of transferring to the *Elizabeth*, for the sake of the better accommodation she could offer him, changed his mind.

" I will stay with the *Doutelle*," he decided, " at least until we see the issue of this business."

The two ships cracked on sail ; but the *Lion*, a far more modern ship than the old *Elizabeth*, came up hand over fist, and the course she was steering made her purpose plain. She meant to overhaul and investigate the two French ships.

The *Elizabeth* and the *Doutelle* altered course slightly, to draw closer together, and Charles, watching, saw a boat lowered from the man-of-war. Her captain himself was coming over to hold a council of war. It was held on the frigate's quarterdeck, and it was brief, for this was an affair for sailors primarily. Captain D'Oe, who commanded the *Elizabeth*, wasted no time.

" I propose, gentlemen," he declared, " that we should if possible avoid an action."

He looked round the assembled adventurers, and saw agreement in every face. Their business was to reach Scotland in safety and with all speed ; a battle at sea might prove disastrous. But they must be ready for any event, and Captain D'Oe and Walsh discussed the situation keenly. In the end, the plan of action was rapidly outlined.

" If action is forced upon us, the *Elizabeth* will receive the enemy's first broadside, and thereupon bear down upon her and attempt to board."

It seemed the most sensible course, for the hundred marines on board the *Elizabeth* would give a good account of themselves and carry the Englishmen by storm.

While the discussion had been going on the ships had been running before the wind, and when Captain D'Oe turned to go down into his boat again he saw that the enemy had closed the range and was bearing down on them steadily. When she was little more than half a mile away she suddenly hove to. D'Oe pursed his lips as he watched this manœuvre, for it could have only one meaning. The *Lion* was clearing her decks for action. He turned quickly to Walsh.

" There is no chance now, it seems," he said, " of avoiding action. Therefore I propose that when I am engaged with the enemy you will close within range of your guns and play upon her on her disengaged side."

Walsh shook his head.

" No, sir," he replied. " I am only lightly armed, no match for the guns of such a ship. I shall not interfere in any shape."

D'Oe tried to insist, but Walsh stood firm. He was not prepared to risk his ship as well as the *Elizabeth*. The little *Doutelle* was fast, she could look after herself, and he meant to keep her well out of harm's way. D'Oe inclined his head, drew the sword from its scabbard, saluted, and went down into his boat. Still with drawn sword in hand, he boarded the *Elizabeth* again as she prepared for action.

He had scarcely set foot on deck when the *Lion* was seen to be bearing down directly upon the ship. Charles, watching from the frigate, saw the two ships drawing steadily closer, and suddenly the *Elizabeth* altered course to bring her broadside to bear on the pursuer. A moment later flame rippled along her bulwarks and the thunder of thirty guns roared out.

Almost instantly the *Lion* too altered course and returned the broadside. The *Elizabeth* was desperately wearing ship to bring her other broadside to bear ; but the English ship, newer and in better shape, proved too quick for her. She hoisted her jib and ran ahead to get across the *Elizabeth's* bows, and got in her broadside before the *Elizabeth* could save herself. As the *Doutelle's* log-book recorded : " The Englishman had time to pass forward and contrived so well that he fired all his port broadside, which raked the *Elizabeth* fore and aft, and must have killed many and done her great damage, so that the Englishman got between our two ships, and fired from his starboard guns three shots, which passed between my masts ; my sails were riddled with his small shots, so much so that we did not fire, being out of range to reach him with our small guns."

But the *Elizabeth* was not daunted by this early misfortune. She continued the fight doggedly, exchanging broadside for broadside until both ships were so heavily damaged that it was a wonder they remained afloat.

Charles, watching the battle helplessly, turned at last to Walsh.

" I beg you to intervene, Mr. Walsh," he cried. " Let us run down upon the Englishman and engage him. We may save the *Elizabeth* if we do so."

Walsh shook his head. " I have refused to interfere," he replied firmly. " The risk is too great."

Charles bit his lip. For himself he cared not a fig. Had he had command of this ship he would have risked her without a qualm, to help her consort. But Walsh remained adamant, and the battle went on just beyond range of the frigate's guns.

The Prince watched anxiously. Now if the *Doutelle* joined in the enemy would be caught unprepared between two fires, unable to defend himself. Again he spoke to Walsh, urging him to take a hand in the fray. But Walsh, suddenly losing his temper, spoke back sharply.

" If your royal highness continues to badger me at this time with these suggestions," he snapped, " I shall be compelled to order you down to your cabin."

Charles accepted the rebuff with as good a grace as he could muster. He knew what was at stake, he knew that rashness should have no place in his actions now ; but the sight of the *Elizabeth* so hard pressed by the enemy's superior guns and heavier broadsides, and at such a disadvantage in speed, was hard to bear, and the enforced inaction riled him.

So for five hours the battle went on, with the *Doutelle* tagging at the heels of the contending ships, taking no part in the action but resolved all the same not to abandon her consort ; and at last the daylight faded, night came on, and the two ships, both badly crippled, drew out of range of each other as if by mutual consent. Neither ship, indeed, was in any condition to carry on the battle.

At once the *Doutelle* closed her consort, and the *Elizabeth's* first lieutenant made a report. The ship had suffered severe losses in men and officers, Captain D'Oe himself was wounded and the ship could not possibly proceed on the voyage without repairs.

Charles listened to this grim news in silence. Adversity had so long been his constant companion that he showed no sign of dismay. The first lieutenant, having finished his report, made a suggestion :

" I am willing to continue the voyage," he declared, " if you can supply me with a mainmast and some rigging." But Walsh shook his head. He had no spare gear on board and could not help.

" I would advise you, sir, to put back," he declared.
" You cannot continue the voyage. You must return to
Brest."

The lieutenant agreed. It seemed the only safe course
in the circumstances ; but what would Walsh decide
to do ?

Charles spoke, for the first time."

" We shall continue the voyage to Scotland alone."

There was a long moment's silence, while every eye
was upon the Prince. Then Walsh nodded and said,
quietly :

" Yes, we shall continue the voyage alone."

§

Seven men, a few hundred broadswords, some muskets
and field pieces. Seven men setting out to conquer a
kingdom ! It had been fantastic enough with only two
ships, and a hundred marines. Now it seemed preposterous. But the seven men did not waver ; and
Charles remained serene. No misfortune, no setback
could alter his determination. He had set out on this
venture, knowing well how desperate it was. He would
carry it through to the finish—whatever that finish
might be.

The two ships parted company, the *Elizabeth* heading
back for Brest, the *Doutelle* pressing on northwards ;
but now she cracked on sail and when, on July 11th, the
look-out raised that cry again : " Sail-ho ! " Walsh
remained unconcerned. The *Doutelle* had the heels of
anything she was likely to meet now. And so, indeed,
it proved, for very soon the stranger was hull down
astern, then lost altogether. The voyage continued.

On the 15th she ran into rougher weather. The wind,
rising suddenly, screamed in her rigging, and huge seas
began piling up ; but Walsh held his course and for two
days the gallant little frigate battled with the storm.
She came out of it unscathed and for several days slipped

along swiftly in fine weather and under clear skies. By now Scotland must be abeam, and Charles, his excitement rising as each hour brought the great moment nearer, remained on deck to stare eagerly into the darkness ahead.

The night was fine and cold ; but presently a sharper chill came into the air, and the wind stiffened, the little ship plunged more and more uneasily into the long mounting seas. By midnight a gale was blowing and seamen, wading in water to the waist, fought and struggled against the storm to save the ship. With dawn the gale increased in fury, and mountainous seas piled up to overwhelm the ship ; but Walsh was a competent master and, so near the end of their voyage, the men were ready to work desperately to bring her to safety.

All day and all night the battle went on, a ceaseless struggle against the savage assaults of the tempest, but next day—the 22nd—it eased, and the *Doutelle*, strained and weatherbeaten but still undaunted, held her course. And suddenly a glad cry went up.

" Land-ho ! "

Duncan Cameron, the man from Barra who had been brought as pilot, came running on deck. Walsh raised an eager finger. The Highlander shaded his eyes and gazed upon that land he had not seen for many years ; and there was emotion quivering in his voice as he said, in a subdued whisper : " The Long Isle ! "

It was the island of Mingulay, on the larboard bow. The seven adventurers looked at each other, in a long silence ; and then another cry was heard : " Sail-ho ! "

It broke in upon their thoughts like a douche of cold water. Walsh, whipping round, raised his spyglass to examine the stranger, which was between the *Doutelle* and the land. He did not have to look twice. Here was another man-of-war, an English ship on the prowl. To be caught at this moment, within sight of the land he had longed for all these years—Charles might well have been dismayed. But Walsh acted swiftly. He altered course at once and stretched along the east side of the island of Barra and soon lost sight of the man-of-war.

The long narrow shape of South Uist hove in sight and the *Doutelle* ran for safety into the little strait that separates the island from Eriskay and its islets ; then she hove to close inshore.

A boat was lowered, and Duncan Cameron slipped down into it and was rowed ashore. He knew these waters ; but it was years since he had been here, and what was needed was some local man to act as pilot.

Ashore, he found one quickly. He had not gone far before he met a sturdy figure walking towards him. The two stopped, stared at each other hard, then let out a cry of greeting. They were old friends, for the stranger was none other than MacNeill of Barra's piper.

Duncan explained the situation. Would the piper help ?

He would ; so he was rowed out to the ship and taken on board. Under his guidance, with Duncan to interpret for them, the ship was brought in to a safe anchor, and Charles, standing on the quarterdeck staring intently at the low rocky land so near them, heard the chain grind out as the anchor went down.

Eighteen days from France—eighteen momentous days. He had put those eighteen days behind him and ahead lay—who could tell ?

A boat was lowered. Charles, still in his plain black clothes, went down into it, followed by the six men who had been willing to risk all in his cause. In silence they rowed ashore. The boat's prow grated on the stones, and Charles stepped out on to the beach of Eriskay—on to the soil of Scotland. He stood silent ; and around him the six men stood silent, in a new homage. They understood that here was no longer the impatient and moody young man they had known in Italy and France, the high spirited, courteous, pleasant fellow round whom

He stood silent.

centred so much intrigue and rumour and idle talk.
Here was a different Charles—Charles Edward Stuart,
Regent for his father, King James III, a man who from
now on would assume command and expect implicit
obedience ; the man who was to become, almost overnight, Bonnie Prince Charlie.

He pulled a kerchief from the pocket of his jacket, and,
unnoticed, some little seeds which chanced to be in his
pocket fell to the ground. In due season they took root
and sprang up—pink convolvulus unknown till then on
Eriskay. The place has been known, ever since, as *Coilleag
a Phrionnsa*, the Prince's Strand.

Around him his followers stood, their eyes paying him
homage, their hearts too full for speech. The Prince had
come home.

CHAPTER SIX

RAISING THE STANDARD

O wha's for Scotland and Charlie?
O wha's for Scotland and Charlie?
He's come o'er the sea to his ain countree,
Now wha's for Scotland and Charlie?

Awa', awa', auld carlie,
Awa', awa', auld carlie !
Gie Charlie his crown, and let him sit down
Whaur ye've been sae lang, auld carlie !

THERE was no sign of life ; but they found a hut nearby, and took shelter there. Then, since they must eat, they went outside, and Charles led the way, wading into the sea after flounders. Soon they had caught a fair bag, and carried them back in triumph to the hut. They handed them over to Duncan Cameron of Barra to deal with.

Duncan was no great cook. But he split and cleaned the fish as well as he could, and roasted them over the glowing coals of the peat fire. Charles's spirits rose, and as Duncan burnt his fingers and made awkward attempts to deal with the fish the Prince, sitting on a heap of peats, laughed heartily at him.

Presently a man appeared. He had watched from the shore as they rowed in, and had come to find them.

But the excitement on his face was only the excitement that any strangers would cause in this wild remote spot.

" You are welcome, gentlemen," he said, looking curiously from one to another.   Tullibardine stepped forward, and Æneas MacDonald the banker, and the rest followed, the Prince keeping well back.   The islander was Angus MacDonald, tacksman or chief tenant of this and some other small islands, and he led them to his home.

Charles looked at it with keen interest.   It seemed little more than a hut, built of stone and roofed with a heather thatch like a pyramid, with a hole at the top out of which trailed wisps of blueblack pungent peat smoke.   They stepped inside, and Charles remembered to linger at the door so that the others should not step aside for him.

" This, gentleman," Æneas MacDonald explained, " is a young Irish priest."

Their host smiled and nodded.   There was nothing unusual in that, for Irish priests often came over to the Hebrides, where many of the people still were Catholics. He accepted the Prince without question, noting his sober black clothes and his air of preoccupation ;   for indeed Charles had much to think about.

The poverty of the place struck him forcibly.   The cottage was almost bare, and their host, embarrassed, had little food or bedding to offer them.   Also it was stifling, for the food he set to cook was fish.   The peat smoke swirled and eddied around the room, finding its way only slowly out of the hole in the roof, and what with this and the fumes from the roasting fish Charles soon felt the need of fresh air.   He went to the door, put his head out, and drew a deep breath.   Then he went back to his seat by the fire.

A few moments later he was up again, his eyes smarting, to get more air.   The Highlanders in the party, more accustomed to these primitive conditions, were secretly amused ;   but their host, now busy making up beds for them, stared at the young man in astonishment, and eventually said angrily :

" What a plague is the matter with that fellow, that he can neither sit nor stand still, and keep neither within nor without doors? "

If he noticed the momentary shock his exasperated words produced, he guessed nothing as to the reason for it.

So they sat and supped, while out of doors the weather had changed, and a heavy persistent downpour blotted out the horizon and hissed on the heather thatch, while raindrops silvered down through the peat smoke and sizzled on the glowing fire.

Æneas MacDonald talked to their host, but to Charles, listening intently, no word was intelligible, for they spoke only in the Gaelic.

" Mac Mhic Ailean and his brother Boisdale are in South Uist," the tacksman said, and the banker leaned forward eagerly ; for Mac Mhic Ailean was the Highland name for the Chief of the MacDonalds of Clanranald, who could muster as many as seven hundred fighting men. " They say, too," the tacksman volunteered, " that young Clanranald, the old chief's son, is over in Moidart."

The banker turned quickly and spoke to his companions. Old Clanranald was known to be a sick man, not likely to be able to help ; but his word was law and they must have his support.

" We must send for Boisdale," the banker declared. " He has influence with his brother, and if we apply direct to Clanranald we may only get a definite refusal for our pains. But if we speak with Boisdale first, he may then persuade the chief to agree to what we want."

It was a sensible proposal, and a letter was immediately sent off to Boisdale, requesting his attendance on board the *Doutelle*.

It was evening now, and the air in the crowded cottage grew drowsy. The host had made up as many beds as he could, but some of the party would have to go without. Charles, jumping up, went over to one of the beds, and beckoned to Sir Thomas Sheridan, who showed signs of weariness and was far less able than the others to stand up to the rigours and excitements of their long journey.

" This will be your bed," Charles declared, and turned back the clothes to satisfy himself that the sheets had been well aired and were completely dry and clean. His old tutor would have protested, but, remembering the need to keep up appearances, restrained himself.

" I am not tired," Charles declared. " I have often slept in a chair. I'll do well enough on the floor."

There was a quick protest ; but he laughed and shook his head.

" The beds are for the weary ones," he retorted, " and I am not weary."

Their host, watching this by-play and understanding enough English to gather the young man's refusal to sleep in one of the beds, looked at him indignantly as he examined the sheets, and called out:

" It is a good bed indeed, and the sheets are so good that a prince need not be ashamed to sleep in it ! "

For a second there was sudden silence ; then a roar of laughter from the whole party, led by Charles himself, and the bewildered tacksman stared at them entirely unable to imagine what the joke could be.

They settled down to sleep, Charles, wrapped in his coat, stared into the heart of the dying embers of the peat fire.

§

A boat came rowing towards the *Doutelle*. A stalwart, middle-aged man sat in the sternsheets, and as the boatmen plied their oars Charles heard, for the first time, the slow and mournful lilt of a Hebridean boat song. It ran alongside, and MacDonald of Boisdale came on board. His face was grave and troubled, and the Prince's friends, noticing his expression, felt their spirits drop.

He was shown below to the Prince's cabin immediately.

Charles greeted him with a hearty handshake and bade him be seated. Then, while he talked, he examined this man upon whom so much might depend. He had met some of the Highland chiefs or their kinsfolk in France ; this was his first encounter with one of them in their native country, and he realised how vital it might be.

" I need not tell you, sir, why I am here," Charles began, striving to be at ease in face of the unbending expression on the Highlander's face. " I have asked you to join me here so that I may lay my plans before you and claim your support."

Boisdale lowered his head. His mind was already made up—had been made up long ago. Since 1715 the Highlands had been savagely treated by the government, the most vicious repressive measures had been enforced, and like all the other Highland chiefs he saw quite clearly the fate in store if they rose in revolt. The government in London was only waiting for some such excuse in order to bring fire and sword again to the Highlands and lay them waste completely.

The people might thirst for revenge for all the wrongs they had suffered at the hands of the redcoats, but it was the plain duty of the chiefs to avoid further suffering and to keep their people in check. He had come to the frigate, because all his loyalty was to Charles and the Stuart cause ; but he had come determined to dissuade the Prince from any rash attempt.

Charles persisted.

" My proposal, sir, is that you should accompany me to the mainland and there endeavour to persuade your nephew, young Clanranald, to take up arms."

Boisdale looked him straight in the eye.

" No, sir," he replied firmly. " That I cannot do. Indeed I will do everything that is in my power to dissuade that young man from listening to any such proposals. I shall use all my influence to prevent the clan from being called out for an enterprise that I consider completely desperate."

Charles listened to these outspoken words with a sinking heart. There was no doubt that Boisdale meant precisely what he said—no doubt, also, that his influence was great, that his advice would be listened to not only by his brother and nephew but by many of the smaller chiefs.

Remembering his early optimism, his high hopes and his utter faith in his " loyal Highlanders," as he had always called them, he refused to allow anger or bitterness to get the better of him.

" Then, sir," he said, " if you will not aid me in this way, will you carry a message to MacDonald of Sleat and the MacLeod, requesting their assistance? "

Again Boisdale shook his head.

" Such a message would be useless," he replied. " I have seen both Sir Alexander MacDonald and the MacLeod but lately, and it was they who told me that your royal highness might soon be expected in the Highlands. They were firm that if you came without regular troops they would not join you, and I am convinced that no other chief will. In fact, sir, I was instructed by these two gentlemen to mention this resolution to your royal highness, should I have the honour of meeting you upon your arrival. They begged me to urge you, sir, should you come without regular troops, to return directly to France."

Charles listened to this plain speech with a growing sense of his own helplessness. Where were the loyal men who would acclaim his landing and spring to arms joyfully at the word that their Prince was among them at last ? Where were his dreams, his hopes, his plans ? Here, at the very outset, he met nothing but refusal, blunt forthright refusal and blunt forthright advice to return whence he came. They did not want him here.

He sat silent and still, with clenched hands, staring into space, thinking, thinking. Was all to go for naught? Desperation laid hold of him, and he roused himself and leaned forward eagerly, persuasively.

" I am sure, Boisdale," he cried, " that you cannot realise the true situation. England has no trained troops. Her army is on the Continent—and has been quite lately heavily defeated by the French. The levies in the south are raw and untrained troops. There will never be a chance like this again. With even a few thousand men we could sweep the Elector of Hanover's supporters out of Scotland, we could sweep into England—aye, right to the gates of London. There is nothing to stop us."

Boisdale looked at him morosely. He felt a lift in his own spirits at this eager flow of words, at the way the young Prince's eyes lit up, his whole face was transformed with enthusiasm. But his decision had been taken, and no eager words could alter it. He shook his head once more. Then he looked up, rose swiftly and crossed to a port to look out.

" We are getting under weigh, sir," he exclaimed.

Charles, recalled to his immediate surroundings, looked up impatiently. He had forgotten the cramped little cabin on board the *Doutelle*, he had forgotten where they were as his brain was fired with visions of what might be achieved if only a handful of resolute men would follow him.

A messenger came down to the cabin to explain that two sail had been sighted making for the strait, and the captain had decided to weigh anchor and stand in for the mainland. Charles waved him away, and turned to Boisdale again.

He argued, pleaded, appealed to his loyalty and his honour, but all in vain, and when at last they rose, seeing that they could never agree, they found that the ship was already some miles away from Eriskay. Boisdale went down into his boat, which was trailing alongside, and was rowed away. Charles returned to his cabin, to face the hard and simple fact. The enterprise was meeting failure at the outset.

§

All night the frigate held her course, and by morning was closing the mainland. There was no sign of the two strange ships that had caused her to leave Eriskay so hurriedly.

When the party was about to go down to dinner, Tullibardine, glancing up, saw something that made him catch his breath. Soaring high above the ship, and circling her in long graceful sweeps, was a great golden eagle. Impulsively, he made a move to call the others to look, then held back, because they might only laugh at him for being superstitious. But his spirits had risen, and over the meal there was little to show that the adventurers were downcast. The Prince, in spite of the severe rebuff he had had from Boisdale, had recovered his spirits and was determined to be cheerful.

They came on deck again, and Tullibardine's eyes instinctively went to the sky. This time there was no doubt about it, and the old warrior, who had been an exile for so long, could not restrain himself.

" See ! " he cried, and pointed upwards. Curiously the others raised their eyes, and Tullibardine turned to the Prince.

" Sir," he exclaimed, " I hope this is an excellent omen and promises good things to us. The king of birds is come to welcome your royal highness upon your arrival in Scotland ! "

Charles was delighted, and the effect on the others, particularly the Highlanders among them, was instantaneous.

Shortly after, the *Doutelle* dropped anchor in Lochnanuagh, which separates parts of Moidart and Arisaig, and Charles sent a boat on shore at once, with a letter to young Clanranald. The uncle might be obstinate ; the nephew was likely to be less cautious.

Æneas MacDonald the banker went ashore in the same boat, to visit his brother, MacDonald of Kinlochmoidart, and soon the boat came back with the pair of them on board. Æneas introduced him to the Prince, and they had an interview—short and satisfactory.

Kinlochmoidart had none of Boisdale's caution. The

fact that his brother the banker, an eminently sensible man, was of the Prince's party was perhaps enough in itself.

" I am ready, sir," he stated plainly, " to engage myself and my people in your service."

Charles wrung his hand, and did not try to hide his emotion at this sudden turn in his fortunes. Boisdale had cast him deep in gloom and misgivings ; Kinlochmoidart restored his faith and his hopes.

He sent him off immediately with letters to Lochiel, the Duke of Perth, Murray of Broughton and others ; and it is the measure of his trust in his loyal Highlanders that it did not occur to anyone, then or afterwards, to consider there was any risk in doing so.

Now the atmosphere on board the frigate was very different. There was a buoyancy, a feeling of high confidence about the Prince as he paced the deck that night ; and next morning he had more cause for optimism. A small party of men appeared on shore and hailed the ship, asking for a boat to be sent to fetch them out.

They came, and Charles grasped the hand of a young man in whom he placed the highest hopes. Handsome, well built, bearing himself proudly as the son of one of the most powerful chiefs in the west, young Clanranald saluted his Prince with a fervour that left no room for doubt. His father was old and sick and in no condition for campaigning, his uncle was cautious and morose and pessimistic, but young Clanranald, clear-headed but impetuous, saw what he conceived to be his duty and grasped it instantly.

Charles took him down to his cabin.

For three hours they talked together, but what they said was never recorded. No doubt Charles plied him with questions and learned all he could about the clans. On deck, the party that had come with Clanranald was being entertained by Tullibardine. They were Clanranald's kinsman, Alexander MacDonald of Glenalladale,

Angus MacDonald of Dalily, and a Highland officer who had served with the Old Pretender in the Fifteen. They found a large tent erected on deck, and inside were tables well furnished with refreshments. Tullibardine—they all referred to him still as the Duke of Athole, for they did not acknowledge the authority of the Elector of Hanover and his London government and therefore did not recognise the forfeiture of the Athole estates and title—welcomed them and kept them talking while Clanranald went below. They did not expect to see the Prince that night.

After about three hours young Clanranald came into the tent, and half an hour later a young man entered quietly and took a seat without seeming to notice the company. He was plainly dressed in a black coat and a plain shirt—not very clean—and a cambric stock fixed with a plain silver buckle. Over his wig he wore a black hat with a canvas string attached to one of his coat buttons ; his stockings were black, and his shoes had ordinary brass buckles. There was nothing here to tell them who he was, although the Highland officer, at sight of him, felt a sudden surge of emotion and knew at once that here was no ordinary man. The tall, well-knit figure, the fine regular features, the large brown eyes that seemed to burn with intense excitement—they made an indelible impression upon a seasoned campaigner, who knew a leader of men when he saw one.

One of the Prince's party introduced him casually. An English clergyman who had long wanted to see and talk with Highlanders. There was no need for anyone to rise, and they simply bowed from a distance while he saluted them and sat down.

The Highland officer happened to be standing close by, and the Prince at once jumped up and begged him to sit down beside him on a chest. The officer smilingly agreed, taking him to be either a clergyman or some other passenger in the ship. They fell to talking, with great familiarity and without any restraint.

" Tell me," said Charles, " don't you feel cold in that dress? "

The Highlander looked surprised.

" Why, no," he replied. " I am so used to it that I should feel cold if I wore anything else."

Charles laughed heartily, then went on, with keen interest, for already he was beginning to see the advantages of the kilt in a campaign.

" How do you lie with it at night? "

" I unbuckle the belt, unfasten the shoulder pin, and at once I have a blanket to wrap myself in. The pleats are held in place only by the belt, and the kilt measures nearly seven yards by two yards. When I put it on, I lay the belt down, pleat the lower part, then fasten the belt round my waist. When I stand up, the plaid falls down over the belt, and I take it and pin it to my shoulder."

The Prince was impressed.

" But," he objected, " if you are so closely wrapped up at night, you cannot be prepared for a sudden surprise. How could you defend yourself? "

The Highlander laughed.

"When we are campaigning," he explained, "we have a special method of using the plaid for a blanket, so that we can leap up clear of it in a moment, with drawn sword and cocked pistol ready."

Charles nodded. There was a lot to be said for such a garment, kilt and plaid in one, and bedclothes as well. He asked a few more questions, fingered the officer's dirk and sgian dubh, examined his claymore, and then, springing up from his seat, he called for a dram.

One of the others whispered quickly to the officer.

" Pledge him but do not drink to him."

The Highlander nodded, and immediately realised who the tall young stranger in black really was. He remembered the easy familiarity with which they had been talking, and if before he had been an enthusiastic supporter of the cause now he was also the Prince's slave. For such a man, such a leader, he and all others like him would gladly risk their lives.

Charles raised his glass, and drank silently to the assembled company in turn, then went quickly back to his cabin. He had work to do—and fresh enthusiasm for that work.

§

He hid his jubilation ; but he knew that young Clanranald was won round, that the MacDonalds, or a good part of them, would rally to the cause. He decided to send the young man off on the very errand his uncle had refused to undertake. So he first wrote to MacDonald of Sleat and the laird of MacLeod, and on July 22nd Clanranald, attended by Allan MacDonald, a younger brother of Kinlochmoidart, who had come on board, went off on his journey to Skye. It was an important mission ; for between them the chief of Sleat and the MacLeod could easily raise 2,000 men.

Soon after the young chief had gone another party reached the village of Forey, opposite the *Doutelle's* anchorage, and came on board. There were two more of the MacDonald chiefs—Donald MacDonald of Scot-house, and Bishop Hugh MacDonald, brother of the laird of Morar. They brought with them Dr. Archibald Cameron, who came on behalf of his brother, Donald Cameron the younger, of Lochiel.

Hugh MacDonald had a story to tell. He had been on his way home from Edinburgh when, as he was crossing the water of Lochy, he fell in with Kinlochmoidart.

" You may see the Prince to-morrow if you wish," Kinlochmoidart told him. " But be careful how you address him. The French crew of the ship have no idea who he is. They think him a French clergyman. You might see the Prince to-night at my house."

" What number of men has he brought along with him ? " asked Hugh.

The Prince was impressed by the Highland dress.

" Only seven."

" What stock of money and arms has he brought with him, then? " Hugh cried.

" A very small stock of either," replied Kinlochmoidart.

" What generals or officers fit for commanding are with him? "

" None at all."

Hugh MacDonald stared with anxious eyes at his informant.

" I do not like this expedition at all," he declared, morosely. " I fear the consequences of it."

" I cannot help it," Kinlochmoidart, said simply. " If the matter go wrong, then I'll certainly be hanged, for I am engaged already."

It was not very heartening news for men who realised, far better than the Prince and his advisers could, what the real dangers were—and what the consequences of failure would be.

So when Charles, hearing who the visitors were, invited Bishop Hugh to his cabin immediately, he was not likely to hear anything to encourage his hopes.

Hugh did not beat about the bush.

" I fear very much the consequences of this attempt, sir," he declared, " and since you have brought no forces with you the most eligible course for you to follow, in my opinion, is to return to France and await a better opportunity. Without regular troops and the help of France you could achieve nothing."

Charles was learning rapidly the kind of men he had to deal with. They were zealous in the Jacobite cause, their loyalty was absolute, they were eager to serve him and longing for the restoration of the House of Stuart. But they were no ordinary men. They had been born and bred in responsibility, trained from infancy in a deep sense of their duty to their people. They inherited their power as chiefs of the clans ; they inherited also the strong feeling of responsibility to their clans, the need to place the welfare of their people before their own private convictions or private wishes. They would gladly lay down their own lives ; they did not consider they could lightly risk the lives of the men—and the women and children, for Hanover would have no mercy on the weak and defenceless—who depended on them.

Charles rose to his feet.

" I have no wish to be indebted for my father's restoration to foreigners, sir, but to my own friends," he retorted with spirit. " I have now put it in the power of my friends to have the glory of restoring my father to the throne. As to returning to France without making the attempt, no foreigner will ever be able to say that I threw myself upon my friends, that they turned their backs on me and that I was forced to seek shelter in a foreign land. If I could only get six stout trusty fellows to join me, I would choose rather to skulk in these mountains than return to France."

Dr. Cameron came next. Like Hugh, he urged the Prince to return to France.

" Lochiel's mind is made up," he declared. " His father is in exile for helping your father. He is not prepared to risk the same fate, and the destruction of the clan that would surely follow. He is determined that he will not join."

Charles listened with a growing sense of frustration. He knew the influence Lochiel wielded in the High-lands. They still called him " the younger," but he was a man of over fifty, a seasoned campaigner, a fine soldier and a man whose opinion was valued every-where. His reputation stood high in Scotland, among all shades of opinion, and not even his worst enemies could whisper a word against his character. Such a man might well make or mar the expedition, for every smaller chief in the West Highlands would listen to his words and copy his actions, knowing that whatever Lochiel did he believed it to be the right and honourable course.

On the heels of these unsatisfactory visitors came young

Clanranald, back from Skye and Sleat. He came on board with gloom on his face, which proclaimed in advance the news he had brought. MacDonald of Sleat and the laird of MacLeod had both returned an absolute and final refusal. They had engaged themselves to serve the cause ; but that had been on the understanding that the Prince would be accompanied by a substantial force of French troops, and that France herself would take a hand in the business. Now, since neither of these essential conditions was fulfilled, they considered they were released from their obligations, and were not prepared to call out their men.

One after another the six other " men of Moidart " came to the Prince, begging him to desist. The attempt was hopeless. They must return to France and wait until the French would move to help them before they tried to raise an army in Scotland. Even Sir Thomas Sheridan, whose opinion weighed most with the Prince, and on whose advice he generally acted, came down to the cabin on the same unhappy errand. The Prince listened to all he had to say with his usual courteous attention ; but afterwards he only smiled slightly and shook his head.

" My mind is made up. It is now or never. Nothing will alter my decision."

They argued and pleaded in vain. Charles was unshakable.

§

Little groups of men were beginning to arrive at the anchorage and Charles, busy in his cabin writing letters to the men in Scotland whose names appeared on the lists of Jacobite supporters, often lifted his head to listen to the skirl of bagpipes from the shore, and sometimes rose to look out of his porthole and watch, with a lift of the heart, the small bodies of men who paraded there, marching and counter marching, drilling, accustoming themselves once again to the feel of weapons in their hands.

Charles gave orders for the stores to be landed, and working parties were formed to bring ashore the muskets and broadswords and powder and shot and the few field pieces the *Doutelle* had brought.

Young Clanranald offered him the hospitality of Borrodale, one of his farms, and on the 25th of July he and his suite went ashore. The tenant of the farm, Angus MacDonald, acted as host and gave him a hearty welcome.

Clanranald went further. He gave orders to MacDonald of Glenalladale and another gentleman of the clan to raise a bodyguard for the Prince, and soon Charles was called out to witness a stirring spectacle—a hundred picked MacDonalds, armed to the teeth, well drilled and disciplined, and proud of the very great honour that had been done them.

Angus MacDonald offered the hospitality of his farm to the entire company, and breathed a sigh of relief to know that the Prince's person would at least be well protected while he remained his guest.

Recruits arrived daily. Here was, indeed, the perfect setting for the Prince's landing, for Borrodale was surrounded by the most loyal of the clans, men who remembered the terrible cruelties inflicted on them after the abortive Fifteen and who burned for revenge against the redcoats who had harried and persecuted them ever since.

Borrodale was besieged. Men and women of every class, even young children, came trooping to see their Prince, and Charlie, mindful of the obligations of royalty, took care to seat himself at every meal where he could be seen. He ate heartily the simple fare that Borrodale could offer, and his high spirits enlivened every meal. At the end of the meal he would rise and give a toast, the clear young voice ringing out firmly.

At one of the earliest of these occasions a guest gave

the toast of the king in Gaelic : " Deoch slaint an Righ ! "
—Drink health to the king ! Charles turned to him at
once, and begged him to repeat the words. He listened
eagerly, and thereafter when he rose to propose his
father's health he did so not in the English which so
few present could understand but in their own language.
The youngster who had mastered French and Spanish
and Italian at fourteen and could talk to soldiers of all
three races in their own familiar tongue was not likely
to neglect the language of the new soldiers who came so
eagerly to offer their services.

From Borrodale Charles sent off fresh messengers to
his various supporters, summoning them to attend him
there. He had no doubt of their adherence, and already
one of the chiefs, MacDonald of Keppoch, had voiced the
feeling with which news of his arrival had been received
by most of them.

"As the Prince has risked his person and generously
thrown himself into the hands of his friends, we are
bound in duty at least to raise men instantly for the
protection of his person, whatever might be the
consequences."

Whether they marched against Hanover or not, they
must at the least be prepared to defend the Prince from
his enemies.

But there was one man whose support was essential—
Cameron of Lochiel. He was a staunch Protestant, a
man of known moderate views and complete integrity.
Whatever lead he gave would be followed by a score of
lesser chiefs, and MacDonald the younger of Scothouse
was selected for the difficult task of winning Lochiel
to the Cause.

"At least, sir," Scothouse pressed, " you must attend
upon the Prince at Borrodale and hear what he has to
say."

Lochiel agreed. His loyalty to the house of Stuart was
absolute. His conviction that a rebellion could only be
a disastrous failure was equally sincere. He went with

Scothouse with his mind firmly made up. Nothing would induce him to commit the Camerons to so desperate an adventure.

On the way to Borrodale he called upon his brother, John Cameron of Fassifern.

The latter came out immediately to greet him.

" What is the matter that brings you here so early in the day? " he exclaimed.

" I am on my way," Lochiel told him, " to attend the Prince at Borrodale. He has landed there, and sends for me."

Fassifern's face grew grave.

" What troops has the Prince brought with him? " he demanded. " What supplies of money and arms? "

Lochiel shook his head.

" I believe he has brought neither troops nor money nor arms. I am resolved not to be concerned in the affair at all, and I shall do my utmost to prevent the Prince from making so rash an attempt."

Fassifern nodded vigorously. He heartily approved his brother's decision ; but all the same he was alarmed.

" I advise you to go no further on your way to Borrodale, Donald," he declared earnestly. " Come into the house, and inform the Prince of your decision by letter."

Lochiel shook his head.

" No," he replied, " I ought at least to wait upon him, and give my reasons for declining to join him. They are far too strong to allow of any reply."

Fassifern looked at him with a slight, grim smile.

" Brother," he said, " I know you better than you know yourself. If this Prince once sets his eyes upon you, he will make you do whatever he pleases."

But Lochiel refused to add discourtesy to his refusal to join the Prince. The least he could do was to go in person and explain his reasons—and, perhaps, succeed in persuading Charles to give up the attempt.

Fassifern watched him go with a troubled face ; for

the truth about Charles had begun to leak out. He was
not like his father. He was a born leader of men, and
the charm of his personality, the strength of his impassioned appeals, the decisiveness and resolution of his
bearing made him a force to be reckoned with.

§

Lochiel had no fears. He was completely convinced
that he could make Charles listen to reason, and that
nothing Charles might say could influence his own
decision. He was the first of the chiefs to arrive in response
to the Prince's summons, and when he was announced
Charles gave him a private interview at once. He knew
very well the importance of Lochiel. His grandfather,
Sir Ewen, had fought with distinction under Montrose
and Dundee ; his father had been attainted after the
Fifteen and lived in exile in France ; he himself had
been commissioned by James to negotiate with the Scots
Jacobites with full powers. Charles wasted no time on
idle preliminaries.

" I mean to be completely candid with you, Lochiel,"
he declared. " I shall hide nothing. The French ministry
have behaved abominably. They have repeatedly made
promises to me, and when the moment arrives they have
deceived me without the slightest qualms. I have only
a small quantity of arms, and very little money. I made
no arrangements before I left France for concerted action.
In fact, I did not take leave of the French court. I simply
came. But before I left I wrote to the French king and
his ministers pleading for their support, and I am convinced they will send help as soon as they see that we
really have a party in Scotland and mean to go on with
the affair. I have appointed the Earl Marischal my
agent at the French court, and I depend upon his zeal
and ability. He will himself superintend the embarkation
of the French troops."

Lochiel listened to this blunt statement with a grave

face, and when his turn came to speak he found difficulty in remembering the carefully prepared statements he meant to make.

" I freely admit, sir," he said, " the engagement I and other chiefs have entered into in support of the Cause. But that engagement can only be binding if the stipulated assistance is forthcoming. As your royal highness has come without that support we must consider ourselves released from our engagement."

It was an argument that Charles had heard already before—with almost wearisome reiteration. He heard it now from the lips of Lochiel with a growing sense of desperation.

" I can only repeat my determination not to join you, sir, in this attempt," the chief declared, firmly, " and I would advise your royal highness to return to France and await a more favourable opportunity."

" There may never be a more favourable opportunity," Charles retorted. " All the British troops are abroad, except for a few newly raised regiments—raw recruits who could do nothing against your Highlanders. There are not sufficient regular troops in the country to withstand us. If we gain any advantage at the outset over the government's forces the whole country will declare in our favour, and our friends overseas will immediately come to our aid."

It was a plausible argument, although not strictly true, for there were certain trained troops on garrison duty at that moment in the Highlands—and there was every reason to doubt the good faith of the French. They might help—or again they might not ; and Lochiel, who had had more experience even than Charles of dealing with the politicians at King Louis's court, was unmoved. But Charles went on impetuously.

" Everything now depends upon the Highlanders," he cried. " If we are to accomplish the restoration of my father all that is needed is for them to declare themselves instantly, and let the campaign begin ! "

Lochiel shook his head stubbornly.

" I cannot agree with you, sir," he replied, gloomily.
" I beg your royal highness will consider returning to
France."

Charles retorted with one sharp word :

" Never ! "

" Then, sir," cried Lochiel, " I entreat you to be more
moderate in your views. The difficulties in your way are
great. I beg you will send your attendants back to France
while you yourself remain in hiding here, and let it be
given out that you too have gone back. Then the court
of France can be acquainted with the state of affairs and
informed that your friends are ready to take up arms
the moment word is received of a landing of French
troops. Nothing can be done without foreign support."

But Charles in turn was stubborn.

" The court of France will never become convinced
that I have a large party in Scotland until there is an
actual rising," he declared. " I am afraid that without
that they will never venture their troops."

It seemed to be a complete deadlock. But Lochiel, torn
between common sense and loyalty, made one last effort.

" Then, sir," he said, " may I venture to suggest that
your royal highness should remain at Borrodale till I
and my friends can hold a meeting and agree upon what
is to be done? "

Charles made an impatient gesture, and sprang to his
feet.

" It is my firm determination, sir," he cried passionately
" to take the field however small my following may be.
In a few days, with the few friends I have, I will raise
the royal standard, and proclaim to the people of Britain
that Charles Stuart is come over to claim the crown of
his ancestors—to win it, or to perish in the attempt.
Lochiel, whom my father has often told me, was our
firmest friend, may stay at home, and learn from the
newspapers the fate of his prince ! "

Lochiel too rose. His face was dark with passion, his

eyes glowing with anger at this taunt.   He touched the hilt of his claymore.

"No!" he declared desperately, all scruple swept away.   "I'll share the fate of my prince—and so shall every man over whom nature or fortune has given me any power!"

And with that he took his leave.

§

Charles was jubilant.   The news of Lochiel's decision would run like wildfire through the glens, everywhere the waverers and the doubters would be confounded, all hesitation would be abandoned and the clans would rise for the sake of the Cause—and their Prince.

Letters were sent off in haste to all the well-disposed chiefs, informing them that the Prince would raise his standard at Glenfinnan on the 19th of August, and that they were required to be present with their followers on that day or as soon thereafter as possible.   Lochiel, returning home to Achnacarry, sent out runners to all the gentlemen of his clan, ordering them to raise their men and hold themselves in readiness to march to Glenfinnan.

Shortly afterwards the Prince moved his quarters, accepting the eager hospitality of Kinlochmoidart, whose house was but seven miles away.

And now, during those busy days before the fateful 19th, a stirring could be felt throughout the western Highlands, and detached parties of armed men were to be seen upon the hillsides.   From the thatches of bothies and crofts and cottages claymores and muskets were pulled down, and cleaned and got into condition again after rusting so long in these simple hiding places. Women, anxious eyed, watched their menfolk at this work, and patched and darned kilts and plaids and shirts, and stitched new brogues for them, and prepared haversacks of food, and hid their terrible anxiety from the men whose eyes burned with eagerness to be up and doing, to strike a blow for the old Cause and hit back at the enemies who had used them so mercilessly in the past thirty years.

Three weeks had elapsed since the landing of the Prince, yet the authorities had received no whisper of it. Men who had bluntly refused to join the desperate enterprise not only knew that he was here, but knew where he was. At any moment they might have given away his secret and won for themselves the approbation and protection of the government, and a substantial reward. It occurred to none of them to do that. They retired to their own homes quietly, resolved to have no part in the whole affair yet fixed in an absolute loyalty to the House of Stuart and to a code of chivalry that, as events were soon to prove, had long since died in the more civilised south.

But Fort William with its garrison was a bare thirty miles from the Prince's headquarters, and inevitably the movement of armed bands through the glens became known. Parties of Camerons and Macdonalds, beginning to converge upon Glenfinnan, were detected by the redcoats, and urgent messages went out to Fort Augustus, where the governor, mightily alarmed, decided on prompt action. On the 16th he despatched two companies of the second battalion of the Royal Scots, experienced Lowland troops, to Fort William to reinforce the garrison there.

Since the Fifteen a chain of forts had been erected between Fort William and Inverness to overawe the clans, and Fort Augustus, the strongest of these, was almost equidistant from Fort William to the west and Fort George to the east. A military road had been built to link the forts, along what is now the bed of the Caledonian Canal, and regular communications were maintained along this road. It was but a short twenty-eight miles that the Royal Scots had to march, and their commanding officer, Captain Scott, had probably no expectation of anything but a rather wearisome trudge ahead of him.

He planned to do the whole journey in a single day, since there was no place in between where he could quarter his men, so he made a start in the early hours of the morning of the 16th.

They had covered about twenty miles of the twenty-eight before he had a hint of any interference. Now, approaching High Bridge, a single-arch bridge of great height spanning the rushing torrent of the Spean, his ears were assailed by a sound which was always calculated to alarm a Southerner—the wail of bagpipes. At first he paid little attention, for pipers were common enough, but almost immediately after he caught sight of a body of Highlanders, armed with claymores and firelocks, on the far side of the bridge—and there could be no doubting their intentions.

They were MacDonalds of Keppoch, under the command of MacDonald of Tierndriech, and they awaited the arrival of the strong force of regulars with evident delight, leaping about and flourishing their weapons and yelling defiance at the enemy. Captain Scott, very much alarmed, gave the order to halt and sent a sergeant and his own servant forward to reconnoitre. As they approached the bridge two of the MacDonalds, darting nimbly across, seized hold of them before they could defend themselves and carried them off by main force across the bridge.

This exploit was hailed with a roar of delight from the Highlanders, and Captain Scott, now thoroughly alarmed, decided to leave his unfortunate men to whatever fate might be in store for them and make his best speed back to Fort Augustus. He felt that he dared not risk an encounter in which his companies might be cut to pieces.

MacDonald of Tierndriech watched his departure with the greatest delight, and a derisive shout followed the redcoats as they turned right about. That shout came from the throats of twelve men, for that was the whole strength of the party. By skipping about and spreading out their plaids between one another and keeping constantly on the move they had given Scott the impression of a powerful force ; and so two companies of King George's soldiers had turned tail before the threat of a brush with a dozen MacDonalds.

But Tierndriech had not come haphazard to High Bridge. He had been watching the soldiers from early that morning, and had immediately sent off runners to Lochiel and Keppoch, whose houses were within three or four miles of the Bridge. So, expecting early assistance, he had determined to hold the bridge and prevent the redcoats from getting across, however much they outnumbered his little party.

Now, determined not to disillusion Captain Scott as to his numbers, he allowed the soldiers to retreat in good order, and followed at a distance until the troops had passed the western end of Loch Lochy and were upon the narrow road between the loch and the steep mountain slopes. Then he led the way swiftly up.

Skilled mountaineers as they were, used to violent exertion in their daily lives and ready for any risk, the little party scaled the cliffs and dropped into cover among the rocks and trees. Then, from this vantage point, they opened fire upon the soldiers.

Captain Scott saw that he was in a tight corner. He had no idea even yet how many enemies he faced, and in any case he could not have risked making a stand. He ordered his men to better their pace along the narrow dangerous road, while the Highlanders sniped at them in comfort, without a shot fired in return.

The sound of the shooting echoed away down the glen, and soon small bodies of men who had hastened to obey Tierndriech's summons to support him at the Bridge came running towards the sound. Keppoch himself appeared with a strong body, and soon Tierndriech's original twelve had swollen to respectable numbers.

Scott, urging his men to their best speed, went hurrying along the lochside to its eastern end, where a narrow neck of land separates it from Loch Oich ; and here he had a fresh shock. Another party of Highlanders was drawn up on a hill above Loch Oich, ready to cut off his retreat. Turn and fight—or go on and fight? The situation was desperate, and he made up his mind instantly. Only a short distance away was Invergarry Castle, seat of MacDonell of Glengarry, and Scott resolved to throw his troops into the castle for protection. Accordingly he ordered them to wheel off the road and cross the narrow neck of land. As he did so, he found himself facing still another body of Highlanders, moving down the hill to attack. They were the MacDonells of Glengarry !

There was nothing for it now but to face the issue.

" Form hollow square ! " he ordered, and the men, falling into formation, continued their march.

They were footsore and weary and more than a little terrified at their situation ; and on their heels came Tierndriech and his reinforced party, swift, nimble men capable of out-marching and out-running any body of Lowland troops in these wild hills. Swiftly they overtook the sweating redcoats, and Captain Scott, seeing that the moment had come upon him, halted his men and prepared for a desperate resistance. But one of the Highlanders advanced alone, with empty hands, to parley with him.

It was MacDonald of Keppoch himself, fearlessly approaching the redcoats with an offer of terms.

" I invite you, sir, to surrender," he cried, " and I will offer you good quarter for yourself and your officers and men. But if you resist, you will be cut to pieces. There is nothing to be gained by spilling blood."

It was a speech that may well have surprised the gallant captain, who no doubt had all the current mistaken notions about these wild savages in the Highlands and who would probably never have thought of offering them quarter if the tables had been turned. But he had been wounded during the sniping, and two of his men killed, and he did not demur. He accepted Keppoch's offer forthwith, and the weary soldiery, no doubt

.delighted at their escape, accepted the situation thankfully
and fell docilely into line between two files of Highland
guards.

The jubilant MacDonalds turned about and headed for
Glenfinnan.

§

The company sat down to dinner.

Charles was in great spirits. He had heard the news
of this first skirmish and had been informed also that
Lochiel had taken charge of the prisoners. The Highlanders were wildly excited. This first swift action was
all that they needed to arouse every man to the highest
pitch of enthusiasm, and to bring recruits pouring in
from the outlying glens. Charles had left Kinlochmoidart two days after the affair, accepting the invitation
of MacDonald of Glenalladale, whose house was by the
side of Loch Shiel, to take up his quarters there.

Now, as the party sat down, there was a clatter and
commotion outside, and presently some new arrivals
were announced. They were Gordon of Glenbucket and
his followers, and they did not come empty-handed. A
young English officer accompanied them.

" Captain Sweetenham, of Guise's Regiment of Foot,"
Glenbucket announced. " He was on his way to Fort
William to take command of the garrison when some
of Keppoch's men surprised him."

Charles and the young Englishman looked at each other
curiously, and suddenly the Prince smiled.

" You are fortunate, sir," he said. " You have fallen
among men of honour and will be honourably treated."
He turned to his attendants. " See that this gentleman
is properly cared for," he ordered, and Captain Sweetenham, who had been expecting to have his throat cut at
any moment, found himself an unwilling but grateful
guest at Glenalladale. He had plenty of time, in the
next few days, to revise his ideas of these wild Highlanders

and of the young man who had so suddenly appeared among them.

Soon after dawn next day there was stir and bustle around the house, and Charles, followed by the whole party of twenty-five, went down to the shore. Three boats were in readiness, and at six o'clock they pushed off to sail up the Loch. It was a still, tranquil autumn morning, the deep blue water sparkling in the early sunshine, and as the oars dipped in unison all eyes were turned towards the head of the loch, until they had passed the little Eilean Dubh and the narrow defile of Glenfinnan came into view, cutting deep into the mountain barrier beyond.

They went ashore close to the spot where the little River Finnan pours down into Loch Shiel.

Charles looked eagerly up the narrow glen. A scattering of small bothies, a handful of people at their doors, staring down upon the strangers—these were all he saw. His mouth tightened, and for a long moment he stood staring around him. All the way up the long narrow loch his excitement had been mounting as the moment approached to make the fateful gesture, to raise the standard and proclaim open war upon the Elector of Hanover and the established government of Britain. The summons had gone out to the chiefs. And now . . .

Now he stood with only his handful of followers upon the shore, looking in vain for the clansmen who should have answered the summons. Even the ardent young Clanranald, whose very presence had been a tonic to him, was missing, for he had gone off to raise his men.

Charles, rousing himself, looked round swiftly. There was a hovel nearby, and without a word he strode towards it, spoke a word to the two old people who stood at the door, and went inside. He threw himself down on the peat-stack beside the smouldering fire, and took his chin in his hands, biting his lip to prevent himself from breaking into an outburst of vexation and chagrin. His

party waited silently, knowing it better to say nothing, to offer no explanations or encouragement.

Time dragged slowly. An hour, two hours. Then suddenly Charles raised his head. Through the open doorway of the bothy there crept a faint high sound. He leapt to his feet, strode out—and raised his eyes to the mountains. The breath caught in his throat. High and clear came the singing of the bagpipes, and suddenly over the shoulder of a hill appeared a sight that sent the blood coursing through his veins—two columns of men, three abreast in each column, swinging over the hilltop and marching swiftly down towards the mouth of the glen. The skirl of the pipes gave a spring to their steps over the heather, and the Prince's keen young eyes recognised, with a thrill of relief, the bright red tartan that swung to the long swift stride of the marching men. The Camerons of Lochiel ! Eight hundred strong they came on, in good order, with the grizzled, powerful figure of Lochiel himself at their head, flanked by the leading gentlemen of his clan ; and between the two columns marched the two captured companies of redcoats, disarmed and docile.

Charles strode forward to greet the clan. Eight hundred men ! It was a tremendous access of strength, for few of the clans could muster so large a number. The majority of them, too, were armed, and the young Prince, who had so often been frustrated in his efforts to go soldiering in Europe, inspected these new soldiers of his with glowing eyes and a flush on his cheeks.

He turned to his followers.

" There is nothing to be gained by delaying any longer," he declared. " Here is a sufficient gathering of loyal men for our purpose. Shall we proceed, gentlemen ? "

They agreed ; and the Marquis of Tullibardine, taking the standard which had been prepared for the occasion—a silk flag of white, red and blue—mounted a hillock in the centre of the glen. To him, as the highest in rank among the Prince's party, had been allotted the honour of unfurling the standard. Two men supported him, and in a tense silence he raised the Prince's banner and in a ringing voice addressed the assembly.

" I proclaim His Majesty James Stuart, Chevalier de St. George, by the grace of God King James the VIII of Scotland and III of England."

At the words a great shout rent the air, and the echoes of that shout, reverberating through the glens, were destined yet to set all London trembling and to make the Elector of Hanover covertly send the crown jewels and all his valuables and his family on board a ship in the muddy Thames, in readiness for instant flight back to the obscurity from which chance and the persevering cunning of his grandmother the Electress Sophia had transplanted his father and himself.

When the cheering had died down, Tullibardine went on to read a commission from James appointing his son Prince Charles regent in Britain ; then followed a manifesto :

James VIII, by the grace of God, King of Scotland, England, France, and Ireland, Defender of the Faith, etc. To all our loving subjects, of what degree or quality soever, greeting.

Having always borne the most constant affection to our ancient kingdom of Scotland, from whence

we derive our royal origin, and where our pro-
genitors have swayed the sceptre with glory through
a longer succession of kings than any monarchy
upon earth can at this day boast of ; we cannot but
behold with the deepest concern the miseries they
suffer under a foreign usurpation, and the intolerable
burdens daily added to their yoke, which become yet
more sensible to us when we consider the constant
zeal and affection the generality of our subjects of
that our ancient kingdom have expressed for us on
all occasions, and particularly when we had the
satisfaction of being ourselves amongst them.

We see a nation always famous for valour, the
highly esteemed by the greatest of foreign potentates,
reduced to the condition of a province, under the
specious pretence of an union with a more powerful
neighbour. In consequence of this pretended union,
grievous and unprecedented taxes have been laid on,
and levied with severity in spite of all the representations that could be made to the contrary ; and these
have not failed to produce that poverty and decay
of trade which were easily foreseen to be the necessary
consequences of such oppressive measures.

The manifesto went on to speak of the oppression of
the Highlands, the Disarming Act, the building of forts
and their garrisoning by troops from the south, and the
fact that the Highlands were now subjected to what
amounted to martial law. It promised the restoration
of freedom to the Highlands and of independence to
Scotland generally, a free pardon to all who had ever
taken up arms against the Royal House of Stuart, the
speedy summoning of a free parliament, complete
religious toleration and respect for the Protestant Church
and schools and universities ; and of course, suitable
reward for all those who should prove their zeal in the
Stuart cause.

Again the glen echoed to the tumultuous cheering of

the assembled men, then Tullibardine marched back to the Prince's quarters with the standard and a guard of fifty Camerons.

An hour later another column of marching men was seen, and presently MacDonald of Keppoch arrived at the head of three hundred of his clan. Other smaller parties followed, and when Charles surveyed the scene his heart rose to his throat with exultation. Where a few hours ago he had found only a few lonely bothies and a handful of people the Glen was filled now with men—twelve hundred of them, every man sworn to fight to the last for their Prince and the Cause.

MacDonald of Tierndriech led forward the magnificent mount he had taken from his prisoner, Captain Scott, and presented it to the Prince, and as evening drew in the gallant young figure, upright and at ease in the saddle, was surrounded by cheering crowds of armed men.

But oddly enough, James himself knew nothing of all this. Charles had kept his secret well, and it was some time before his father knew that he had thrown caution to the winds, disregarded filial duty and set out boldly and almost alone upon his mad adventure.

When he heard of it, James was deeply upset. But his heart was filled with pride as well, and he wrote to the Duke of Ormond, who had sent him the news: "I cannot but say that the courage and sentiments he shows upon this occasion will always do him honour."

Thereafter, with an energy he had seldom shown in pushing his own affairs forward, he threw himself into the delicate and difficult task of securing help for his son and doing all that lay in his power to stir the court of France to action.

But Charles, wearied of politics, sick of inaction and delays, had come home at last. What need of help from the tricky foreigner? The clamour of an army was in his ears, and he was already, in spirit, speeding south to win a throne.

CHAPTER SEVEN

Cam ye by Athole, lad wi' the philabeg,
Down by the Tummel or banks of the Garry?
Saw ye the lads with their bonnets and white cockades
Leaving their mountains to follow Prince Charlie?

> Follow thee, follow thee, wha' wadna follow thee?
> Lang hast thou lo'ed and trusted us fairly.
> Charlie, Charlie, wha wadna follow thee?
> King o' the Hieland hearts, bonnie Prince Charlie!

PRINCE CHARLES swung himself into the saddle and rode out to inspect his army.

At sight of the tall, athletic figure a ripple of cheering ran along the ranks, drawn up in marching order in the glen, and the Prince, looking upon the inspiring scene, felt his heart swell with pride and his pulses quicken with excitement. How often he had pictured this moment! And how far the reality transcended anything he had been able to imagine!

These were, in the opinion of any professional soldier, raw undisciplined troops; yet there was no sign of lack of discipline, and they bore themselves like veterans.

Indeed the clan system lent itself to military organisation. When Lochiel had sent round the fiery cross throughout his territory the first to respond had been the gentlemen of the clan. Lochiel was their chief, the supreme authority; but under him came many gentlemen, minor chiefs in reality and all closely related to him. They called out their men at Lochiel's summons, and marched to the rendezvous at Achnacarry; and the men who marched with them did so freely and without a thought for themselves. Even the humblest of them carried in his head a genealogical table that traced his ancestors in direct descent from the original founder of the clan. The poorest Cameron of them all had an equal claim with every other to be a cousin of Lochiel. The honour of the family was his first thought, and the chief he regarded as the head of the family. His quarrels were family quarrels, in which all, rich and poor alike, considered themselves directly involved.

When the clan gathered, it fell naturally into separate companies, each under its own officers, according to districts, with the chief in supreme command. And so it was with all the clans.

But their devotion was to the clan, not to the chief in person. If he went against the wishes of the clan, they were quick to criticise, to take action if necessary. So it occasioned no surprise when a party of gentlemen reached Glenfinnan and, having spoken to Lochiel, were introduced to the Prince. Their spokesman came forward.

" Your royal highness, we are gentlemen of the MacLeods. We disapprove of our chief's decision not to join your standard, and we have come to offer you our swords, and, if you desire it, to return and raise our people for your service."

The Prince was overjoyed. The MacLeod's refusal had been a bitter blow, for the clan was powerful and could have raised a considerable force. This offer of support from the Isles was particularly welcome.

So the party went off in haste to call out their men and join the Prince as soon as they could, while runners went off to other chiefs to acquaint them with the route of the Prince's march, and appoint rendezvous along the way.

The first was at Kinlocheil, a bare six miles away, and the little army was soon on the march, with pipes playing and banners flying up the wooded defile by the Callop River, and then by the track that led down to the head of the long and narrow Loch Eil.

Here Charles pitched his first encampment, the day after the raising of the standard, and here he was joined by 300 of Clanranald's men, and by Murray of Broughton, who had acted for the Edinburgh Association. Because of their former dealings and Murray's excellent work in that respect, the Prince appointed him Secretary. He was almost the only old acquaintance Charles met in Scotland, and speedily ingratiated himself with the Prince.

The camp was a scene of bustle and constant activity. A working party of 250 Camerons had been despatched to fetch the baggage and arms and ammunition that had been landed from the *Doutelle*, and their arrival was hailed with delight by the troops. At the same time men arrived singly or in small parties to join the flag or to bring news of the outside world.

One piece of news was startling enough—a copy of a proclamation issued in London for the apprehension of the Prince. It offered a reward of £30,000 for him, dead or alive, and Charles, reading it, burst into a shout of laughter. But there was no laughter on the faces of the men who crowded round him. It might amuse him; but to them it was a deadly insult, and they turned on him passionately to demand that he should retaliate.

" Your royal highness must issue a proclamation for the apprehension of the Elector of Hanover ! " they exclaimed.

The Prince shook his head.

" No, no, gentlemen," he protested. " Such a thing is absurd."

" Honour demands it ! " they pressed, and the Prince, smothering his laughter, listened to them courteously. Murray of Broughton immediately set to work ; but when Charles glanced at the draft he expostulated again.

" Thirty pounds should be enough ! "

But the Highlanders were in deadly earnest. They could not see this as any joking matter, and reluctantly Charles agreed, and signed the proclamation.

The government's offer of the reward for the Prince's capture was not simply a dishonourable and shameful act ; it was also a stupid one, and showed how little the gentlemen in the south understood the character of the people whom they hoped to bribe. Already many thousands knew the Prince's exact location, and his probable future movements ; but the Commander-in-Chief of the government forces was still completely in the dark, with no means of gaining intelligence. He might have remained much longer in the dark, but for a typical gesture made at Kinlocheil.

Captain Sweetenham was summoned.

" We have no desire," he was told, " to carry prisoners of war along with us, nor to imprison a gentleman for an indefinite period. We therefore offer you your freedom, in return for your parole as an officer and a gentleman."

The gallant captain, who had had time to alter his views about these Highland savages, received this announcement with delight, and readily gave his parole. He was released on August 21st accordingly, and set off for home. But he placed his own interpretation upon a question of honour, and hastened off to find his Commander-in-Chief.

§

On the 23rd the Prince marched on to Fassifern, where he spent the night with Lochiel's brother, and heard news that raised his spirits and offered the prospect of immediate action.

Sir John Cope had left Stirling with a strong force to march into the Highlands. Only much later it transpired that the suggestion for this move had come originally from some secret Jacobites, who hoped thereby to shift him from Stirling.

By an odd coincidence, the two commanders had started their march on the same day, the 20th, and with approximately the same number of men, for Cope's troops consisted of twenty-five companies of foot totalling 1400 men, and some of Gardiner's dragoons. The dragoons he left behind in Stirling, as mounted troops could be of little use in the Highlands, but he brought four small field-pieces and 1000 stand of spare firearms with which to supply the recruits he expected to join him on his march.

He reached Crieff on the 21st, where he was visited by the Duke of Athole and his younger brother, Lord George Murray. He had ordered them to furnish reinforcements, but the Duke excused himself. He had not been able to persuade a single Highlander to join the redcoats.

Now he was in full march towards Dalnacardoch, and the Prince realised that he would proceed from Dalwhinnie towards the great mountain mass of Corrie-arraick and cross it to sweep down into the glens beyond, where the disaffected clans were most numerous.

Next morning he moved to Moy, and on the 26th crossed the water of Lochy and reached the Castle of Invergarry, where he spent the night. While there he had fresh news. It came from old Gordon of Glenbucket, who had gone home to collect his men, and now sent an express to say that Cope had advanced considerably along his line of march and intended to cross Corrie-arraick.

A council of war was held. Fraser of Gortlech, who had just arrived, and came in the name of his chief, Lord Lovat, with assurances that his lordship offered his services to the Prince, advised a march to the north, to raise the Frasers of Stratherrick and secure reinforcements among other clans.

The Marquis of Tullibardine intervened.

"I cannot recommend such a plan, sir," he declared. "The enemy is marching to meet us. We must show ourselves ready and eager to meet *him*."

Mr. Secretary Murray concurred.

" In Edinburgh there is a strong Jacobite party, only awaiting your royal highness's arrival in order to declare themselves. Edinburgh should be our objective. To be in Edinburgh—that is the crux of the matter."

Charles listened keenly to the discussion. Edinburgh ! It was a bold suggestion. But it fell in admirably with his own inclinations. Days were precious, since every delay meant further strength of opposition.

" We march for Edinburgh, gentlemen," he decided, and the conference broke up.

At Low Bridge, Stewart of Ardshiel met him with two hundred and eighty of the Stewarts of Appin, and at Aberchalder, at the north end of Loch Oich and only five miles from Fort Augustus, six hundred of the MacDonells of Glengarry, under MacDonell of Lochgarry, four hundred of the Grants of Glenmoriston, and sixty Macdonalds of Glencoe were waiting.

Another council was called.

It was essential to reach the summit of Corriearraick before Cope could get there—and Cope, according to the latest reports, was dangerously near. But Charles knew his Highlanders.

Campaigning in the mountains was no novelty to them, and he could count on doubling the speed of the redcoats without undue exertion.

" We start at dawn," he announced, and his officers dispersed to snatch a few brief hours of sleep.

§

In the clouded darkness before a misty dawn the pipes summoned the men from their beds among the heather. Fires kindled in the valley, and by the light of them, while a hasty meal was being cooked, men strapped on their kilts and looked to their arms. The Prince, stooping to tie the latchets of his shoes, looked up at the men surrounding him.

" I declare, gentlemen," he cried solemnly, " that I

shall not unloose these latchets until I have come up with Sir John Cope and his army !"

As the grey light of dawn penetrated into the deep glen, the clansmen saw a tall young figure moving among them, upright and handsome. They looked, puzzled at the tartan he wore, for he was in Highland dress ; and then he was recognised, and the cheering began. It went down the glen in a ringing shout of triumph and enthusiasm, and as the men fell in under their officers every eye was upon the Prince. He spoke to them in Gaelic, for since the landing at Borrodale he had practised hard every day and was already fairly fluent. Then he gave the order to march.

It was a gruelling climb, although General Wade had made it easier for them with his military road. But for all they knew Sir John Cope and his regulars were even then ascending the long winding traverses of that road on the southern side of the mountain. It was to be a race to the top, and the Highlanders breasted the steep slopes with a will.

Now was the moment for Charles to bless his vigorous youth, his long sturdy legs and those days and nights among the mountains near Albano, when he had trained his body for just such an ordeal. They climbed ; and their Prince climbed with them, leading the way, proving at the outset that he was no mere parlour prince but every inch a man as good as the best of them.

The sun rose, the mists cleared from the mountains and the day was fine and clear. The men toiled on without fatigue, inured to any hardship. Born and bred among their mountains, where they tended their sheep and the great herds of black cattle that were the real wealth of the clans, they thought nothing of sleeping in the heather, of climbing a thousand feet in a morning, of scaling heights that no other troops in the world could have tackled. With targets and haversacks slung on their backs, the belted plaids leaving their limbs free and unhampered, and only their firelocks and claymores to burden them, they moved swiftly towards the summit ; and when the vanguard came swinging over the top they halted to stare down into the deep valley of the River Spey where no sign of a redcoat could be seen.

Here and there a solitary figure could be picked out, toiling up the glen ; but of Sir John Cope and his army, marching to occupy the Highlands, there was no trace.

The Highlanders surveyed the empty glen in puzzled silence ; and then the first of those toiling figures reached them. He was a deserter from Cope's forces, a man who had enrolled, a while ago, in Loudon's Highland Regiment and who, learning the object of the Commander-in-Chief's march, had taken the first opportunity to follow his true loyalty.

He had much to report.

Cope had reached Dalnacardoch on the 25th, and there Captain Sweetenham joined him. He had given the general the first authentic news of the rising, describing how he had been captured and had witnessed the raising of the standard, how he had been released on parole, how at that time the Prince's force did not number upwards of 1,400 men, and how, on his way south, he had met various bands of Highlanders marching to join the Prince.

At Dalwhinnie Sweetenham had heard that the rebel army had been swollen to nearly 3,000 and was in full march for Corriearraick. Cope had gone on as far as Dalwhinnie himself, and there had held a council of war ; but what the result of that council had been the soldier could not say. Whenever the news of the rising had leaked out among the troops, most of the Highlanders among them had made up their minds to desert, and there would soon be others with later news.

It was clear what the news was to be, and it came almost at once. That very day Cope's council of war had decided not to risk battle with the Prince, but to march instead for Inverness.

So the Highland army, halted on the summit of

Corriearraick, looked in vain for the enemy, and heard the news of his flight with a great shout of joy.

The Prince, standing before his troops, took a glass of brandy and raised it high.

" Here's a health to Mr. Cope ! " he cried. " He is my friend, and if all the usurper's generals follow his example, I shall soon be at St. James's ! "

A shout of laughter and a storm of cheering greeted this sally, and the Prince ordered a glass of whisky to be issued to every man, so that the whole army could drink the toast. Then the descent started.

It was no longer a grim march. It was the pursuit of a fleeing enemy, and the Highlanders, swift as they had been in their ascent, went swinging down the steep twisting road at a pace that must have been a revelation to their young Commander, whose notions of soldiering were those of the south and who had yet to realise the capabilities of these men who had so eagerly answered his summons.

They were soon in Garvamore, and here the Prince summoned another council of war. This rapid pursuit could not be kept up indefinitely ; it was time to decide what should be done.

" The enemy has a long start of us," Secretary Murray pointed out. " We might not catch him up before he shut himself in to Inverness—and we are in no condition to carry out a siege. Also Cope could escape by sea, and get south again and dispute our march to Edinburgh. I therefore propose, gentlemen, that we should abandon the pursuit of Cope and march for the south and endeavour to seize Edinburgh before measures for defence of the city can be completed."

The Prince saw the wisdom of his words. But the chiefs objected. Their men knew that the retreating enemy were only a little distance away. They were burning with impatience to get to grips with the redcoats, for they had many old scores to settle. To ask them to break off the pursuit and turn south instead was to invite disagreement. But wiser voices prevailed. Lochiel and Keppoch and Clanranald and Lochgarry might long to smash Cope's army at the very start of the campaign ; but there were greater issues involved and Charles, young and impetuous as he was, had too firm a grasp of strategy to yield to the temptation of an easy victory.

The council wrangled and argued and at last came to its decision, which Charles endorsed with satisfaction. They would march to the south.

Consternation greeted the order. Murmurings of discontent ran along the lines. Six hundred of them sent a deputation forward, offering to detach themselves from the main body, overtake Sir John Cope, and smash his forces without assistance. The chiefs, having agreed to the council's plan, dissuaded them ; but it wanted all their authority to restrain the men, and only the Prince's exhortations prevailed upon them in the end.

Charles, however, saw that some concessions must be made. He summoned MacDonell of Lochgarry.

" Take a party of two hundred men," he ordered him, " and seize the fort at Ruthven. If we cannot destroy the whole breed at one blow, we can at least smoke out a few of the hornets' nests."

The MacDonells set off in great fettle for the job, and Dr. Cameron was summoned next.

" It is but a short way to Cluny Castle, where MacPherson sits idly while we march to the south. He commands a company of soldiers in the service of the Elector of Hanover. Take a party of your Camerons and apprehend him, and bring him to me, so that we shall see whether he will return to his proper allegiance."

Cameron, too, set off in the best of spirits on his errand, while the Prince's army resumed its march. Lochgarry's men, as it happened, failed to take Ruthven fort ; but at Dalwhinnie a party was seen rapidly overtaking the army, and soon Dr. Cameron came up, bringing MacPherson of Cluny. The Prince sent for him.

It was a brief interview. MacPherson had taken service

with the government simply because he had given up all hope of a Stuart rising. The disarming of the Highlanders had been a bitter blow to men like himself, and his commission as an officer in Lord Loudon's Regiment at least salved his pride by allowing him to retain his own arms. But the news of the Prince's landing had put him in a serious quandary. His wife, a daughter of Simon, Lord Lovat, chief of the Frasers, was a zealous Jacobite, but she insisted that as he had taken a commission under the government he could not join the Prince. So Cluny had stayed at home—he would certainly not rejoin the regiment and take the field against the man whom he regarded as the rightful heir to the throne.

Now the final choice had been forced upon him, and within a few minutes it had been made. When a man so firm and far-sighted as the Gentle Lochiel had been entirely unable to withstand the charm of the Prince's presence, what hope had Cluny ? A less magnanimous prince might have reproached him with disloyalty in taking service with the government ; but Charles had no reproaches to make to him, and without more ado the chief undertook to throw up his commission and go home and raise the clan for the Prince's service.

On that promise he was instantly released, and set off to explain the situation to his wife and call up the six hundred MacPhersons who would obey his summons. He would have no difficulty there, for two MacPhersons had been shot after the mutiny of the Black Watch three years before—and the clan thirsted for revenge.

§

The Marquis of Tullibardine wrote a letter. It was to an old friend, Mrs. Robertson of Lude, a mansion situated close to Blair Castle, the Marquis's old home. He had not been home for thirty years, since his attainder for his share in The Fifteen ; perhaps the thought of revisiting Blair Castle had influenced him in the councils of war at which he had pressed for the decision to march south. Now he had had news of the Castle. His brother had fled, like so many other Perthshire gentlemen, when word came of the advance of the Highland army. The Castle was untenanted. So the Marquis wrote to Mrs. Robertson, asking her to go and put it in readiness to receive his royal guest, and to stay and do the honours as hostess.

On the 30th of August the Prince and his army arrived —and Mrs. Robertson was there to receive him. A few local gentlemen, including Lord Nairne, came to offer their services ; but as yet there was little response among the people.

Next day Charles inspected his army.

He was still in high spirits, and as he rode out at the head of his officers his clear young eyes were alert and keen. At sight of the regiments drawn up before him his brow furrowed in sudden vexation ; for there were gaps—wide, alarming gaps—in the ranks. He spoke to various officers. Some of their men, they admitted, had fallen behind.

" Then go and bring them in," he ordered, and sent off a party of officers to round up the stragglers. They returned presently with the missing men, and Charles, hearing the only excuse they had to offer, found himself face to face with the one serious defect in these Highland troops.

They had loitered behind solely because they were disgusted at not being allowed to go in pursuit of the redcoats ! Their chiefs had promised them the chance of revenging the many injuries they had suffered at the hands of the soldiers in the past ; yet when the opportunity offered they were ordered to call off the chase and march south instead.

It was as well the Prince had sent their officers to round them up, for if a sufficient number of them had got together as they loitered behind they would certainly have put their heads together and gone off after Cope on their own account.

§

On the same day George II returned to London from Germany ; and the MacGregors captured the fort of Inversnaid.

Robert MacGregor of Glencairnock had raised three hundred of them to form a regiment and join the Prince ; but another branch of the clan, which regarded William MacGregor (or Drummond) of Bochaldy as the rightful chief, formed a separate corps under MacGregor of Glengyle, James Roy MacGregor, a son of Rob Roy. The corps, in fact, consisted at first of only twelve men, remnants of the famous freebooter's band, and before setting out to join the levies raised by Tullibardine James conceived the idea of striking a shrewd blow on his own account.

As part of the measures for pacifying the MacGregor country, a strong fort had been built at Inversnaid, and here a garrison was maintained. James led his men in a sudden descent upon the fort, and after a brief sharp struggle they smashed their way in, captured the remaining eighty-nine soldiers of the garrison, and burnt the fort to the ground. It was an exploit that would have done credit to Rob Roy himself, and it set all Loch Lomond-side by the ears.

§

Mrs. Robertson of Lude, delighted as she was with the great honour that had been done her, conceived an ambition. She wanted to entertain the Prince under her own roof ; and Charles, never able to refuse a favour, readily assented. So after two days at Blair Castle he went on to Lude ; and his hostess took care that he should be royally entertained.

The gentlemen of Perthshire might have departed in haste for the south ; but not all their ladies had gone with them, and that evening witnessed a scene that was to live in the annals of the old house. Mrs. Robertson gave a ball for the Prince.

He had been working hard, perfecting plans of campaign, writing despatches, reviewing and drilling his troops, attending to the multitude of detail any commander in the field must deal with. Now, for one evening, he could afford to relax ; and this evening he showed that he knew how to relax. After all he was only a youngster still, full of high spirits and great hopes and surrounded by men devoted heart and soul to his cause.

So the Prince led his hostess out in a graceful minuet, and for the first time the ladies of Scotland were able to watch the superb dancing that was to delight so many hearts in the months to come. For all his adventures he had not forgotten the social graces in which he had excelled as a boy, and after the minuet he called for a Highland reel, and the tune he called for was appropriate enough : " This is no' mine ain hoose ! "

Reel followed reel, and Charles delighted the gathering with his dancing of the strathspey minuet, and his ready smiles, his laughter, his splendid bearing and his unfailing charm carried the evening with a swing.

It was a brief interlude in the grim, enthralling task upon which he had set out—a delightful interlude that strengthened his determination and gave him new zest for the work ahead ; but it could not tempt him from that work, and early next day, the 3rd September, he sent Lochiel and Lord Nairne ahead with four hundred men to occupy Dunkeld, along the road to Perth. They entered the little cathedral town during the morning and proclaimed James VIII at the market cross.

The Prince himself, at the head of his troops, rode through the town the same day, and went on to Lord Nairne's house for the night.

Meanwhile the advance party of Camerons had been pressing down on the road to Perth, and they marched into the Fair City that same day. They took possession of it quietly, without fuss, and without a trace of opposition. Many of them had never seen a large town before, and the sight of so many people all at once, and all in the strange outlandish dress of the south, must have been astonishing enough ; but they knew the honour that the Prince had done them in selecting them for this work, and they had already listened to more than one harangue on the question of their behaviour. They had been reminded, in clear set terms, that the people they were going among were the Prince's subjects just as much as they were, countrymen to be treated as such. They might be wrongheaded, misled into disloyalty through the machinations of the London government ; but they were not enemies.

So the Camerons behaved themselves, mounting guard at strategic points smartly and quietly, interfering not at all with the douce citizens who poured out into the streets to stare at these wild Highlandmen with their kilts and bonnets and targets and their antiquated weapons ; and next day the whole of Perth was lining the streets or streaming out on the Dunkeld road at the first distant skirl of the pipes and the first rumour that the Prince was coming.

He came, riding at the head of his troops and attended by a body of gentlemen on horseback. The good burgesses, ever with an eye for a fine figure of a man, stared at this youth who sat his horse so magnificently, whose face, with the large glowing eyes, the delicate mouth and the pointed chin, was so mobile and animated and yet had an underlying cast of melancholy to offset its pride and recklessness. They saw an athletic, dashing figure, in a superb dress of tartan trimmed with gold, with his own yellow hair brushed up over the small white periwig, and as they stared, and the Prince looked down upon them from his mount, riding slowly past, they began to cheer.

They cheered and cheered, they threw their bonnets in the air, they shouted and swarmed into the roadway, they called friendly greetings to the marching High-landers and raised cheer after cheer for every known figure that went past—for Lochiel, and Clanranald, and Keppoch, and Lord Nairne, and Tullibardine, and Murray of Broughton, and all the rest. The Fair City rang with the acclamations of its citizens, hailing the Prince and his men.

It was a spontaneous tribute to a gallant young man and his gallant adherents ; but it was more than that.

The Union of Parliaments had had many effects entirely beneficial to the industrial areas of Scotland, and therefore to the country as a whole ; but outside these areas there had been results far less favourable, and the loss of independence, the removal of the seat of government from Edinburgh to London, had been a bitter pill to swallow, and one which had done serious harm. Taxes had been imposed that no Scots Parliament would have agreed to ; repressive measures in the Highlands, often accompanied by barbarous cruelty, had been taken that no Scots Parliament could have countenanced. In Perth, too, the affair of the mutiny of the Black Watch, whose headquarters were Perth, had caused lasting bitterness. As the Mutiny had many repercussions in the Forty-Five, a brief outline must be given.

The Black Watch had been recruited solely for the policing of the Highland border ; almost every man belonged to one of the leading Highland families, and when it was on the march *Am Freiceadan Dubh* was followed by servants almost as numerous as the regiment itself. The humblest private regarded himself as a gentlemen in his own right. The terms of enlistment stipulated that they should not be required to serve outside Scotland.

In 1742 the regiment was summoned to attend a great

review of troops in London. Its officers required
assurances that this did not involve service outside
Scotland, and that immediately after the review it would
be sent back to Perth. These assurances were instantly
given. But no sooner had the regiment arrived in
London than word got about that it was to be sent
overseas. This was no mere rumour ; it was plain fact,
and in a regiment where officers and men all belonged
to the same social stratum it was not long before the
news was known to all. The government intended
to take this golden opportunity of shipping a large
body of the most energetic of the younger Highland
gentry out of the country, and so being rid at one sweep
of these men whose natural sympathies were probably
Jacobite.

It was the sort of treachery best calculated to horrify
and infuriate men who regarded personal honour as the
greatest of all virtues. The officers, because of their oath
of allegiance to the government, could do nothing ; but
the men were not so bound. The morning after the
news had got about the Black Watch had disappeared.
Their officers were still in their quarters, but not a man
was to be found.

They were not found for days. They left London by
night ; they hid during the day, marched north again
at night, in utter silence, undetected. It was a superb
feat, the kind of military manœuvre commanders dream
about and never hope to accomplish ; but these men,
born and bred among the mountains and the glens,
were expert in the art of the foray and tireless and swift
on the march. They had passed York before they were
detected. By then the whole of England was searching
for them, and large bodies of troops were moving about
the country seeking to intercept them. Eventually
several regiments of cavalry succeeded in surrounding
them, and demanded their surrender.

They agreed to surrender—on conditions. They
required that the government should fulfil its obligations

and keep its word given to return the regiment to Perth ; they demanded that there should be no victimisation as a result of the mutiny and that no measures should be taken against the ringleaders. On these conditions they were willing to march back to London, take part in the review, and return quietly to Scotland.

The English general consulted his superiors. He was instructed to agree to these terms. The alternative to agreement would have been a bloody and terrible battle in which the Black Watch could have been expected to give a very good account of itself. With these assurances, the regiment returned to London.

It was immediately confined to barracks, the ringleaders were summarily tried and shot and almost the whole of the regiment was transported overseas to a convict settlement, for life.

If it did nothing else, this incident should have shown the Highlanders what they might expect from the government in London. It was typical of the " Scrap of Paper " mentality which had been introduced into the country and was to be the keynote of official dealings thereafter. But the Highlanders, still obsessed with their outmoded ideas of personal integrity, refused to learn their lesson, and even the Prince, whose experience of politics and courts should have taught him better, subscribed to these sentiments and persistently conducted his campaign accordingly.

Now the city of Perth declared itself without reservation, giving the Prince and his army a royal welcome in spite of the absence of the provost and magistrates, who had avoided a difficult situation by retiring discreetly to Edinburgh. From every window the fair maids and matrons of the city smiled down upon the Prince and fluttered their kerchiefs and cheered themselves hoarse, while the population flocked through the streets to gather at the Cross.

There James VIII was proclaimed amid wild huzzas, and then the cheering populace escorted the Prince

through the streets to the house of Viscount Stormont,
where he took up his quarters.

As he rode into Perth, Charles had pulled from his
pocket a single golden guinea and showed it to Kelly,
who was riding close beside him. He had laughed as
he tossed it up and slipped it back into his pocket.

" There's the sum of my wealth ! " he cried merrily.
" It is all I have left of my fortune. But, praise God,
the army has received a fortnight's pay in advance, and
before that time is up more funds will be forthcoming."

But for all his lighthearted jesting, that single guinea
in his pocket was a source of serious worry. It meant
that he had to remain in Perth until more money could
be found, and although he had written round to various
friends from Kinlocheil, requesting advances, it was
some time before he could expect a response.

It came eventually, and much of it came anonymously,
from secret adherents who for one reason or another
dared not avow themselves openly. But more positive
measures were needed, and Charles issued an order levying
a sum of £500 from the city. He also appointed collectors
for Dundee and other towns in Perthshire and Angus,
to collect the public funds and remit them to him. In
this way his coffers were soon replenished, and sufficient
funds were gathered to continue the march to the south.

MacDonald of Keppoch was sent forward with an
advanced party to capture Dundee as soon as the army
reached Perth, but on the way he met some citizens of
the town who warned him that his force was too small.
He accordingly sent back word requesting reinforcements,
and young Clanranald was selected for this task. He
set off with his men at midnight, and at daybreak the
MacDonalds burst into the town and, racing straightway
for the docks, succeeded in capturing two ships lying
there loaded with arms and ammunition. Keppoch sent
them up the Tay to Perth, a welcome addition to the
Prince's armoury.

At Perth, too, a new adherent arrived who was to take

a leading part in the subsequent campaign. The Marquis of Tullibardine brought his young brother, Lord George Murray, to meet the Prince.

Lord George's reputation was well known in Europe. He had been out, like his eldest brother, in the Fifteen, and in 1719 had joined the small Spanish force which had landed in the Highlands in an abortive attempt to restore the Stuarts. After the defeat of that force at Glenshiel he had gone abroad and had served with great distinction as an officer in the army of the King of Sardinia. Subsequently, his brother, the new Duke of Athole, had secured him a pardon and had presented him to George I. Tall and powerfully built, still robust and vigorous although well past middle age, he had a natural military genius in addition to long experience, and was resourceful and brave to a fault. His favourite address to his men before an engagement was always : " I do not ask you, my lads, to go before, but to follow me ! " and he had always interpreted his own words literally.

Now he had come to offer his services to the Prince, and Charles wrung him warmly by the hand and, knowing well his great ability, appointed him lieutenant-general on the spot. The Duke of Perth had been given the rank of lieutenant-general, while O'Sullivan, one of the seven men of Moidart, held the post of quarter-master general, and adjutant-general, which had been given him at Glenfinnan. It was inevitable that Charles should favour the men he knew of old, without realising that they were mere adventurers.

Lord George knew the magnitude of the task ahead, and he got to work at once. His previous experience had taught him that the greatest disadvantage of High-land troops was their inclination to straggle in search of food.

" Your royal highness must first appoint a regular commissariat department," he pointed out to Charles, " so that the men have regular meals. Without that we shall never keep the army together and at full strength."

He soon had the new department organised. He also ordered large quantities of haversacks to be made, to carry a peck or two of meal, and to be issued to every man, so that the army could march ahead of its commissariat. A thousand of these knapsacks were sent to Crieff for the use of the Athole men, who were to gather there and march south.

The delay in Perth was irksome; but the very speed of the Prince's advance into Athole had rendered it necessary. There had been no time for the Athole men to gather, and it would take many days to collect all the available troops. Meantime fresh batches of men continued to arrive, among them a regiment two hundred strong raised by the aged Robertson of Struan, who at seventy-five was unable to lead his clan himself but appointed a deputy in command.

Charles worked unremittingly. However much he had enjoyed the ball at Lude, there was no time for enjoyment, and he accepted invitations only when he could not, out of courtesy or policy, refuse. Then he would lay aside the cares of the campaign and become once more the soul of charm; but for the rest he devoted every waking moment to his task, writing despatches, studying reports that arrived at frequent intervals from all over the country, dealing with all the complicated detail of organisation and, most particularly, drilling and training the troops.

On the Sunday, remembering the manner of his upbringing, he went to church in Perth, and took part, with complete assurance, in the Presbyterian service, listening attentively to the Rev. Mr. Armstrong as he preached a rousing sermon on a text from Isaiah xiv, verses 1 and 2 : " For the Lord will have mercy on Jacob, and will yet choose Israel, and set them in their own land ; and the strangers shall be joined to them, and bring them to their place, and the house of Israel shall possess them in the land of the Lord for servants and handmaids ; and they shall take them captives, whose captives they were ; and they shall rule over their oppressors."

§

After riding out to Glenalmond to inspect the troops raised by the Duke of Perth, the Prince returned to the city to find urgent news awaiting him. Cope had left Inverness on the 4th of September for Aberdeen, and had ordered transports to be ready there to convey his troops south to the Forth.

" He means to occupy Edinburgh," the Prince exclaimed. " His transports might reach Leith in time."

A council of war was summoned at once, and the situation set forth.

" There are two courses open to us. Either we may make a dash to the north to intercept Cope at Aberdeen and force him to give battle, or we can continue our march to the south and hope to cross the Forth before his transports arrive."

The first alternative was tempting. The Highlanders to a man would greet such a decision with a thunderous cheer, and set off at once by forced marches with the wildest enthusiasm. But would they be in time ? There was a serious doubt—and this was no time for a gamble.

" We must reach Edinburgh before him, whatever happens," Murray of Broughton declared emphatically ; and so it was decided.

CHAPTER EIGHT

HOLYROOD HOUSE

'Twas on a Monday morning,
Right early in the year,
That Charlie cam' to our town,
The young Chevalier.

O Charlie is my darling,
My darling, my darling,
O Charlie is my darling,
The young Chevalier !

EDINBURGH was in uproar.

My Lord Provost and the Magistrates of the city had
kept the news from the north to themselves. They
misdoubted the effects it might have upon the lieges ;
so the people knew nothing, beyond the fact that the
Prince had landed, that he had collected a certain number
of wild Highlanders and was making a move. They
knew, of course, that the valiant Sir John Cope had set
out from Stirling to deal with the situation, and it
never occurred to them that the rebellion would get
beyond the stage of being another local disturbance
behind the Highland line.

People were not wanting, either, to keep this opinion current. The Jacobites in the city put it about assiduously that the Prince had only a very small number of adherents with him and did not contemplate a descent upon the south. They pooh-poohed the idea of a real rising and jeered at the elaborate preparations that Cope had made to smother a mere momentary unrest among the clans.

At this point Rob Roy's son James came calmly into Edinburgh, volunteering information. Many of the Whigs, taking their line from the Duke of Argyll, who had always shown a partiality for Rob Roy and his family, were glad to see him. Here was a Highlander who, of all people, ought to be in a position to tell them things. He did so, with relish.

He was taken along and introduced to the public functionaries of the city, who wanted nothing more anxiously than to be reassured ; he reassured them.

" The Highland army," he declared positively, " is not fifteen hundred strong. And most of them are old men and boys. As for arms—why, sickles and scythes are all the most of them have. Let them once come face to face with Johnnie Cope and his men, and they'll turn tail and never stop till they're back in their own glens. I know. I've seen them."

For one brief moment the worthy bailies allowed themselves to rejoice. But James Roy had no sooner gone from the meeting than other voices rose. All very well to take the matter so lightly : but what if the Highlanders did not run? What if they stood up to Cope, or out-manœuvred him, and came on south? And that very day, the 26th of August, a piece of intelligence reached the city which threw the Town Council into wild confusion.

Sir John Cope, breaking off his march into the western Highlands, had hastened off and shut him in Inverness. The Prince had marched on unopposed and was in Perth. A wag, less overawed by this announcement than his frightened colleagues, gave a pawky grin and cried :

" Why, then, they are doing a country dance, and now they have changed places ! "

Next day a special meeting was called, some of the leading private citizens being included. They must discuss what was to be done—and there was no time to lose. The city was in no condition to defend itself. Its walls were not designed to withstand a siege, but only to keep out smugglers. In places they rose to a height of twenty feet ; but in others they were no more than ten feet high, and easily scalable. They possessed some embrasures and bastions, but no guns had ever been mounted on them—and no guns were available. Also they surrounded only three sides of the city, leaving the fourth protected only by the North Loch, a sheet of water occupying what are now the Princes Street Gardens.

The Castle was strongly garrisoned, and, with an aged fire-eater in command, could be expected to hold out firmly against any assault. General Guest, at eighty-five, had no intention of being dislodged from his comfortable quarters by any rebels—and since all reports showed that the rebels had only a negligible quantity of field pieces and no siege guns at all, he knew he was safe from attack. His second-in-command, at the age of eighty-six, felt equally secure.

But the Provost and his Magistrates got no consolation from this security. So they agreed hurriedly to repair the walls and set about what defences they could contrive.

As for the men who were to defend the city, the good Provost Stewart found himself in even more of a quandary. True, there were the Trained Bands, supported by the town—sixteen companies with from sixty to a hundred men in each. But since the Revolution the only time they appeared under arms was on the King's birth-day, when they drew their arms from the city magazine, which contained about 1,200 firearms, mostly without bayonets. One day a year being rather inadequate training, the Magistrates wagged solemn heads and tried to gain courage from the fact that they had, at least, the Town Guard, a company of foot armed with muskets and bayonets and serving under the orders of the Provost.

The meeting decided to raise a regiment of Edinburgh volunteers a thousand strong, and they forthwith sent off a petition to London applying for the warrant without which they could not proceed to enrol a single man.

A few days later Sir John Cope's aide-de-camp, Captain Rogers, came galloping into town with an order to General Guest to requisition a number of transports at Leith and send them north to Aberdeen at once, to embark Cope's army.

This was on September 4th, the very day on which word came that the Prince's advance guard had entered Perth, and the worthy bailies breathed sighs of relief and prayed fervently for fair winds for the transports. Perth was perilously near, and the Highlanders had a name for swift movement ; they might cover those forty miles in a single day !

Now the news leaked out and swept through the city and scared burgesses collected in knots and crowds at every corner, arguing, quarrelling, whipping themselves up into a panic with tales of the horrors in store ; and at this point local politics took a hand.

Five years before, Provost Stewart and his friends had swept the polls, and from that time on they had governed the city without challenge from their rivals. But the Municipal Elections were due to start on September 10th —and the contest was bound to be fierce. The ex-Provost and ex-bailies were ready to make a fresh bid for power, and they jumped at the chance of a little astute electioneering.

Three-quarters of Edinburgh was staunchly Whig, as became the citizens of a thriving town with a flourishing trade and a large number of lawyers to keep the people's minds occupied with local disputes. The other quarter was as staunchly Jacobite ; but it was the Whig vote that counted. So to ex-Provost Drummond came the inspiration of being the most zealous Whig of all.

On Friday, the 6th of September, a petition, signed by about a hundred people—most of them ex-Magistrates and their friends—was presented to the Town Council, seeking authority to form a body of volunteers for the defence of the city and asking the Provost to apply to General Guest for arms from the King's magazine in the castle.

Next day a Council was summoned, and promptly granted its prayers in every article except one—the petitioners could not be permitted to choose their own officers, but must accept those appointed by the Provost. That wily gentleman had his eyes wide open.

On the following Monday the warrant from London arrived, and the Council appointed Provost Stewart colonel in command both of the regiment it permitted the Council to raise, and of the volunteers as well.

Next day the elections began. Whatever the danger from without the walls, the good burgesses of Edinburgh were determined at any rate to cast their votes ; so all work stopped for the day, and no doubt the Jacobites were as assiduous as any in urging the artisans to leave their work on the walls and go to the polls. The same day a fleet of transports sailed from Leith to Aberdeen, and the anxious Council had opportunity, in among the excitements of electioneering, to pray that they might get back to the Forth before it was too late.

So Edinburgh prepared for whatever should come, and stalwart citizens determined to defend their homes to the last ; but while some citizens clamoured for arms to defend their homes others clamoured, with equal zeal, for a policy of appeasement and humble submission to the rebels' demands.

Meanwhile Charles, with the able help of Lord George Murray, had produced order out of chaos and was almost ready to resume his march. On the 11th of September he set out, at the head of a detachment of his troops, on the road to Dunblane. They camped overnight near the town, and the Prince and his commanders waited impatiently for the main body of the army, with their field pieces and supply columns, to catch them up.

They did not arrive until next day.

Charles, obsessed with the need for haste, was vexed at the delay, and demanded explanations.

Lord George, that seasoned veteran of many campaigns, knew the answer.

" For the last eight days they have been living in comfortable quarters in Perth. Apart from some drilling they have had no exercise. They have got out of condition. An army in the field had better remain in the field."

Charles agreed, and new orders were given. Hereafter the army would encamp in the open instead of taking up quarters in the towns, and it would be kept constantly in motion. The fatigued appearance of the stragglers had contrasted strongly with the fit, keen, vigorous air of James Roy's MacGregors, and of the sixty further Macdonalds of Glencoe who, under their chief, had joined the Prince on his march to Dunblane. Both regiments had made long forced marches through difficult country and at high speed, and arrived in splendid fettle ; and Charles did not fail to notice that.

On the 13th he ordered the whole force to be put in motion again.

§

The army was approaching Doune. As the Prince rode along with his entourage a gentleman appeared, coming to meet him. It was Edmonstone of Cambuswallace, whose house lay close to the line of march. He had put everything in readiness to receive the Prince and regale him with a hearty meal. Not only that, but many of the ladies of Menteith had assembled at

Cambuswallace, in order to pay their respects and wait upon him.

Charles received this warm invitation with his usual courtesy. But he was still consumed with impatience at the recent loss of time, and intent upon the march.

" I beg that you will excuse me, sir," he exclaimed, with real concern at being obliged to refuse. " But time is pressing and I cannot delay."

" Then at least permit me to offer your royal highness a glass of wine," Mr. Edmonstone pleaded, and the Prince, unwilling to appear ungracious, smiled and nodded. The ladies meantime had come out of the house and were gathered round, and Mr. Edmonstone's daughters came forward to serve the wine. The Prince raised his glass gallantly and toasted them and drank without leaving the saddle, whereupon one of the girls, summoning all her courage, begged leave to kiss his hand.

Smiling, he granted her request, and the other daughters followed her example. But not so their cousin Robina. The favour she sought was something much more worth having—" to pree his royal highness's mou'."

Charles wrinkled his brows in bewilderment. For all his upbringing, broad Scots was still beyond him. He looked round for enlightenment, and one of the men around him laughingly translated. " The lady desires to kiss you on the mouth ! "

For answer, Charles swung out of the saddle, gathered the lady into his arms, and impulsively kissed her from ear to ear. Her cousins looked on enviously amid the laughter and cheers of the crowd.

A moment later the Prince was on his way, in great good humour.

Poring over his maps, he had selected the only safe route, by the Ford of Frew. It was an obvious point for the crossing of the Forth, and at least one experienced soldier on the other side realised that. Colonel Gardiner,

One of the girls begged leave to kiss his hand.

whose home was near Preston Grange, had brought his regiment of dragoons here in order to prevent the Prince from using the ford. When the Highland army came in sight the dragoons were ready for them—or so, at least, their Colonel fondly thought.

The Highland advance guard approached the river.

By great good luck it was unusually low, for there had been drought for some weeks, and the crossing would not be difficult. Charles, still in the highest spirits, rode out to the van, leapt from his horse, drew his sword, and waved it above his head. Then he dashed into the river.

In a great surge the Highlanders came after him, racing across the broad stream, and the gallant dragoons wheeled about, set spurs to their horses, and made off in a body. Their worthy colonel had no option but to follow, and they did not draw rein until they saw the welcoming walls of Stirling within easy reach.

Now indeed the die was cast. For a Highland army to cross the Forth was the most decisive step it could take. It was committed to a campaign in the Lowlands, in strange unknown country ill suited to the tactics of the clans and where difference of language and of outlook would make it unwelcome. But the decision had been taken, and now the Prince, standing on the southern bank, watched each detachment as it crossed, and called out his congratulations to the commanders. Whatever happened now there was but one course open to them— to go on, and on, and on ; for with the Forth behind them there could be no retreat.

On the moor of Sauchie, a few miles south of the ford, the army camped for the night, while Charles dined at Leckie House in the absence of his host, Mr. Moir, who had been seized by Gardiner's dragoons and carried off to Stirling Castle.

Charles passed the night at Bannockburn House, whose owner, Sir Hugh Paterson, was a zealous Jacobite, and it was while he was there that an incident happened that had a profound effect on the Highland army. In spite of Lord George Murray's splendid efforts to provide an adequate commissariat, some of the men got out of hand. After all, they were ignorant clansmen who had never before been away from their own glens, and they regarded themselves now as in enemy territory. The Lowlands, remote and legendary, had always seemed to them a strange and hostile country. So it was the most natural thing in the world, when you saw a great flock of sheep in a field, to shoot one and secure a hearty dinner for yourself and your friends.

The chiefs took stern measures to put a stop to this, and Lochiel, enraged at the conduct of his men, is said to have shot one of them himself as an example to the rest.

There was no further trouble. The chiefs, knowing well the Prince's attitude, harangued their men on their duty towards fellow-countrymen and respect for property, and the few thoughtless offenders were speedily subdued.

The Prince's next objective was Falkirk, and soon the towers and battlements of Stirling Castle came in sight. There was no way of avoiding passing fairly close to the Castle except by making a long and tedious detour, and when the guns opened up the Highlanders cheered derisively and continued their march. The gunners, picking out the Prince by the number of mounted attendants with him, trained their pieces upon his party ; but he had been under fire before and had shown his contempt of danger. He rode on without paying any attention to the brief and ineffectual bombardment.

Lord George Murray had sent a message to the Stirling magistrates, requiring a supply of provisions for the army, and they promptly opened the gates of the town and gave notice to the people of the Prince's demands. The shopkeepers were quick to respond, and soon a great trek was under way towards Bannockburn, near which the army had halted, and a brisk trade began. Then with the commissariat well supplied the army resumed its

march, and camped for the night in a field to the east
of Falkirk.

The Earl of Kilmarnock was the Prince's host that
night, at Callander House, and besides informing his
guest of his devoted attachment to his cause he gave him
a piece of important news. Gardiner's dragoons had
repeated their performance of the previous day, and,
unwilling to risk being trapped in Stirling, had continued their retreat to Falkirk. Then they had learned
that the Highland Army was after them again, and they
had retired still farther, in the direction of Linlithgow,
at which point their colonel had taken them firmly in
hand. He was determined to put up a fight at Linlithgow
Bridge, and had camped for the night in the neighbourhood.

Charles immediately summoned a council of war.
The dragoons were regular troops and by no means to
be despised. Here in the south cavalry could do a great
deal of harm to an army that was almost exclusively
infantry, and the dragoons were a constant menace. It
would be well to deal with them once and for all.

So a detachment of a thousand well armed men from
the different clans was ordered to prepare for a night
march, and at one o'clock in the morning they filed out
of the camp, with Lord George Murray himself in
command. But with them went also a tall young man
with the light of excitement in his eyes and a look of
eagerness on his face. The Prince had no mind to miss
such a golden chance of action at last.

In perfect order and utter silence they marched, swiftly
and eagerly. This was the sort of foray they understood,
the adventure they loved, and the thought of falling
upon the elusive dragoons keyed them up to a great
pitch of excitement and anticipation ; but as they
approached the camp of the dragoons in the darkness
the silence remained unbroken. None of the jangle of
harness, the creaking of leather, the soft sounds of
movements, of breathing and snorting that a cavalry

camp gives out at night, could be heard. The dragoons had gone again. They had retired during the night to Kirkliston, only eight miles from Edinburgh.

The detachment continued its silent march, and the muffled tramp of deerskin brogues failed to awaken the sleeping citizens of Linlithgow. When dawn broke, the town was completely occupied, and later in the day the whole army marched peaceably in. The provost had avoided a difficult situation by taking an early departure, but his wife and daughters, dressing themselves in bright tartan gowns, went down to the Cross with white cockades in their hats, to pay their respects and kiss the Prince's hand.

Next morning, Monday, the 16th, the army reached Corstorphine. All this time Gardiner's dragoons had kept just one jump ahead, and the Highlanders had never had a sight of them.

To avoid exposing his troops to the fire of the Castle guns, Charles made a circuit towards the south, and fixed his headquarters at Gray's Mill near Slateford, a mile from Corstorphine and less than two from the city walls. The men bivouacked in a field known as Gray's Park.

Meanwhile the uproar in Edinburgh had got almost out of hand. The Edinburgh Regiment mustered, and was found to consist of 189 men. The volunteers paraded, all 363 of them. The Town Guard turned out. General Guest decided to send the two regiments of dragoons— Gardiner's, which was near Corstorphine, and Hamilton's —out to do battle supported by the Edinburgh Regiment, the Edinburgh Volunteers, and the Town Guard. Hamilton's, coming in from their camp on Leith Links, made a brave show clattering through the town, down the Lawnmarket where the infantry had been drawn up. As they rode, they clashed their drawn swords and looked as bold and dashing as they could ; but the effect on the spectators was not what they had intended.

The womenfolk of the Volunteers, seeing the naked

steel, suddenly realised what all this meant. Their men
were going out to fight. They were going to meet the
broadswords of the Highlanders—and it was well known
what these claymores could do. At Killiecrankie they
had cleft men's skulls clean down to the breastbone at
a single stroke ; they had lopped the tops off men's
heads, neatly above the eyes, so that they were strewn
on the ground like nightcaps ; they had cleaved men's
bodies in two at the waist, through belts and bandoliers
and all. They had . . . but the ladies of Edinburgh
knew quite well what they had done. And suddenly
they saw that happening to their men.

Pandemonium followed.

The troops received the order to march. The dragoons
rode out gallantly to join forces with Gardiner's. The
foot set off down the Lawnmarket, and at every yard
their ranks thinned rapidly. They marched out of the
city, westwards. . . .

General Gardiner, not coming into contact with the
Highland army, since it had made the wide sweep to
Slateford, retired to bivouac for the night in a field
between Edinburgh and Leith ; but he left a strong
detachment of dragoons to keep watch on the rebels'
movements. And the rebels spotted them, on the morning
of the 16th.

" Send a mounted party to reconnoitre," Charles
ordered, and a number of young Highlanders, well armed
and well mounted, rode out towards the dragoons'
piquets. They laughed as they rode.

" Who's for first blood ? " cried one.

" Shall we give them a taste of our lead ? " cried
another.

It was not just Highland bravado. They were a mere
handful, against the strong party of dragoons. But they
had come with the Prince to fight—and here was the
chance of a scrap. They rode straight up to the piquets
and got within pistol shot and let fly a volley. There
was no return fire. The astonished Highlanders saw the

dragoons jerk their horses' heads round, clap spurs into their sides, and gallop off pell-mell in the wildest confusion.

They sat and looked at each other, blankly ; then they began to laugh.

But the dragoons did not laugh. They galloped non-stop until they reached the regiment's lines, and when they arrived they yelled and shouted the alarm.

" The rebels are after us ! A whole regiment of cavalry ! They'll be here in a moment ! "

General Fowkes, who had just arrived from London and had been sent out by General Guest to take charge of the little army, instantly ordered a retreat. But there was no retreat. There was only a rout ; and the startled people of Edinburgh looked fearfully out of their windows and over their walls and saw the two gallant regiments flying along the Long Dykes, where Princes Street now runs, as if the devil himself were after them. But there was no sight of any pursuit.

The dragoons did not draw rein until they reached Leith ; but they did not stay there long. They went on almost at once to Musselburgh, while the abandoned infantry, the Edinburgh Regiment, the Volunteers, and the Town Guard, made surprising speed in their retreat back into the city.

§

Meanwhile a message had come from the Prince.

It was brought by an Edinburgh man, Mr. Alves, who reported that on his way to the city he had passed the rebel army, and, being recognised by the Duke of Perth, whom he knew personally, had been called over. The Duke had given him the message to deliver, informing the people of Edinburgh that if they would admit the Prince peaceably into the city they should be civilly dealt with, but if not they must expect all the rigours of military occupation.

The Provost, listening to this demand, treated the worthy Mr. Alves to a contemptuous sneer and refused to pay any further attention ; whereat Mr. Alves lost his temper and went out and informed the people in the streets, upon which the Provost had him arrested and thrown into prison. But the mischief had been done.

The Provost called a meeting at the Goldsmiths' Hall, attended by the magistrates and town council and most of the principal inhabitants. A deputation was sent off to the law officers of the crown, but these gentlemen were not to be found. They had left the city. The captains of the trained bands and the volunteers were sent for next ; but they had no advice to offer. Tempers became frayed, harsh words were bandied back and forth and the meeting degenerated into complete pandemonium.

The Hall was chock-a-block ; so they adjourned to the New Church aisle, which became jammed with people in a twinkling, and most of them yelling for surrender. Then a letter was handed in at the door, addressed to the Provost, magistrates and town council. It was put into the hands of Orrock, the deacon of the shoemakers, who opened it with trembling hands and announced that it was subscribed " Charles, P.R."

The Deacon began to read the letter aloud, but the Provost snatched it away from him.

" I will not be witness to the reading of such a communication ! " he exclaimed furiously. " Treason—rank treason ! "

He rose from his seat and marched out. But presently he had no option but to march back again, and with the assembly clamouring to hear the letter he eventually gave way and allowed it to be read :

" From our Camp, 16th September, 1745.
" Being now in a condition to make our way into the capital of his majesty's ancient kingdom of

Scotland, we hereby summon you to receive us, as you are in duty bound to do ; and in order to it, we hereby require you, upon receipt of this, to summon the town-council and take proper measures for securing the peace and quiet of the city, which we are very desirous to protect. But if you suffer any of the usurper's troops to enter the town, or any of the cannon, arms, or ammunition in it (whether belonging to the public or private persons) to be carried off, we shall take it as a breach of your duty, and a heinous offence against the king and us, and shall resent it accordingly. We promise to preserve all the rights and liberties of the city, and the particular property of every one of his majesty's subjects. But if any opposition be made to us, we cannot answer for the consequences, being firmly resolved at any rate to enter the city ; and in that case, if any of the inhabitants are found in arms against us, they must not expect to be treated as prisoners of war."

As the reading ended, pandemonium broke out again ; and through that pandemonium the Provost realised the dominant demands of the populace. Defeated, he agreed to appoint a deputation of four to wait upon the Prince and request that he would grant the citizens time to deliberate on the contents of his letter.

Meantime out in the Lawnmarket things were happening.

Four of the six companies were drawn up there, still in considerable confusion, when suddenly a figure on a large grey horse came thundering along the street from the West-Bow. He was well dressed, and his voice, when he spoke, carried authority. He galloped down the lines of the volunteers, shouting as he passed.

" I have seen the Highland army. There are sixteen thousand men ! "

He was gone in a moment, and no one every discovered

afterwards who he was. But his ruse worked well.
Captain Drummond consulted with his brother officers
and then promptly marched the four companies up to
the Castle and delivered up their arms. The remaining
companies copied their example soon after, and the men,
the mock heroics scared right out of them, hurried off
home to assume innocent expressions in their own back
parlours.

About eight o'clock that night the four deputies drove
in a coach out to Gray's Mill ; but they had no sooner
left the city gate behind them than another messenger
arrived for the Provost. General Cope and his transports
had arrived at Dunbar, only twenty-seven miles away !
As the wind was unfavourable for proceeding higher up
the Firth, Cope intended to disembark his men at Dunbar
and march immediately to the relief of the city.

The Provost, jubilant, waved this wonderful news in
the faces of his councillors.

§

Charles and his advisers received the four gentlemen
from Edinburgh with every courtesy. They listened to
what they had to say with great deliberation, and Charles
eyed the four of them with a well-hidden amused contempt. They could not cast dust in his eyes. He knew
all about Sir John Cope's race for the Forth, he knew
precisely what was at the backs of the minds of these
four frightened gentlemen. He had no intention of
being hoodwinked.

He signed to Mr. Secretary Murray. A brief consultation, and that gentleman indited the Prince's
reply.

" His royal highness the prince regent thinks his
manifesto, and the king his father's declaration, already
published, a sufficient capitulation for all his majesty's
subjects to accept with joy. His present demands are,
to be received into the city as the son and representative

of the king his father, and obeyed as such when there. Lastly, he expects a positive answer before two o'clock in the morning, otherwise he will think himself obliged to take measures conform."

The Provost, when he read this letter to the council, pursed his lips and exclaimed, vigorously : " Delay ! We must have time. We must put them off. Time for Sir John Cope to reach the city . . . "

The council eagerly agreed. They decided to send a second deputation in the naïve belief that they could hoodwink the Prince into giving them more time. They set off in a hired coach and came to Gray's Mill shortly after two o'clock in the morning.

Charles had not gone to bed. He was determined to be in Edinburgh before Cope's transports could arrive in the Firth and disembark his army—and he had learnt enough of the military art to make alternative plans. If the town council proved obdurate the city would have to be taken by stratagem or assault. He was busy now with plans for both.

Lord George Murray received the deputation. He listened to all they had to say with quiet courtesy.

" The Provost and the council feel, sir," said their spokesman, " that the decision they are called upon to make is too onerous to be taken without reference to the principal private citizens. And these good people have all gone to bed long ago. We have come to beg an extension of time—until nine o'clock in the morning. By that time it will have been possible to consult the desires of the more important gentlemen of the city, and we promise a definite answer . . . "

Lord George remained cool and patient.

" The Prince is much engaged. He has already shown great patience in this matter, and I fear he will not grant this new request," he pointed out. But the deputation pressed him. They reminded him of the terrible things that might follow a military occupation of the city, the loss of life and the destruction of property, and they pleaded eloquently with him to go to the Prince and lay their request before him. Lord George gave way.

Charles glanced up sharply at his entry.

" Well, my lord? "

" Sir," Murray reported, " a deputation has come from Edinburgh—— "

" I know that."

" —They request an extension of time until nine o'clock—— "

" My last intimation to them was explicit enough," Charles retorted. " I gave them until two o'clock. It is past that hour. I know perfectly well what they intend. Send them away."

Lord George expostulated. At least the Prince must hear their argument, and he begged him to listen ; but Charles, consumed with impatience now that he was so near his goal, and seriously concerned about Cope, was in no mood, at that hour of the morning, to be lenient.

" Send them away," he repeated, and Lord George retired.

The deputation met him with a chorus of entreaties. Could he not try again ? So much depended upon this, and all they sought was to avoid bloodshed and confusion. . . . Lord George once more gave way, against his better judgment ; and had he but known it this kindly intention was to set a train of actions in motion that led eventually to disaster.

He returned to the Prince's room. The Earl of Wemyss's son, Lord Elcho, who had recently joined the Prince's staff, was with him now, and both young men looked up impatiently at the lieutenant-general's entry.

" Your royal highness," Lord George began, " I beg of you to reconsider your decision, and at least hear the deputation—— "

" Certainly not," Charles replied sharply. " They are trying to gain time—while Cope makes his way here. I am not to be tricked by these Edinburgh gentry." He turned to Elcho. " My lord, tell these people to go immediately."

Elcho leapt up eagerly and did as he was bidden, and Lord George, vexed and conscious of having done himself some harm in the Prince's eyes, went back to his own quarters.

The Prince, seriously annoyed, considered the situation. There was not a moment to lose. He knew that the city could not resist assault by a body of determined men, and he already had such a body standing by, awaiting his orders—nine hundred picked clansmen, Camerons, MacDonalds and MacGregors mostly, well armed and eager to be off.

He had discussed the affair already with their chiefs, and one point they had made which weighed heavily with him was that opposition might inflame their men. If there was a struggle, the Highlanders would become exasperated and when they eventually burst into the city they would be mad for revenge for the deaths of their own clansmen. The clan system had its dangers, as every man regarded every other member of his clan as a kinsman, a relative whose death was a personal loss. The chiefs, taking their example from the Gentle Lochiel, were urgent that surprise or stratagem should be tried, if only to save the people of Edinburgh from the anger of their men.

The plan was complete. Charles, summoning Lochiel and Keppoch and Ardshiel, and O'Sullivan, spoke to them briefly.

" You have your orders, gentlemen. The moment has arrived to carry them out. God speed you."

The four left ; and a few minutes later, while the Edinburgh deputies were still rattling back towards the city, the nine hundred fell into their ranks and set off.

They marched swiftly, in absolute silence. They met no one who might give the alarm, they avoided dwelling houses and they covered the ground at a swinging pace that took them to the Borough Moor in short order.

There they halted. There was no need for words. The junior officers understood their night's work perfectly, and two parties of twenty-four men each went on to the Netherbow Port, on the east of the city, and took up positions one on each side of it. The guards patrolling the walls heard nothing, saw nothing, for the Highlanders were all expert deer-stalkers and supremely competent.

Behind them sixty other men crept forward half way up St. Mary's Wynd, and lay there ready to lend support ; a third party remained at a greater distance, while the main body waited in readiness to rush forward when their help was required.

One of the Highlanders had been dressed in Lowland garb for the occasion. Rising, he walked forward towards the Port and knocked on the wicket gate.

A sentry challenged.

" Who goes there? "

" Friend."

" Approach, friend."

He stepped closer.

" I'm a sodger in Gairdiner's dragoons," he said, in a broad Lowland accent. " I'm servant to ane o' the officers. My maister left something ahint him in the toon, and he's garred me come back and fetch it."

The sentry glowered at him.

" This is no' the time o' day to come here wi' sic a tale," he growled. " Awa wi' ye, and come back the morn. There's naebody goes in or oot this port this nicht, and a' yon rebels rinning up and doon the country-side. Awa' with ye, man."

The Highlander protested.

" Aiblins we'll be fechting the rebels the morn. My maister gie'd me his orders, and man, I cannae wait till daylicht. I maun do as I've been tellt."

" Ye'll do as I tell ye and no' argue. Awa' wi' ye."

The Highlander, nonplussed, stepped back a yard or so under the sudden threat of the sentry's levelled musket.

What to do now? Only a short distance away the men waited, ready to rush forward the moment the wicket was opened. Another sentry called from the walls.

" Back, there ! Aboot face and march, or I fire ! "

The Highlander glanced up. Several men had appeared on the wall, their muskets levelled at him. He had no option but to retire.

A few paces carried him to safety in the darkness, and he dropped down beside his officer and reported his failure. Young Captain Ewen MacGregor, a younger son of Glencairnaig, who was in charge of the party, glanced at the sky. It was beginning to lighten already. They must soon be discovered. He sent a runner back to Lochiel, to consult him, and prepared to withdraw. Now they would have to put the alternative plan into effect, bring up their reserve and launch a direct assault upon the gate. It was annoying, for he knew that it meant serious losses—and these men were his kinsmen. But just as he framed the order to retire his quick ears caught a faint sound, a clattering in the distance, inside the city.

" That is a coach ! " he breathed, and strained his ears. " It is coming down the High Street—it is coming to the Netherbow Port ! "

Sudden excitement seized him. He remembered the deputies' carriage. It must have deposited these four gentlemen, with a flea in their ear, by now. It must be coming out of the Netherbow Port for the night, since most of the hackney proprietors lived in the Canongate.

He spoke a swift word.

" Ready, lads ! When the port is opened we go in."

The coach rattled to a halt. Then the tramp of the sentries could be heard, the creak of iron hinges as the gate was opened. The dim twin lights of the coach's lamps cast a glow upon the ground, and upon the sweating horse. The coachman clicked his tongue.

At the same moment MacGregor rose and started

forward. Behind him his men followed—lithe, swift figures, sprinting silently for the gate. Dark shadows in the night, they streamed round on either side of the coach and darted through the gate.

The other party followed. Naked steel flashed, and as the men rushed through they leapt right and left, grabbing the astonished guard, pouring into the guard-room, leaping on the parapets and dragging the sentries off the wall. In a matter of seconds the gate was captured, and the supporting parties, warned by the noise, came racing forward.

They surged into the street, and the silence of the night was shattered by one triumphant shout, the stirring war cry of the clans. Windows were thrown up, nightcap-covered heads were thrust out, and terrified citizens looked down upon a moving mass of blue bonnets and streaming white cockades as the Highlanders raced up the street.

They expected opposition. They expected barricades, and armed men behind them to dispute their advance. They found neither.

An order rang out, and the nine hundred fell immediately into their ranks. Leaving a party to mount guard at the Netherbow Port they set off swiftly through the sleeping city, for only near the Port had the disturbance roused people from their uneasy slumbers.

They marched at a fast trot, with drawn claymores in their right hands, targes and cocked pistols in their left. But there was no need for this precaution.

. They separated, racing through the streets in different directions, making for all the ports. The operation was going exactly according to plan. Silently in their deerskin brogues they padded through the deserted streets. A party of Camerons came swiftly to one of the gates, burst into the guardroom. Their officer looked coolly at the officer of the Town Guard, and his startled men, who had leapt to their feet.

" Gentlemen," he said, " the guard is relieved. This

is the changing of the guard. You may dismiss your men."

So it happened at all the ports, with no more fuss or confusion than if it had been an official changing of the guard. The Highlanders, disarming the Town Guard and the volunteers who reinforced them, simply took over their duties like trained and disciplined soldiers. No violence was offered—none was needed.

Edinburgh was occupied.

§

Charles had thrown himself, still fully dressed, upon his bed. He slept for just two hours. When he awoke he leapt out of bed immediately and strode out.

" Any news? " he demanded of the officer of the guard, who sprang to his feet at his sudden appearance.

" No, sir. No news yet."

" It will soon be dawn."

" Yes, sir. It is after five o'clock."

" Very well."

Charles went out, stood staring towards the city. Slowly the sky lightened, the grey of dawn spread upwards from behind the city and Charles, drawing a deep breath, stared about him and listened keenly. Faintly he caught the sound of running feet, then heard a sharp challenge ringing out, in the now familiar Gaelic. The reply was in Gaelic; and then a man came running. He pulled the bonnet off his head at sight of the Prince, and went down on his knee and kissed his hand and spoke, in a torrent of words.

The Prince stood still, his head thrown back, the chill morning wind ruffling his hair. He drew in a long breath ; and then he smiled, a brilliant smile that transfigured the thoughtful, almost melancholy young face.

He spun round, went back into the house, and called sharply.

In a moment men were running, heavy riding boots clattered on the stairs, crisp orders rang out. Then, from the camp, came the high clear skirl of the pipes. As dawn broke, the army was astir, laughing, shouting, singing, snatching a handful of food while accoutrements were strapped on, firelocks cleaned and loaded. An orderly led out the Prince's horse.

He came striding out.

At sight of him the army raised a tremendous cheer. He was dressed in a tartan short coat, and a blue sash wrought with gold instead of a plaid. The star of the order of St. Andrew glittered on his breast, and he carried a silver hilted broadsword at his side. On his head he wore a light coloured peruke with his own hair brushed over it, and a blue velvet bonnet with a band of gold lace, and a white cockade of satin. Red velvet breeches and a pair of riding boots completed the costume, and when he sprang into the saddle the army gazed in a passion of devoted admiration at the splendid figure of their leader.

He turned to Lord George Murray.

" Give the order to march," he said ; and in a few moments the army was on the move.

The route he had chosen was a wide circuit to avoid the guns of the Castle, and it took him south of the city to the Braid burn, and thence towards Morningside. At the Black Stone, a great granite boulder close to the turnpike road, he swung off along a narrow unfrequented by-road to what are now Causewayside and Newington.

Near Priestfield the Prince led his army through into the King's Park, and headed for the Hunter's Bog, a deep sheltered valley running between Arthur's Seat and Salisbury Crags. Here he was completely protected from the Castle guns, and as the army came out of the defile he halted, his cheeks flushing and his eyes sparkling ; for there before him, less than a quarter of a mile away, lay his ancestral home, the palace of Holyrood House.

The park was crammed. The fickle populace, waking

that morning to discover their city occupied by the Highlanders, had had a change of heart. No longer was there any blustering talk of chasing these ragged rebels away from their precious Edinburgh. No longer was the Prince a foreign adventurer, a figure of fun or hatred. The people had flocked to Holyrood House to see this youth who had achieved so much in so short a time.

Charles, sitting motionless upon his horse, looking down upon the great throng, felt this moment with an emotion too deep for words. He was exalted, carried away, scarcely able to realise yet what had happened. It was less than a month since he had raised his standard at Glenfinnan. Not even the most rabid optimist could have predicted such a triumph.

He touched his horse's side with his heel, and started down towards the palace. Beside him rode Lord Perth and Lord Elcho, and behind came a train of gentlemen, well mounted and splendidly dressed, as befitted the attendants of a prince returning into his royal birthright.

On reaching the high ground below St. Anthony's well Charles dismounted. He was entirely without fear. He meant to go among his people on foot.

As he set foot on the ground he was surrounded immediately by a great throng, all pressing forward to kneel before him and kiss his hand. It was some time before he could move, and he stood smiling and bowing and looking out over the heads of the great multitude that filled the entire space between him and the palace.

Then, as he started to descend to the park below, a shout went up—a great huzza that gathered volume as the vast crowds, their imagination captured by the tall, upright young figure, cheered and cheered. When he reached the Duke's Walk, named after his grandfather James VII when Duke of York, he stopped again so that the throng might gratify its curiosity and its enthusiasm.

Among the crowds at least one man watched with disapproval. He was John Home, who later wrote one of the most comprehensive accounts of the rebellion—

from the Whig angle. But even his prejudiced eyes were filled with grudging admiration as he watched the Prince.

" The figure and presence of Charles Stuart," he afterwards wrote, " were not ill-suited to his lofty pretensions. He was in the prime of youth, tall and handsome, of a fair complexion. . . . "

Another spectator, Dr. Alexander Carlyle, who rubbed shoulders with him twice, managed to measure his height against his own, and reported : " He was a good-looking man of about five feet ten inches ; his hair was dark-red and his eyes black. His features were regular, his visage long, much sunburnt and freckled, and his countenance thoughtful and melancholy."

Five feet ten was tall for those days, and brought him well above the average.

Presently he mounted his horse again, a fine bay gelding. that had been presented to him by the Duke of Perth. The cheering grew louder now, since he could be seen by all, and he rode slowly towards Holyrood House. The throng, pressing after him, cheered and cheered, thrilled by his splendid presence, by the strange magnetic charm of his personality ; only here and there among them were there black looks and dour glum faces and grim silence, from the more stubborn of the Whigs who refused to be carried away by the popular acclaim.

Charles alighted again and, entering the gate of the palace, walked along the piazza within the quadrangle towards the Duke of Hamilton's apartments. As he was about to enter the porch, whose door stood open, a man stepped forward from among the crowd and drew his sword.

He was an East Lothian gentleman, James Hepburn of Keith, who had fought in the Fifteen not out of any devotion to the House of Stuart but because he considered that Scotland had been betrayed by the Union of Parliaments. As the only hope of repeal of that measure lay in the restoration of the Stuarts, who had favoured its repeal, he had for thirty years kept himself in readiness to join the Jacobites if the time arrived. He had kept also his wide reputation among the Jacobites and Whigs alike for the highest integrity, and was revered by everyone as a model of the ancient Scots simplicity, manliness and honour.

Now he raised his sword aloft, and stepping forward walked up the stairs in front of the Prince and disappeared with him into the palace. His dramatic accession to the Stuart cause raised a tremendous shout of enthusiasm from the delighted crowds, and when the Prince came to one of the windows of his apartments and showed himself with his bonnet in his hand the cheering swelled into a mighty shout of acclamation from the people who had surged forward into the great courtyard below.

For a while he stood there, bowing and smiling, acknowledging the cheers ; then he turned away and the cheering gradually died down, and people began to stream back towards the city. Crowds were congregating at the cross.

Presently a great procession appeared, the heralds and pursuivants of the city at their head—and armed men close beside them. The Highlanders, determined that the royal proclamation of the Chevalier of St. George as James VIII and III, should be carried out with the proper ceremony, had thoughtfully taken the precaution of securing the persons of the city's functionaries. They had ordered them to dress themselves in their official uniforms and now, a little before one o'clock, they took up their position beside the cross and proclaimed King James.

Edinburgh roared its approval and its loyalty. Every window was crammed with gaily dressed Edinburgh ladies, straining their voices to the utmost and waving white kerchiefs in honour of the handsome young Prince. One of the leading beauties of the time, Mrs. Murray of Broughton, gave a colourful touch to the scene by

sitting her horse throughout the ceremony with a drawn
sword in her hand, and her clothes covered with white
favours. She distributed white cockades and kisses right
and left and was the envy of all the other ladies at the
windows, who had not thought of doing anything quite
so dashing.

Afterwards, Charles returned in triumph to Holyrood
House. But his heart was with his army, encamped at
Duddingston, and as soon as he could escape from the
palace he slipped away to spend the night among his
men.

CHAPTER NINE

HEY, JOHNNIE COPE !

COLONEL GARDINER was disgusted. An experienced and courageous soldier, he had felt the bitterest shame galloping after his regiment in full flight and in full view of the populace of Edinburgh. Now the regiment, and Hamilton's as well, were camped in a field near Gardiner's home, not far from Preston Grange.

The colonel, satisfied that for the moment the dragoons' predilection for galloping in the wrong direction had been overcome, rode the short distance across to his own house to spend a night in tolerable comfort. He had had a good dinner, and presently locked the front door and went up to bed. He fell asleep, and slept soundly, a tired and angry man.

Meanwhile one of the dragoons, searching for fodder for his horse, strayed a few yards away from the lines and, in the darkness, lost his footing and pitched headlong into an old disused coalpit, half full of water. He let out a yell, and as he floundered about shouting desperately for help. His shouts were heard. In a matter of moments the whole camp was on its feet, desperate fingers were fumbling with girths and stirrup leathers, and before the unfortunate dragoon could drag himself out of the pit not a man remained in camp. They had thrown themselves on their horses and gone thundering off into the night.

The unlucky dragoon scrambled out, found his own horse, and not knowing what the alarm was about went pelting after his companions. And Colonel Gardiner went on sleeping.

In the early morning he sallied out to inspect the lines. There were no lines there—only a bare field scattered with blankets, and harness, and muskets, and cooking pots. He glared about in desperation, and followed a trail of discarded accoutrements across the field to the Dunbar road. Down the road he went, and the trail was easy to follow. It was like a paper chase, with muskets and swords and pistols and helmets for the paper trail.

A very angry colonel rode off and commandeered some covered carts, and set off for Dunbar, collecting the arms and equipment off the road as he went, and presently he met up with his gallant dragoons. They had reached Dunbar in record time, and the worthy Mr. Home, who, after watching the Prince's reception in Edinburgh, had hurried off to join Sir John Cope with a full report of the Highland army, reported on their arrival in the mildest terms possible. They had come to Dunbar, he wrote, " in a condition not very respectable."

What Colonel Gardiner thought of their condition was not recorded.

But at any rate the dragoons could not retreat any further, for Sir John Cope was busy landing his army. He completed the disembarkation of the foot on Wednesday the 17th, and of the artillery and stores next day. He listened, with great satisfaction, to Mr. Home's account of the rebels, armed for the most part with scythe blades lashed to pitchfork shafts, and not over 2,000 in strength.

So, on the 19th, Cope began to move. His little army, about 2,400 strong, made a brave sight, for most of his troops were veterans of Dettingen and other brilliant battles overseas.

He spent the night encamped near Haddington, sixteen miles easy of Edinburgh, and in order to prevent a surprise attack he sent of a party of sixteen young volunteers to picket the roads. They went out in couples, and in due course all but one of the patrols returned to report all quiet. The remaining patrol had ridden off towards Musselburgh, and, avoiding the high narrow bridge over the Esk, crossed the river near its mouth at extreme low tide. But when they got to the other side the first thing they noticed was a snug little tavern belonging to a famous old woman called Luckie, renowned for her oysters and sherry.

Now it happened that the two young men, both volunteers from Edinburgh, regarded themselves as *bon-viveurs*, and could not resist the allure of Luckie's sign. They went into the tavern and settled down to sample her oysters and sherry.

Presently along came a youth from a north country town, fired by the spirit of adventure to join the Prince's army. He was a writer's apprentice, and perhaps was tired of musty legal documents and a sedentary life. At any rate, reaching the tavern, he peeped through the window and recognised the two who sat there so confidently. In a moment he guessed their errand, and decided that here was a golden opportunity for striking a blow for Charlie. He went and placed himself in ambush on the bridge, for as the tide was on the make the gallant patrol would have to use the bridge.

The two bold scouts emerged eventually from the tavern, mounted their horses, and rode along to the bridge. Now how he contrived it no one ever knew, but, in the words of a chronicler, the Norland whippersnapper single-handed surrounded and captured the patrol before they could draw trigger ; so Sir John, all unknowing, had already suffered his first casualties.

§

Charles scanned the reports that had arrived.

Intent on preparing to meet Cope at the earliest opportunity, he had left Holyrood House on the evening of the 18th for the camp at Duddingston, and now he assembled a council of war and stated his views :

" I propose to march immediately against Cope. We must give him no time to make contact with the garrison in Edinburgh Castle. We must give him battle at once."

The council acclaimed his decision, and the Highland chiefs, called upon to assess the fighting powers of their men, declared that although they had had no previous experience of battle they would follow their chiefs anywhere ; the majority of the officers had already seen military service in Britain or in foreign armies.

" In that case," Charles cried, his eyes sparkling with excitement, " I will lead the clans myself ! "

At that there was a cry of consternation.

" Your royal highness cannot be permitted to expose your person in such a way," one of the chiefs declared emphatically. " And unless you are prepared to accept a station of greater safety I for one will withdraw and go home. If our Prince is killed our whole enterprise is doomed."

A chorus of approval greeted these words and Charles, curbing his ardour, finally gave way. He would take up his position with the reserves of the centre, about fifty yards behind the front line.

On the 18th a hundred and fifty MacLachlans had joined the army, and on the 19th and 20th there were additional recruits, the men of Athole and the Grants of Glenmoriston, bringing the total strength up to about 2,500. Early that day, Friday the 20th, the Prince placed himself at the head of his troops and, presenting his sword, exclaimed : " My friends, I have flung away the scabbard ! "

A great huzza greeted his words, and the army moved off in one long column three files deep.

They crossed the Esk by the bridge at Musselburgh and advanced towards Pinkie. Here Lord George Murray, who was leading the van, was brought intelligence of Cope's movement towards some high ground, and immediately decided to forestall him. He swung off the road without waiting for a consultation, and in half an hour had gained the heights long before Cope's more slowly moving forces could come up.

Charles joined him presently with the main body, and from the heights he looked down upon the Hanoverian army, drawn up in battle order. A wide bog or morass protected them from direct attack, and Lord George Murray sent Colonel Ker of Gradon to reconnoitre. He rode down on a little white pony in full view of the enemy, who opened up a brisk fire ; but he coolly went on exploring the bog, trying to find a way across, and he even dismounted and broke down a loose stone wall in order to lead his pony through the gap.

He returned to report that the morass was impassable, and Lord George decided to attack from the east. Towards sunset he led his force down towards the village of Tranent, and sent word back to the Prince to follow him.

At this point occurred a minor incident that was to have unhappy repercussions. O'Sullivan had posted fifty Camerons to watch Cope, and he had chosen the ground badly, leaving them exposed to the enemy's fire. They had suffered some casualties without flinching, but now Lord George ordered them to retire and join him. O'Sullivan, coming up, demanded to know who had countermanded his own orders to the men, and there was a brief altercation, Lord George replying mildly and quietly to the Irishman's angry words.

Charles, leaving the Athole Brigade of 500 men under Lord Nairne to watch the enemy, hastened after Lord George, and presently, when the army encamped in a field near Tranent, a council of war was held. A local gentleman, Robert Anderson, confirmed most of Ker's report on the morass, but declared that it could be crossed ; he knew the path and thought it might be used.

It was a dangerous expedient. The path was barely wide enough for three men abreast, and a very small number of men could hold it indefinitely and inflict grievous harm on any army attempting to force the passage. But the council agreed to accept the risk, which Charles was eager to do, and they forthwith lay down to sleep. Charles, dragging a sheaf of pease over for a pillow, promptly went to sleep on the stubble-ground, with his staff following his example around him.

About midnight Anderson, remembering further details, came and roused Lord George to acquaint him with these, and together they woke the Prince. He slept lightly, was wide awake at once and delighted to hear what Anderson had to say ; then he lay down again to resume his interrupted sleep.

The camp lay wrapped in utter silence. The horses had been left behind so that they should not betray the army's position, no fires were lighted, and talking had been forbidden. The Highlanders, wrapped in their plaids, slept like logs, and the Prince's orders had been scrupulously obeyed.

Cope meantime was in a quandary. He had no certain idea where the rebel army lay, or what Charles's plans were. There might be a surprise attack at any moment. So the bulk of his troops had to stand to their arms throughout the night, while the Highlanders enjoyed their slumber. Cope, vexed by this possibility, kept firing his guns at intervals, in the hope of giving the Highlanders a restless night ; but he might have saved his ammunition. They went on sleeping, and Cope went on puzzling about the future. Already he had been compelled to change his dispositions several times on account of the Highlanders' movements, and he was completely on the defensive. It was galling, and hardly in keeping with the situation as an experienced soldier like himself could see it.

The night was bitterly cold, and he lit lines of fires to keep his men warm; but no answering fires flickered to give away the position of the enemy.

Nairne had been sent orders to join the main body, starting at 2 a.m., and had been enjoined to preserve absolute silence and secrecy. He did so with complete success, and at 3 a.m. reported his arrival. But now a difficulty arose. Cope's dispositions were known, the plan of attack was complete, but because of the changes of dispositions it was discovered that the MacDonalds would be upon the left wing. That could not be allowed, for since Bannockburn the clan had traditionally claimed the honour of forming the right wing, and none of the other clans would dispute the claim.

The entire order of march had therefore to be reversed. This difficult manœuvre was entrusted to Ker of Gradon, who had already shown his prowess in his reconnoitring of the bog. He went down the lines on foot, speaking to each company, ordering them to remain still and preserve utter silence until he personally returned. When he reached the rear, where the MacDonalds lay, he set them moving first, and so coming back up the lines put the whole army in motion. In pitch darkness, in perfect order and in silence, the evolution was carried out and by four o'clock the whole army was in full march.

MacDonald of Glenalladale, major of the Clanranald regiment, went ahead with sixty men to seize the enemy's baggage; the Duke of Perth, in command of the right wing, went with the van. Not a whisper was heard, only the soft swishing sound of brogues upon the wet grass. No weapons clashed, no accoutrements jangled, and Perth led his men across the morass without difficulty. Yet a mere handful of men could have stopped him and turned the affair into a ghastly rout. The path was barely wide enough for two abreast, and men often floundered up to the knees in mud.

Charles, leading the second column himself, came to the path. He had first to leap a four-foot wide ditch and in the darkness he stumbled to his knees as he landed. The slip vexed him deeply, and he began to wonder if it might not be an omen of ill-luck ahead. But he was committed now, and he led on without hesitation, hurrying as the first lightening of dawn appeared in the sky.

The whole army was safely over. Suddenly the vanguard heard a cry :

" Who is there? "

It was repeated again and again. Cope's advance pickets had caught the tramp of feet and given the alarm. A voice could be heard distinctly, yelling :

" Cannons, cannons ! Get ready the cannons, cannoneers ! "

Charles moved swiftly. As the wan light strengthened his army was drawn up, Clanranald, Keppoch, Glengarry and Glencoe forming the right wing under Perth, the Duke's own men forming the centre, and Lord George Murray commanding the Camerons and the Stewarts of Appin on the left. The second line, fifty paces in the rear, consisted of the Athole men, the Robertsons of Struan and the MacLachlans under Lord Nairne.

Cope, receiving intelligence of this, was forced to change his own order of battle all over again, and there was some confusion as the soldiers and the dragoons and artillery shifted places. But as the sun rose and full daylight came Cope realised, with satisfaction, that he was to give battle on ground most favourable to himself. It was a great, level field, recently harvested, and free of trees or bushes—ideal for cavalry. His cavalry should win the battle by themselves, for the Highlanders had few firearms, and it was an accepted tenet of military tactics that infantry could not withstand a cavalry charge except by fire-power. Without that, these ill-armed mountaineers should be cut to pieces in short order. He reckoned without the spirit of the clans.

The moment was drawing near, and Charles rode out to address his men.

"Follow me, gentlemen," he cried, "and by the assistance of God I will this day make you a free and happy people !"

He was cool and self-possessed, exhibiting less signs of strain than many of the seasoned veterans among his commanders. He went to the right wing for brief conferences with the MacDonald chiefs, then, returning to his post, he encountered the officer who had been teaching him Gaelic.

"*Gres ort !*" he cried to him, "*gres ort !* (Make haste !)" and the Highlander, delighted, called back a cheery reassurance.

The morning mist, rising from the field, still hid the opposing armies from each other. The Highlanders, removing their bonnets, knelt for a brief prayer ; then Lord George ordered the left wing to advance and sent his aide-de-camp to request Lord Perth to put the right wing in motion. The men moved forward so swiftly that they had to halt several times to reform their rank. The Camerons, who had been ordered to incline to the left so as to cover the flank, came out of the mist to find themselves directly in face of Cope's artillery. Instantly those with firearms threw up their muskets and let fly at the artillery guard, and as the bullets whistled among them the gunners, taken by surprise, turned and ran. Their officers, cursing, loosed off the pieces, but the Camerons recoiled from the fire only for a moment ; then, throwing away their muskets, they drew their claymores and charged.

Their rush carried them through the artillery lines and beyond, and at once they were faced by the dragoons. The testing time had come. The dragoons set spurs to their horses and came on at an increasing gallop, to ride through the Highlanders and cut them to pieces. But an officer shouted :

"Cut the horses' noses. Never mind the men !" and

with wild shouts the Camerons raced on, straight at the charging cavalry. Broadswords rose and crashed down, horses screamed, reared, fell to the ground with their skulls split open. Riders were thrown in every direction. Scythes, swung by lusty arms, cut down men and horses together, and in a few moments after the initial shock the dragoons had wheeled and taken to their heels.

Gardiner, bringing over his squadrons, ordered them to charge. They too came forward full of confidence ; they too were stopped dead by the first shock of impact, they too turned and bolted. Their gallant colonel was thrown and mortally wounded. He died soon after.

Now the whole army was on the move, and the Highlanders, after receiving the fire of Cope's infantry, charged in a mass with their claymores before the enemy could reload. Finding themselves to their horror directly exposed to this charge, with no cavalry to screen them, the astonished redcoats hurled away their muskets, turned their backs, and ran for their lives. The Highlanders ran after them. One boy of fourteen cut down fourteen men with his claymore. Another, finding himself pelting down a road close behind a party of soldiers, overtook them, cut down the hindmost with his claymore and called to the rest to throw down their arms. Without pausing to look round they obeyed, and turned too late to find themselves captives of a solitary Highlander. With his sword in one hand and his cocked pistol in the other he drove them, like a flock of sheep, back up the road and handed them over to a guard. And these were the men who shortly before had covered themselves with distinction on the fields of Dettingen and Fontenoy and ranked among the bravest troops in Europe !

Hamilton's dragoons, seeing what had happened to Gardiner's, had wheeled and fled without firing a shot or drawing sword. Only one regiment of Cope's army remained on the field, Murray's, a Scots infantry regiment. It fired several volleys, but even this regiment, when the Highlanders prepared to charge, turned and ran. Not a single bayonet was stained with blood. The sight of the flashing claymores had been enough.

Home had reported to Cope that the Highlanders were strong, active and hardy, and he had mentioned how muscular their limbs were. One of many incidents shows this. A Highland gentleman, breaking through the ranks of one of the regiments, came face to face with a grenadier who threw up his hand to parry the blow of the claymore. The blade lopped off his hand and buried itself an inch into his skull, killing him instantly—proof of the almost irresistible power of this weapon in the hands of a strong man.

So swift had been the action that the Prince's second line, only fifty paces in the rear and advancing at a fast run the whole time, had never managed to catch up with the first line or get a sight of the enemy !

Charles hurried forward. In the fury of the onset the Highlanders were bound to inflict heavy casualties, and uppermost in his thoughts now was the need to intervene. Many of the soldiers, after throwing away their arms, found themselves hemmed in by high walls, with no escape. Charles and his officers were just in time to save their lives, although indeed the Highlanders, once the first fury was spent, quickly regained control of themselves and sheathed their swords.

Everywhere cowering redcoats begged quarter, and everywhere quarter was given them. Recovering from the impetuous rush of their onset, the clansmen went even further, calling out to parties of fleeing troops to offer them quarter. They had no desire to go on killing. Some Highlanders ran to Port Seaton to fetch ale and other comforts for the wounded, and no distinction was made between friend and foe. One rugged clansman was seen to lift a wounded redcoat tenderly up and carry him to the nearest house, where he made him comfortable and left him in charge of the people, even giving the redcoat a sixpence to buy himself some luxuries.

Lord George Murray busied himself with the wounded.

The local people refused to help, and he had to organise parties of Highlanders to carry the redcoats to the villages. Charles, who had issued strict orders, remained on the field until twelve o'clock to see that they were carried out.

He had brought as many surgeons as he could with him to the battle ; but so terrible had been the injuries inflicted that he had to send to Edinburgh ordering every surgeon in the town to repair to the field forthwith, while carriages and carts were commandeered to convey the wounded to the hospitals.

The field was a shambles. The MacGregors, having no arms, had brought only scythes, and with these they had lopped of horses' legs and even in some instances cut their riders clean in two. Almost all other wounds had been inflicted with the claymore, and arms and legs and noses and mutilated bodies strewed the blood-soaked ground. Of Cope's whole army only 170 of the infantry escaped, although the bulk of the dragoons had got away. They had been rallied several times, but had always turned and bolted whenever the Highlanders charged, and Cope had been compelled in the end to take to his heels in pursuit of them. Between sixteen and seventeen hundred of his men, including seventy officers, had been captured ; hundreds had been killed, many more wounded, and all his baggage and his artillery had been taken. His military chest, containing the sum of £4,000, fell as booty to the Prince.

The stricken general did not draw rein until he reached the village of Coldstream, and next morning he entered Berwick-on-Tweed, a saddened and disillusioned man.

As for the Jacobite army, they had lost four officers and about 35 men killed, and five officers and between 70 and 80 privates wounded. Rob Roy's son, James Roy, was among the casualties. He had fallen at the very beginning of the battle, with five bullet wounds ; but, raising himself on his elbow, he had called to his men : " My lads, I'm not dead ! By God, I'll see if any of you

does not do his duty!" Whereupon the MacGregors, cheering wildly, had shouted their war-cry and rushed forward with their scythes to do great execution.

Charles, having done everything in his power for the relief of the wounded and the proper care of the prisoners, sat down at last to a hasty meal, and went on to Pinkie House, a seat of the Marquis of Tweeddale, to pass the night; and from there he wrote to his father:

"'Tis hard my victory should put me under new difficulties which I did not feel before, and yet this is the

case. I am charged both with the care of my friends and
enemies. Those who should bury the dead are run away,
as if it were no business of theirs. My Highlanders
think it beneath them to do it, and the country people
are fled away. However, I am determined to try if I
can get people for money to undertake it, for I cannot
bear the thought of suffering Englishmen to rot above
the ground. I am in great difficulties how I shall dispose
of my wounded prisoners. If I make a hospital of the
church, it will be lookt upon as a great profanation, and
of having violated my manifesto, in which I promised
to violate no man's property. If the magistrates would
act, they would help me out of this difficulty. Come
what will, I am resolved not to let the poor wounded
men lye in the streets, and if I can do no better, I will
make a hospital of the palace and leave it to them."

It was an attitude of mind far beyond the compre-
hension of any of his enemies, who certainly had no
intention of showing any mercy to him or his adherents ;
but Charles persisted, and his officers supported him
enthusiastically, so that accommodation was presently
found for all, and those officers who were able to walk
or ride were sent off to various houses, and, giving their
parole, set free, while the more seriously wounded were
put into Colonel Gardiner's house and attended there by
Edinburgh surgeons.

Yet Charles had other things to occupy his mind, and
few men would have been able, in that moment of
triumph, to pay attention to these humanitarian details.

He had won a signal victory. It was not merely his
first victory, it was in point of fact a decisive one, for it
put him in undisputed possession of the whole of Scotland,
and at such a moment he could well have been forgiven
had jubilation blinded him to all else.

However elated the victory had made him, however
uplifted his spirits might be, he refused to give way to
such thoughts and feelings, and quietly set to work at
once to plan his next moves.

But some at least of his subjects rejoiced, and one of them put his feelings into words, to an air that has become a favourite reveille with pipe bands :

Cope sent a message frae Dunbar :
" Charlie, meet me an ye daur,
And I'll learn you the art o' war
If you'll meet me i' the morning."

Hey, Johnnie Cope, are ye waukin' yet?
Or are your drums abeating yet?
If ye were waukin' I wad wait
To gang to the coals i' the morning !

When Charlie looked the letter upon
He drew his sword the scabbard from :
" Come follow me, my merry merry men,
And we'll meet Johnnie Cope i' the morning ! "
    Hey, Johnnie Cope . . .

" Now, Johnnie, be as good's your word,
Come, let us try baith fire and sword,
And dinna flee like a frichtet bird
That's chased frae it's nest in the morning ! "
    Hey, Johnnie Cope . . .

When Johnnie Cope he heard o' this
He thocht it wadna be amiss
To hae a horse in readiness
To flee awa' in the morning.
    Hey, Johnnie Cope . . .

When Johnnie Cope to Berwick cam',
They speired at him, " Where's a' your men? "
" The deil confoond me gin I ken,
For I left them a' i' the morning ! "
    Hey, Johnnie Cope . . .

CHAPTER TEN

THE PRINCE ENJOYS HIS OWN AGAIN

Come boat me owre, come row me owre,
Come, boat me owre to Charlie !
I'll gie John Ross anither bawbee
To row me owre to Charlie !

> We'll owre the water, we'll owre the sea,
> We'll owre the water to Charlie.
> Come weal, come woe, we'll gather and go,
> And live or die wi' Charlie !

ON SUNDAY evening, the 22nd of September, Charles
returned to Holyrood House. It was a triumphal progress
through the streets of Edinburgh, through cheering
throngs who, forgetting their former terrors, lined the
streets to hail the victor of Prestonpans.

The army paraded through the town, with pipes
playing, banners streaming, the captured standards of
Cope's army triumphantly displayed, and the long trains
of baggage and artillery bringing up the rear. The
booty was considerable. The whole town stood and
cheered. But Charles had little inclination to rejoice in
his triumph. On the eve of the battle he had sent
messengers to all the Edinburgh clergy desiring them to

conduct their services as usual next day, and guaranteeing them his protection. When the douce and God-fearing citizens streamed to their favourite churches in the morning to listen to their favourite preachers the pulpits remained empty. Only one of all Edinburgh's numerous clergy appeared in his place—Mr. Hog, morning lecturer of the Tron Church.

In the neighbouring parish of St. Cuthbert's, however, the two ministers, Mr. Macvicar and Mr. Pitcairn, ascended their pulpits as usual and preached to full congregations. And, as usual, they offered up fervent prayers for George II. Mr. Macvicar went further. He expressed the hope that God would soon take Charles unto Himself, and that instead of an earthly crown He would give him a crown of glory.

Charles was finding that he liked these Scots better and better, and when Mr. Macvicar's prayer was repeated to him he roared with laughter.

All the same, the situation was serious. He was determined that freedom of worship should be maintained, and that religious observances should not be interrupted. Accordingly he issued a proclamation next day urging the clergy to return to their duties. None of them did so, and to their lasting shame they deserted their flocks throughout the entire period of the Highland occupation of the city.

Knowing that the populace was planning a great celebration of the victory, Charles added another paragraph to his proclamation, peremptorily prohibiting " any outward demonstration of public joy."

As he wrote to his father :

" If I had obtained this victory over foreigners, my joy would have been complete ; but as it is over Englishmen, it has thrown a damp upon it that I little imagined. The men I have defeated were your majesty's enemies, it is true, but they might have become your friends and dutiful subjects when they had got their eyes opened to see the true interest of their country, which you mean to save, not to destroy."

But he could not prevent a great wave of jubilation sweeping over the country.

A party of armed Highlanders marched into Aberdeen, seized the Provost, and held their swords over his head while they proclaimed King James. But in other parts of the country other forces were at work. Lord President Forbes of Culloden, a man of great integrity, wisdom, and far-sightedness, had set his face against the Jacobites from the start. Now he worked night and day to undermine the Prince's position, feeling in duty and honour bound to do so. His influence was great, and it was he who had prevented MacLeod of MacLeod and Sir Alexander MacDonald of Skye from declaring for the Prince. He also sought to prevail upon Simon Lord Lovat, the sly old fox who was busy playing the game both ways and was trusted by neither side.

In the Lowlands, too, there might be an upsurge of popular national feeling, and a new attitude towards the Highlanders, who on the whole had behaved remarkably well. But there was little corresponding influx of recruits.

In England, the Jacobites failed to act.

In England a wave of sheer panic swept the country. The news was so astounding, so unbelievable, that it knocked the sanest off their balance, and terror-stricken Londoners started a run upon the banks. Had not prompt measures been taken, a financial crisis of the first magnitude might have followed. But the government played a clever card. It assiduously spread the belief that the rising was a national one, for hatred of the Union of Parliaments and its effects was known to be widespread in Scotland. This propaganda had its effect; even the English Jacobites, alarmed, held back and refused to commit themselves to supporting the Prince.

§

Except for the Castles of Edinburgh and Stirling, and a few small forts, the whole of Scotland was in Charles's hands. The old urgency lay still upon him, and when he summoned his Council it was to tell them that he designed to continue his march immediately into England, to drive for London before the government could recover from its confusion and dismay.

But few voices were raised in support.

The Highland chiefs knew that numbers of their men had gone home, laden with the spoils of Prestonpans. They would come back, of course ; but it might be weeks before they did so.

The experienced soldiers pointed out bluntly that the army now barely exceeded two thousand men. It was, admittedly, much better equipped than at first, but even so it was deficient in many things—and it would have to face trained and veteran soldiers in England in over-whelming numbers. It was reckoned that at least 16,000 troops must even now be moving north.

Charles argued passionately. Time was short, his affairs were urgent, military strategy demanded that he should not remain idle, that he should press home his advantage. But more cautious opinion prevailed, and Charles at length yielded to the almost unanimous decision of the Council and agreed to remain in Edinburgh.

" Let us establish ourselves firmly in Scotland," urged one faction, " and so be able to defend our position against the Hanoverians."

" Set up the Scots Parliament again," urged another. " Proclaim a general election straight away. The whole country will respond with great alacrity and joy."

" Let us have a free and independent Scotland again, with our own king. The country would welcome it, and rise to a man to defend it."

But, however great his liking for the Scots had become,

Charles refused to forget his original intentions. He would never willingly give up the right to the throne of England, he would never rest until he had established himself in St. James's.

However, he did agree to remain in Edinburgh for the present, and plunged immediately into his work. There were letters to be written to the Highlands, to France, to Spain, to Rome ; emissaries to be sent into the Highlands and the Isles to raise recruits, others to be sent to France, where brother Henry waited impatiently for news of his adored elder brother, and eager to help him in every way possible. To Henry was entrusted the task of winning over the French court.

There was the army to drill, and train, and discipline— and feed. There was endless work.

One of Charles's first acts was to issue an edict guaranteeing protection to the inhabitants of Edinburgh and the surrounding villages and countryside. The death penalty would be inflicted on any soldier taking goods without giving a fair equivalent, and the edict was scrupulously obeyed.

A guard of Highlanders was stationed in the Weigh House, an old square building at the head of West Bow, a few hundred yards from the fortress, and this guard made no objection to provisions being taken up to the Castle. There seemed a tacit armistice agreement between the Castle and the Palace. But one night, without either provocation or warning, the garrison opened fire upon the town.

Charles reacted instantly, giving orders on the 29th to block all avenues to the Castle. In reply to this General Guest sent a letter the same evening to the Lord Provost —intended, of course, for Charles's eyes—in which he declared that unless communication between the Castle and the city was renewed he would dislodge the Highland guards with his cannon and bombard the city. The Council heard this barbarous and inexcusable threat in stunned silence. They could not at first believe it. But

General Guest had left no room for doubt of his meaning, and the appalled councillors sent a deputation at once to the Castle.

What could they do ? They had no power over the Prince or his army, no hope of restoring communications without the Prince's agreement. They begged Guest to reconsider his threat ; but the Governor was inflexible. He attempted to excuse himself by stating that he had received peremptory orders from London to bombard the city if it fell into rebel hands, and these orders absolved him from any responsibility for his action—a theory that has often been advanced, before and since, in extenuation of criminal or barbarous acts. He did, however, agree to grant a respite for one night, so that the Council could approach the Prince.

Charles received their six deputies promptly. As he scanned Guest's letter and its full import became clear a cold rage succeeded to the horror and pity that had been his first reaction, and in the written reply he sent to the waiting deputies he expressed his surprise at the barbarity of the threat, especially when the garrison had six weeks' provisions in hand, and pointed out that the Elector of Hanover plainly had no thought for the citizens of Edinburgh ; but should he comply out of compassion with the Council's request to lift the blockade he might as well quit the city at once. He promised to indemnify anyone who suffered as a result of Guest's action, but he could not, of course, accept the blame for it.

Next day Guest was as good as his word—or as bad. He opened fire on the Weigh House, and later sent a message to the Provost to say that he intended to demolish all the houses in which the guards were stationed. On the 4th of October a cannonade was opened from the half-moon battery, and was kept up until the evening. There were many casualties among the citizens, although none of the Highlanders was hurt, amd much damage was done to property in the town. A strong party from the garrison sallied out and, throwing up a long earthwork, began firing with their muskets into the streets.

People flocked out of the gates. The normal life of the town was soon at a standstill, and hourly the casualties mounted. General Guest remained indifferent to the consequences of his action, although the Princes' casualties throughout amounted to only one or two killed. The garrison appeared to fire indiscriminately at anyone appearing in the streets, and Charles, receiving frequent reports, became more and more perturbed.

In the end, he felt that he must give way. If the English general was devoid of human feeling, the Prince at least was compassionate, and on the 5th he issued a fresh proclamation removing the blockade. It was with the greatest regret, he wrote, that he was hourly informed of the many murders committed upon the innocent inhabitants of the city by the inhuman commander of the garrison and Castle, a practice contrary to all the laws of war, and even exceeding the orders which the government was alleged to have given upon the occasion. He had therefore allowed his humanity to yield to the barbarity of the common enemy.

The cannonade ceased ; but the garrison continued to fire upon any Highlanders who showed themselves within range, and although the life of the city returned almost to normal bullets were still apt to whistle through the streets and anxious eyes were turned towards the battlements.

In order to secure a return to normal conditions, he guaranteed the funds of the banks, and at the same time he assumed all the functions of royalty and set to work to put his finances in order. The needs of his army were considerable and growing daily, and to meet these he assessed the burghs for taxation. From Edinburgh he demanded 1,000 tents, 2,000 targets, 6,000 pairs of shoes and other equipment to a total of £15,000. For this a tax of 2s. 6d. in the pound was laid on. Of Glasgow, a city growing yearly more wealthy, he demanded the sum of £15,000, but the astute Glasgow Town Council offered to compound with an immediate payment in cash of £5,500, which was accepted.

All smuggled goods seized and lying in the customs' houses in Leith and elsewhere were impounded, and these yielded an additional £7,000, while the taxation of the burghs helped to swell the exchequer ; but the malt tax, one of the most unpopular of the impositions of the London government, was left in abeyance.

Gradually the army swelled in numbers, and Charles looked forward eagerly to the moment when he could prevail upon his council to agree to give the order to march.

§

So far throughout the campaign Charles had shown himself invariably dignified, honourable and compassionate, and if the response of the menfolk was slow and grudging these princely qualities made a vivid appeal to the women of Scotland. Charles, keenly alive to the advantages to be gained from fostering national feeling, responded to the enthusiasm of the ladies of Edinburgh by holding a levee every morning at the Palace.

This sudden resumption of a brilliant and gracious life in the capital, after so many years, had a profound effect. People flocked to Edinburgh to witness the spectacle, to present themselves at court and offer their loyal attachment to the cause. The milliners worked night and day fashioning new gowns for the ladies ; the gentlemen appeared in their most resplendent costume and tartan became the rage.

The Prince appeared, most often, in Highland dress, sometimes with breeches, sometimes with the kilt. His unvarying courtesy and charm of manner soon had their customary effect, and enchanted the ladies. Even although he refused to dance himself at the balls he gave, and always wore boots as if to remind his guests

that he had come here on sterner business, his consideration and his graceful bearing won all their hearts.   Truly
here was a prince who richly deserved to ascend a throne !

At ten o'clock in the mornings, immediately after the
levee, the council met, consisting of the Duke of Perth
and Lord George Murray, O'Sullivan, Lord Pitsligo and
Lord Elcho, Sir Thomas Sheridan, Mr. Secretary Murray
of Broughton, and all the Highland chiefs.   When the
council rose, he dined in public with his principal officers,
then rode, attended by his life guards, to the camp at
Duddingston.

There his heart lay, among the men he knew and
trusted, and often the gay and brilliant throng at Holyrood House looked in vain for the Prince.   He was supping
with his soldiers, and frequently slept at the camp.

The sense of urgency had never left him.

§

The army was growing in strength.

On the 3rd of October Lord Ogilvy, eldest son of the
Earl of Airly, brought 600 men, mainly from Forfar.
Next day old Gordon of Glenbucket reached Edinburgh
with 400 men from Strathdon, Strathnaver, Glenlivet
and Auchindoun.   Lord Pitsligo, who arrived on the
9th, came with a large number of gentlemen from
Aberdeen and Banff, with their servants, all well armed
and mounted.   They formed an excellent corps of cavalry.

On the 10th Charles issued a manifesto, justifying his
actions in coming to Scotland, proclaiming his father's
gracious intention of redressing every grievance, repeal-
ing the Act of Union, and saying in conclusion :

" Civil wars are ever attended with rancour and
ill-will, which party-rage never fails to produce in the
minds of those whom different interests, principles, or
views set in opposition to one another ;   I therefore
earnestly require it of my friends, to give as little loose
as possible to such passions :   this will prove the most

effectual means to prevent the same in the enemies of our royal cause."

On the 14th of October the Marquis Boyer d'Eguille reached Holyrood House, having landed at Montrose with some arms, ammunition and money. He was represented to be the ambassador of the French court. Two other vessels laden with quantities of warlike stores also reached Scotland from France—brother Henry had been assiduously at work.

By the end of the month the army had increased to about 6,000 men. It was a severe disappointment, for Charles and his Council had been counting upon twice that number. Lord Lovat alone had assured them he could raise between four and five thousand. There was only one thing to be done in such circumstances, and Charles took energetic measures.

He kept shifting the cantonments, splitting the army up into numerous detachments quartered in or around Edinburgh or encamped on different sites, and thus the spies who attempted to assess his strength were completely baffled. So, inevitably, the most exaggerated reports soon got about and caused the greatest consternation in London.

The Hanoverian forces had been concentrated in considerable strength in the north of England, and large additions were on their way from the south and from the Continent. Marshal Wade had been put in command ; yet he did not make a move. Dread of the Highlanders and their amazing and terrifying method of conducting a battle kept his army immobilised and unwilling to enter Scotland.

An elaborate and carefully exaggerated account of his situation was sent off by the Prince to France, in the hope that this would spur the French to action ; but he had no intention of waiting indefinitely until they chose to move. He meant to move himself.

Towards the end of the month he recalled all the scattered detachments, and on the 26th shifted to a new camp near Inveresk Church. Two days later he held, for the first time, a general review of his troops on the sands between Leith and Musselburgh.

His supporters issued a long manifesto. " The declaration and admonitory letter of such of the nobility, gentry, and free-born subjects of his majesty as, under the auspicious conduct of his royal highness, Charles, Prince of Wales, Steward of Scotland, etc., have taken up arms in support of the cause of their king and country."

But Charles could not wait to assess the effect of this, or to collect more recruits. Time was speeding past, money was running short, and he spoke bluntly to the council. They had dallied long enough. Now they must act.

There were dissentient voices. But in the end the council's decision was unanimous.

" Very well, gentlemen," the Prince cried at last. " It is agreed. We march for London."

But by what route? At once the arguments broke out again. Most of the council, listening to the Prince's clear exposition of the situation, agreed that they should head straight for Berwick, then go on to Newcastle and give battle to Marshal Wade. If the issue proved successful, they would then have a clear route to London.

Lord George Murray alone shook his head.

" I cannot agree," he declared. " The western route, which is undefended, is much the better. We should divide the army into two separate columns, in order to confuse the enemy's intelligence—one column to march by Kelso and the other by Moffat, to join forces again at Carlisle. With Carlisle in our hands we can march south in greater security."

The council, apt always to be swayed by the last speaker, respected Lord George's reputation, his experience and skill, and despite the Prince's protests—since he favoured the eastern route—it was decided at length to make for Carlisle.

The decision taken, Charles wasted no further time. The army moved to Dalkeith, six miles south of Edinburgh, and on the evening of Thursday, the 31st of October, the Prince left Holyrood House accompanied by his life-guards.

A great throng had gathered to see him go, to regret his going, and to wish him God-speed. As he rode out towards Dalkeith he felt that a great weight had been taken off his mind. He had left the pedestrian and wearisome details of royalty behind, he had escaped from the restraints and artificialities of the court, he could feel almost as he had done in the old days, running away from the Muti Palace to burn up his tremendous energy on a strenuous hunting trip.

His fortunes lay in the palm of his own hand. He was going to win a crown or, he firmly believed, to perish in the attempt. Head high, eyes bright and clear, the exhilaration of action at last flushing his cheeks, he rode out to place himself at the head of his army.

CHAPTER ELEVEN

SOUTHWARDS

Wha wadna fecht for Charlie?
Wha wadna draw the sword?
Wha wadna up and rally
At the royal Prince's word?

ON THE 1st of November the march south began.

The first division of the army set off on the Peebles road, and, in spite of failing health, the Marquis of Tullibardine assumed the command. His force consisted of the three regiments of the Athole Brigade, the Duke of Perth's, Lord Ogilvy's, and Glenbucket's regiments, and the Edinburgh Regiment raised by James Roy Stewart. Most of the horse and all the artillery and baggage went along with it. The available cavalry force, although small, was well equipped and efficient, and consisted of a hundred horse-grenadiers under the Earl of Kilmarnock, Lord Pitsligo's cavalry corps of

120 men, and 70 hussars under the nominal command of Secretary Murray.

For convenience, the seven foot regiments of the first division were referred to as the Lowland Regiments, but in point of fact many of their number were Highlanders, and all the infantry wore the Highland dress.

Charles gave the first division a start of two days, then led off the second himself. It consisted of the six regiments of the clans proper—three MacDonalds and the Camerons, the Stewarts of Appin, and the 600 MacPhersons whom Cluny had brought, and the lifeguards—the first troop, under Lord Elcho, numbering 120, of whom 62 were gentlemen and the remainder their servants, and the second troop amounting to only 40 horse, under the Hon. Arthur Elphinstone, later Lord Balmerino.

The pay of the army had been fixed at 6d. a day for a private soldier. In the clan regiments, the front rank was composed mainly of gentlemen without fortune or estates, and they received 1s. a day ; they were well armed, carrying musket and broadsword, brace of pistols, dirk, and target. Some also wore the *sgian dubh*, the little black knife carried in the stocking. Ensigns received 1s. 6d. a day, lieutenants 2s. and captains 2s. 6d.

Charles had elected to march with the clans, and they had not proceeded far from Dalkeith when he dismounted and took his place in the van of the infantry, with his target slung over his shoulder like the rest. The men were pleased at this mark of favour, and swung along in high spirits, although they expected him soon to remount. He did not do so, and the example he set himself he maintained throughout the march southwards. He went invariably on foot, wading through mud and snow, splashing through rivers, rarely allowing himself to be persuaded to cross rivers on horseback, and then only when the water was deep and swift.

He appeared tireless, indifferent to discomfort, proud to be able to set an example to his men, and just as he never gave a thought to his own personal safety so he completely disregarded his own comfort or convenience. To save time, he would eat nothing between breakfast and dinner, and seemed not to mind going hungry.

He reached Lauder on that first day's march, and was entertained at Thirlstane Castle by the Earl of Lauderdale. That night he sent off a detachment via Selkirk and Hawick, in order to confuse the issue still further, and next day he marched to Kelso. There he gave orders to his life-guards.

" Cross the Tweed and do what you can to keep Wade occupied."

Grinning, they set off, and trotted away down the road to distant Newcastle, where the English Marshal lay with a force of about 11,000 men. At a village along the road they drew rein, and Elcho proceeded to make urgent enquiries about quarters for the army. The terrified villagers promised their help—and sent an urgent message south to Wade. The Highland army was in full march to Newcastle !

Charles remained in Kelso until the 6th, to allow this ruse to operate, and he dispatched a party of 40 men across the Tweed to proclaim the Chevalier on English ground.

On the 6th, he himself crossed the Tweed. The river was in spate, but he plunged in cheerfully, and the men, linking arms, followed him, shouting and cheering and firing off their muskets.

Immediately after, the Prince turned off for Jedburgh, where he remained overnight to rest his men in preparation for the long and arduous march next day across wild and desolate country where no quarters would be found.

Accustomed as they were to walking on rough ground, the Highlanders tackled the march in high spirits. They went up the Rule Water into Liddisdale, then over the Knot o' the Gate to reach Haggishaugh on Liddel Water that night, a march of twenty-five miles. Early next morning they were on their feet again, with no signs of fatigue, and they entered England that evening, Friday, the 8th of November. As they crossed the border the clansmen drew their swords and gave a loud huzza.

Charles's cavalry detachment, after its detour by Hawick and Langholm, joined him that day at Longtown, and next day Charles reached Rowcliff, four miles below Carlisle, and crossed the Eden. Just two hours later Tullibardine came up with the first division and all the baggage. The rendezvous had been safely made—and with an accuracy that would have done credit to any commander, considering the state of the roads and the inadequacy of the maps available.

Wade had been completely deceived. He remained in Newcastle, convinced that the rebels were marching to meet him there, and none of his spies had been able to get at the truth in time. Indeed, only Charles and his close advisers knew the actual route.

On the 10th the army proceeded to invest Carlisle on all sides. It was known that the Castle was well furnished with artillery, and the entire militia of Cumberland and Westmoreland had been collected inside the town ; but Charles was completely confident. At noon he sent a letter to the mayor demanding that the gates should be opened, promising to protect the city if this was agreed to, but threatening assault if the mayor did not comply. He demanded a reply within two hours but none came, and shortly afterwards the guns of Carlisle opened fire. The city meant to fight.

Shortly after news came—Wade was marching to the relief of the town !

Charles, cheered by the prospect, drew off the greater part of his army to meet the Marshal. He reached Bampton at eleven o'clock on the morning of the 11th, and sent Colonel Ker off with a detachment of horse to reconnoitre. Ker, spurring hard, was soon back to report that the news was false. Wade was still at Newcastle. The Prince accordingly summoned a council of war.

There were three separate proposals put forward. First, to march on Newcastle, meet Wade and give him battle. Charles, inspired by the high spirits of his men and well knowing how eagerly the clans looked forward to meeting the enemy, immediately concurred.

" That is my own view," he declared, emphatically. " Wade is far stronger than we are—in numbers. But we possess an advantage that far outweighs that—the claymore. No seasoned troops can withstand the shock of a charge with the claymore, by men who are not only individually brave but who are inspired by the utmost zeal."

But the council heard him with grave faces, and objections were instantly made. The plan was far too dangerous, for even if completely victorious the army might suffer serious casualties which it could not afford. It might be impossible to pursue and destroy Wade's forces before they could reach Newcastle—and Newcastle was far too strong to be taken by assault.

Another proposal followed—that they should retire to Scotland and await reinforcements. It was known that considerable numbers of recruits were being gathered in the Highlands, and that men and arms were coming from France. It would be prudent therefore to retire until the whole available force would be consolidated into one army.

Lord George Murray shook his head over that.

" My proposal," he declared, " is that we should split our forces, and that one division should besiege Carlisle while the other waits here in Bampton in case Wade comes up."

The Duke of Perth, leaning forward eagerly, seconded this suggestion.

" If Lord George will command the blockade," he offered, " I am prepared to take command of the battery."

The council argued. Murray of Broughton, hearing

growing approval on all sides of Lord George's plan, frowned and bit his lip in vexation. He could not oppose the plan ; it was the best in all the circumstances, and he had no desire either to risk the gamble of going to meet Wade or to abandon all the advantages so far gained by retreating into Scotland. But he resented the respectful deference shown to Lord George, and looked for an opening to vent his growing spite.

He had been selected to represent the Edinburgh Association because of his abilities. He was known for his sound common sense, his business efficiency, his hard-headedness ; but what the members of the Edinburgh Association had not realised was his boundless ambition. Meeting the Prince in France had fired him with an ambition that blinded him to the dangers and difficulties ahead, and, flattered by the Prince's good opinion, he had readily seen that the surest way to win his favour was to propose to him the course of action the Prince himself wanted to pursue.

Apart from the Men of Moidart, Murray of Broughton was almost the only old acquaintance Charles met in Scotland, and the ambitious Secretary had not failed to improve the occasion.

He had recognised in Sir Thomas Sheridan and O'Sullivan the two Men of Moidart closest to the Prince and most likely to influence them. He set about winning them over to his own side, and with these two to support him he had little to fear in the way of rivalry.

But the sudden appearance of Lord George Murray had upset his plans. It was known that as a soldier he was head and shoulders above any other of the Prince's adherents. Also he was an aristocrat, assured in his position by birth and breeding as well as by his natural gifts, and the Secretary had nursed a passionate envy and hatred of him from the start. He had hidden it well ; but on occasion he had found the opportunity of dropping a word in the Prince's ear to undermine his confidence in the lieutenant-general ; and now at this vital council of war he looked for a fresh opening.

The plan having been agreed to, Lord George went on to details.

"It is essential," he pointed out, "that your royal highness should have the terms of capitulation prepared in advance. If the city offers to surrender, much valuable time will be wasted if I have to send despatches back and forth before terms are drawn up."

The Secretary, scowling, interposed.

"I consider, sir," he declared, "that the terms of capitulation are entirely an affair within my province. In such matters you have no right to interfere."

Charles, taken by surprise, looked from one to the other. Lord George, not accustomed to being addressed so bluntly, flushed with anger but held his tongue, and the Prince, relying as he did upon his Secretary's advice, said quietly :

"I have not yet been able to reach a decision as to the terms."

"In that case," Lord George Murray replied, "I shall be grateful if you will send your instructions after me in good time, so that I shall know how to act when an offer of surrender is made."

Charles nodded, and Lord George rose. When the council had broken up, the Secretary had a word with the Prince.

"You see, sir, what is happening. Lord George Murray forgets that he is a soldier, and desires to take too much power into his own hands."

Charles, vexed by the situation that had arisen, listened —and remembered the occasions, which had not been few, when Lord George had been more than outspoken. He had not hesitated to criticise the Prince to his face, and had never disguised his impatience with many of the men who offered their advice.

The seed of doubt which the Secretary had long ago planted had taken root, and was growing rapidly.

§

Lord George was given the Lowland Regiments for the blockade, which was established in full on the 13th. For the battery, the Duke of Perth employed his own regiment, and they proceeded immediately to break ground well within musket shot of the city walls. They were constantly under fire, but suffered no casualties, and soon the darkness gave them cover while they laboured. Before dawn the trenches were completed, the cannon had been brought up—thirteen pieces in all—and trained to play upon the city. Next morning the fire from the town was renewed with greater intensity, but the besiegers, instead of wasting time and ammunition replying to it, or breaking off their work to take cover, held their bonnets up on the ends of their spades in derision, cheered—and went on working.

Meanwhile Lord George, still without his instructions, tried to forget the annoyance he had suffered by immersing himself in the job in hand.

It was lively work in the trenches and on the picket lines surrounding the town. The men were continuously under fire, to which they could not profitably retaliate, and Lord George, with all his continental experience to give him wisdom, realised that there must be a definite rotation of duty. He wrote to his brother, Tullibardine, pointing out that it was unfair to expect one section of men to face all the hazards and rigours of the investment. He alluded to the indefatigable exertions of the Duke of Perth, who worked in the trenches himself as an example to his men, and he proposed that there should be turns of duty for the whole army at the post of danger. He suggested that fifty men from each of the regiments at Bampton should be chosen by lot and sent over.

Tullibardine laid this proposal before the Prince and a council of war was called. But there was little opportunity for any of the chiefs to give their views. The Secretary spoke immediately.

" Lord George undertook the blockade and was allotted the force he asked for," he pointed out.   " The regiments remaining here had a very arduous march, and also they bore the brunt of the investment and capture of Edinburgh. It would be unfair to expect them to take part in this other blockade now. Let the Lowland Regiments do that. When the whole of the blockading force has taken turns as guards, then it will be time for the division here to occupy its place. But we cannot send off detachments of men from here."

It was an astute speech, for the Highland chiefs would hardly object to the special consideration it showed for their men. Only Tullibardine raised a dissentient voice ; but by this time he was a sick old man, and his words carried little weight. Charles agreed promptly, and the Secretary went off in high glee to prepare this direct snub.

Lord George received it with amazement and consternation. He knew precisely why the council had decided to reject his proposal. He knew precisely what Murray of Broughton was aiming at. The Secretary wanted the entire direction of the campaign in his own hands.

There seemed only one thing to do. He had no hope of defeating the Secretary's machinations, for the simple reason that he could never get the ear of the Prince, nor could any who might support him. The Secretary had got too long a start over him, and had the support of all those who were out to make their fortunes—which included the two Irish gentlemen who, because of their old associations, were firmly established as personal friends of the Prince.

The Secretary was jealous of others as well as Lord George. He used his position to ensure that only those who would support him should get near the Prince, and he carefully excluded all others. Every new recruit who joined was interviewed by the Secretary, who then reported on him to Charles. All the appointments close to the Prince's person were in the Secretary's hands, and except among the clan regiments all the commands in the army were virtually at his disposal. Charles, convinced of his integrity and ability, would never have thought of doubting the advice he gave.

Lord George was perfectly aware that the Prince did not like him. Now he was beginning to understand why. It was the Secretary's doing. True, his very gallant behaviour at Prestonpans had had its effect, and for a while the Prince had been more affable ; but as he thought over the past few weeks, and began putting one incident after another together, a conviction grew in his mind that shocked him deeply. Charles regarded him with the utmost suspicion.

There could be no doubt about it. Now here was the last straw. His advice as a military expert had been flouted, he had been deliberately snubbed. Yet he was venturing his life and fortune and family for a third time in the Stuart cause. It was an intolerable situation for a man of honour. So long as his opinion held weight in the council, so long as he felt that he could counteract the evil influence of the Secretary and prevent any rash or stupid mistakes, he had been prepared to go on. Now it appeared that his voice no longer dominated the council's deliberations, and on the 15th he wrote to Charles pointing out how little weight was now attached to his advice as a general officer, and tendering his resignation. At the same time, because of his firm attachment to the House of Stuart, and particularly to the king, Prince Charles's father, he would serve as a volunteer if the Prince agreed.

Murray of Broughton scarcely concealed his delight at this development, and improved the occasion by hinting to Charles that it was indeed peculiar for a general to throw up his commission in the middle of a campaign, and to offer to serve as a private soldier. Plainly, Lord George had some scheme in mind.

Tullibardine, seriously alarmed, wrote to his brother

to say that Charles wished to see him, and Lord George hastened to wait upon the Prince. But there was no welcoming smile in the young face, no softening of expression, no friendliness in the eyes.

" Well, my lord? " Charles greeted him.

" My brother informed me that your royal highness desired to see me."

Charles raised his eyebrows.

" I did not require your attendance," he retorted drily. " I have nothing particular to say to you."

Lord George swallowed the affront.

" Then, sir, I can only repeat my offer to serve as a volunteer."

" You may do so, my lord."

The interview terminated. Lord George retired, and called on Sheridan.

" It is intolerable," he told him angrily. " While I am given all the drudgery to do, everything of moment is done without consulting me. I have ventured my all —life, fortune and family—all but my honour. I have some honour to lose and none to gain, and I am determined therefore to serve only as a volunteer in some humble capacity. I shall certainly not undertake a command again."

Sheridan listened without comment. He too had suffered a little from Lord George's outspokenness, and although he knew that without this capable and experienced soldier the army might just as well disband and go home, he could not help being pleased at Lord George's defeat.

The Secretary could not leave it at that.

" We know very well," he declared, " why Lord George has thrown up his commission. He resents having to act under the orders of the Duke of Perth. He knows that the Duke is inferior to himself in ability and so he resigns out of pique."

But there were other voices to be heard. The Highland chiefs, who also had ventured their all, were not likely to accept a situation brought about by men with nothing to lose and everything to gain. Others supported them, and Charles realised that he must take steps to persuade Lord George to retract his resignation.

The Prince's suspicions were by no means stilled ; but he yielded to necessity, and to solve the difficulty it was pointed out to the Duke of Perth, who was a Roman Catholic, that now they were in England, where popery was abhorrent to the great bulk of the people, it would be most impolitic to have a Roman Catholic in supreme command. The good Duke, quite seeing the point, cheerfully resigned, and Lord George was appointed in his stead.

It meant that he would be in actual fact the supreme commander, for his brother Tullibardine was now too ill to exercise that office and would leave everything to his second in command. On these conditions, Lord George accepted the new appointment and prepared to continue his work with redoubled energy and zeal. But the incident rankled yet.

§

Meantime, the siege had gone on without interruption, and after a very short time the inhabitants of the town gathered and held a meeting to discuss the situation. For seven days the garrison had been constantly on the *qui vive*, had had no proper sleep and had been turned out almost hourly for alarms. Large numbers had deserted, slipping over the walls at night and getting past the pickets (who let them go with pleasure) and dispersing to their homes. It was impossible to hold out much longer.

Accordingly a white flag was displayed from the walls, and a messenger despatched to the Duke of Perth to ask for terms. So far none had been received from the Prince. The Duke sent an express to Bampton to know Charles's pleasure, and the answer came promptly. No terms would be granted unless the Castle surrendered at the same time.

The Mayor requested a truce until next day, but long before the time limit expired the Governor of the Castle, Col. Durand, had announced his willingness to surrender.

The conditions were simple. The liberties and properties of the inhabitants and all the privileges of the town would be preserved inviolate ; both garrisons must take an oath not to serve against the House of Stuart for a twelve-month, and they would then be permitted to retire unmolested ; all arms and ammunition in the Castle and the city and all militia horses were to be delivered up to Charles. The capitulation was signed on the night of the 14th by the Duke of Perth and Col. Durand, and next day at ten o'clock the Duke entered the city. Simple-hearted, kindly, and direct, he reviewed the garrison and shook hands with them all, told them they were brave fellows and offered a large bounty to any who would volunteer for the Prince's service.

Charles took up his quarters in the house of a Mr. Hymer, an attorney, to whom he paid five guineas a day in rent. This liberality shocked the master of his household, James Gib, who was particularly indignant because the Hymers supplied neither coal nor candle, yet were given three hearty meals a day from the Prince's kitchen ! But Gib was always worried by his royal master's ways, for at every house Charles visited he invariably left five guineas as a *pour-boire* for the servants.

§

Marshal Wade had been completely outwitted by Lord George's strategy. As soon as he learnt of the fall of Carlisle he set out energetically to redeem his mistake and, leaving Newcastle on the 16th, struggled through deep snow to Hexham, which he reached next day ; but his rear did not come up until nearly midnight, and for three days he lay at Hexham awaiting a thaw, his troops exhausted and in no condition to go on. As the road still remained impassable, he gave up the attempt and turned about, reaching Newcastle again on the 22nd.

The capture of Carlisle had galvanised the country. The wildest rumours were circulated and the scenes of panic which had followed the news of Prestonpans were repeated. But the government was taking energetic steps, and an army of 10,000 men was being assembled in Staffordshire under Sir John Ligonier, while another army was being raised for the defence of the capital, and had already gone into camp nearby.

Charles was soon aware of these moves, and when the council of war met in Carlisle the intelligence that had been received had been collated and digested thoroughly.

The enemy forces, consisting largely of veteran troops under experienced commanders, totalled over 60,000 men. Against that the Prince's army now numbered little more than 4,500, France had made no move towards invasion—which would have drawn off a great portion of the English troops—and, most important still, none of the English Jacobites, who so recently had renewed their assurances of support, had yet declared themselves or attempted to raise men for the cause.

But Charles faced the council with his mind already made up.

He was obsessed entirely with the great object in view —the capture of London, the return of the Stuarts to St. James's. No difficulty, no danger would deter him, and he proceeded to give a statement of the situation that approximated more to his wishes in that respect than to the hard unpalatable facts.

He was fighting for his cause. He had no hesitation in risking his own life to win it—rather he welcomed the risk. He would use any argument that might help him to get his own way, to persuade his advisers to consent to going on. On—on—that was all that mattered. Press the advantage, put it to the test, rely on the tremendous fighting quality of his loyal Highlanders, who could easily sweep any regular troops off the field like chaff before the wind. But a sober voice took up the argument as soon as his exposition of affairs had finished.

" I propose that we should return to Scotland and fight a defensive war there until our prospects become brighter, until the army is strengthened and the French carry out their promises."

" If we wait until the French keep their promises," Charles retorted sourly, " we shall die of inaction."

A few earnest voices supported the proposal, until another voice cut in with a fresh proposal.

" Could your royal highness not remain at Carlisle, quarter the army in the neighbourhood, and await a sign of the reaction in England to our enterprise? "

There was no doubt already as to that reaction—it was entirely unfavourable.

" Then," said a new voice, " let us march upon Newcastle and give battle to Marshal Wade ! "

The Prince leaned forward eagerly, his eyes lighting up, for this was more in accord with his own inclinations. He had not the slightest doubt of the result of such a meeting. But, as before, there were serious objections. With the tiny force they possessed it would be suicidal to incur heavy losses, and even a signal victory over Wade's 11,000 could only be achieved at the expense of serious casualties. Charles realised that, and when a further proposition was made he readily assented. It was to continue the march upon London by the western road, through Lancashire, which would at any rate ensure their line of retreat if retreat became necessary.

He was entirely in the hands of his advisers, since the army's primary allegiance was not to him but to the various chiefs, and he knew that he must defer to their opinions. Now, determined to show that for his part there need be no division of council, he turned to Lord George Murray and desired him to give his opinion.

Lord George had been silent throughout. But he had

listened keenly, and now he proceeded to go into each
of the four proposals in the greatest detail ; then he
concluded :

" I cannot advise your royal highness to march far
into England without more encouragement from the
country than we have so far received, but I am persuaded
that if your royal highness is determined to go on your
army will certainly follow you."

Charles, his face clearing at once, declared emphatically:
" I am ready to venture the trial."

The council, pleased to have reached at least a measure
of agreement, signified its unanimous approval of the
decision, and Lord George rose to put it into instant
effect.

§

Once again the army was split into two divisions.
There had been an unfortunate muddle over the baggage,
and all the tents had been left behind. Lord George
solved the difficulty by proposing that the first division
should march a day in advance of the second, and that
it should quarter itself each night in a town or village,
the second division coming up the following night to
occupy the billets left vacant by the first. The plan,
simple in itself, was not an easy one to put into effect ;
it meant that there must be no delays, no stragglers, no
muddle ; but Lord George was capable of ensuring that.

Accordingly on the 20th of November he rode out of
Carlisle, accompanied by the life-guards under Lord
Elcho and followed by the six Lowland regiments. He
reached Penrith the same day, a march of eighteen miles.
The second division, under the personal leadership of
Charles himself, and comprising the clan regiments and
the remainder of the cavalry, started out next day.

So the march progressed through Penrith, Kendal, and
Lancaster, until the whole army reached Preston on the
26th.

All this way the countryside had been silent, unfriendly, dour. There was no ringing of bells, no joyful reception for the gallant young Prince and his men, no trace of enthusiasm—only the stolid, sullen enmity of people to whom the Stuart cause meant nothing, who resented this intrusion into their lives, and who went about in lively fear of the strange, wild appearance of the Highlanders. But at Preston things were different.

People lined the streets, hailing the Prince with loud huzzas, waving and cheering the marching men while the bells rang out their peals of joy. But it was spurious joy, a kind of delirium that seized the people ; and their hard-headed English caution remained. A few recruits responded to the appeal made to them, joining the ranks as privates ; but only one man of any consequence came forward, a certain Francis Townley, a Roman Catholic gentleman who had been in the French service. When the council of war was summoned in Preston, Mr. Secretary Murray was compelled to report this unflattering response.

Charles refused to be downcast. He saw from the gloomy faces of the chiefs that they were in a difficult mood, and he began straightaway to overcome their reluctance by repeating the categorical assurances he had given before of speedy help from France and reinforcements from the English Jacobites.

" Manchester," he cried emphatically, " will rally to the cause in great numbers. We shall soon be among Jacobite families. We must go on ! "

But even his assurance was being gradually worn down. Each time it was he, and he alone, who had to keep their spirits up and insist that the best course was to go on.

Now, however, the chiefs were won over. The Prince's eloquence had not deserted him, and he knew exactly how to play upon their pride, their loyalty, their emotion. Seeing that the council was unanimous, Lord George, who had always borne the possibility of a retreat in mind, now made a generous and far-sighted gesture.

" May I suggest, your royal highness," he said, " that
I march with my column direct to Liverpool? The
occupation of that city is bound to have a profound
effect, and secure us large recruitment from among the
English Jacobites in the neighbourhood who as yet dare
not declare themselves openly."

Charles considered the proposal. It certainly had merit
as well as courage. But Mr. Secretary Murray had a
word to say. His enmity had grown all the more bitter
since he had been compelled to invite Lord George to
resume his commission, and he was ever on the look-out
for any chance to vent it. He certainly had no intention
of allowing Lord George the opportunity of winning
the Prince's goodwill by outstanding service.

" Your royal highness," he cried, " that would be most
unwise. Our enemies are near at hand, we cannot
afford to split our forces and perhaps have them overwhelmed piecemeal by the vastly superior strength of
our enemies."

The Prince, immediately convinced, agreed, and Lord
George's suggestion was rejected. He bit his lip and
swallowed this fresh affront with as good a grace as he
could ; and next day he set the army in motion again.
They entered Wigan on the 28th, and took the road for
Manchester the following morning.

§

It was at this point that a young Lowland Scot won
himself a page in history.

After Prestonpans Charles, determined to be lenient,
had invited his prisoners to take service with him.
Most of the officers were allowed to give their parole
and depart, although one of them promptly broke his
parole ; the men were permitted to go home on taking
an oath not to serve against him. But a considerable
number, particularly among the non-commissioned
officers, volunteered to join the army. They proved of

great value in drilling and training the troops while they lay near Edinburgh, although the majority deserted later on the southward march.

One of those who did not desert was young Sergeant Dickson, and at Preston he reported himself to his commander, the Chevalier Johnstone—on whom had fallen the duty of enrolling these ex-prisoners and commanding the detachment they formed—and laid a proposal before him.

" Let me tak' ae drummer wi' me," he said, " and I'll gang to Manchester my lane, and raise the toun for the Prince. I ha'e a glib tongue in my heid, and nae fear o' thae English ava. Gie me leave, sir, and when the Prince comes tae Manchester a hale regiment o' thae Manchester lads will be paraded tae greet him there."

The Chevalier Johnstone stared at him in blank astonishment.

" Havers, man ! " he retorted sharply. " You're mad. They would tear you to pieces. You might do infinite harm to the cause. The mob would set upon you—— "

" I've nae fear o' the mob ! "

" Then more fool you. Get back to your duties."

Dickson retired with, as he told his sweetheart, a flea in his lug ; but he refused to be downcast. If only he could get to Manchester he would soon set that city by the ears ! He had already spoken to a drummer, who was quite willing to run the risk ; as for his sweetheart, she had followed his fortunes devotedly for long enough, she would not desert him now. It would be a good ploy, this, and she did not mean to be left out of the fun.

She was one of the very few camp followers who went with the army, for Charles, in no way interested in women himself, had set his face against the usual practice of those times, when large numbers of women would accompany troops on the march. It was a practice encouraged by the German soldier princes on whom the English officers now liked to model themselves, but to

Charles it seemed a mere encumbrance and something of a disgrace.

Dickson, however, being a recruit from the Hanoverian forces, had not been interfered with, and had been allowed to bring his sweetheart with him ; so now the three slipped out of their quarters as soon as it grew dark, and took the Manchester road. They walked fast, the drummer panting as he lugged his instrument, the girl and her soldier laddie swinging along in great spirits.

They came into Manchester in the morning, marching proudly along, and Dickson spoke to the drummer.

" Noo, strike her up, lad ! "

The rattle of the drum brought crowds gaping as the three paraded boldly down the street, with their white cockades and their tartans streaming in the wind, and Dickson set to work.

" Who's for joining the Yellow Haired Laddie ? Who's for fighting for Charlie? Come on, lads—strike a blow for your rightful king ! Up and fight for the bonnie Prince ! "

Throngs lined the streets, in silence, while terrified eyes glanced towards the north. The Highland army must be at hand, it could not be more than a few minutes away. They did not dream of interfering with the intrepid three. But at last someone cried out—and got an answer.

" And when will he be here ? "

" This very day ! " cried Dickson, to his own undoing. " He'll be here before the night."

A shout went up. Not before the night ! The crowd surged forward. Then there was time—ample time to tear these impudent foreigners to pieces, to wreak their vengeance on them in advance.

" Take them ! " they yelled. " Dead or alive ! "

In a moment Dickson and his girl and the drummer found themselves the centre of a milling throng, crazed with fear and mob violence, fighting each other to get at them. Dickson grinned, as cool as ever. He raised the blunderbuss he had thoughtfully brought, and had charged with slugs. As he swung it round he cried :

" I'll blow oot the brains o' the first that tries to lay hands on me or those wi' me ! "

The crowd, suddenly brought to a halt, stared at the fearful weapon, at the calm and confident bearing of the soldier who handled it—and at once those in front began to press to the rear and those in the rear began to retire to a safer distance. Soon he had cleared a wide circle round about, and kept turning constantly to cover the whole mob, while the drummer beat and the girl shouted defiance and taunts at the frightened crowd.

But the drumming had had its effect. There were plenty of secret Jacobites in Manchester, and now they began to collect in small numbers. Then, seeing the predicament Charles's unofficial beater-up had got himself and his companions into, they raced for their homes, armed themselves, and came back in a body into the street.

In a moment the scene was changed. Several hundred armed men poured down the street, and the mob dispersed and ran for its life. Sergeant Dickson grinned, shook hands with his deliverers, and bade them form themselves into a regiment forthwith. They willingly agreed, and after he had drilled them enough he set out at their head to parade, for the rest of the day, through the streets of Manchester, collecting recruits as he went. When, that evening, the vanguard of 100 horse arrived, they found a guard of honour drawn up to receive them —and a bill for three guineas from Sergeant Dickson, for that was all it had cost him to secure a whole regiment of recruits.

Manchester had been captured by a sergeant, a girl, and a drummer !

CHAPTER TWELVE

FATEFUL DECISION

AT TEN O'CLOCK next day, the 29th of November, the citizens of Manchester lining the streets raised a cheer as another body of the rebel cavalry came clattering into the town, and at two o'clock, to the pealing of bells and the waving of flags and handkerchiefs from all the windows, Charles himself came striding in, surrounded by a picked body of the clans.

In a light tartan plaid, belted with a blue sash, with a grey wig and a blue velvet bonnet trimmed with silver lace, and a white rose on top to distinguish him from his officers, who wore their cockades at the side, he was an inspiring figure, and his face showed his elation. The fickle populace of Manchester responded to his gallant bearing with a storm of cheering, bonfires were lit and, in the evening, all the houses illuminated. Crowds gathered outside the Prince's lodgings and cheered and cheered. Charles, sitting down to dinner, had never been in such high spirits.

" What shall I wear when we enter London? " he cried. " Shall it be the kilt? Or shall I go in on horseback? "

His enthusiasm infected the rest ; but there were

strange meaning glances exchanged here and there across the table, glances of real distress, and young Lord Elcho, who had never liked Charles, sat listening in a contemptuous silence. He knew perfectly well what was in all their minds—what Charles refused to see.

This could not go on. Charles was supported by his vision, by his passionate conviction which blinded him to the hard facts. But others saw the situation with clearer eyes.

One of Lord George's friends sought him out.

" Hech, my lord," he said, with a heavy sigh, " we've come a lang gait. And now—now there's only the lang gait back."

Lord George listened gloomily, and nodded. His friend went on, with lowered voice : " We counted on an insurrection in England and a landing from France. Neither the one nor the other has come about, nor is likely to come about now. It's my thought we have gone far enough into this wilderness of Whigs and Hanoverians."

Lord George, who had laid his plans with the possibility of retreat in view, rallied him gently.

" We might make a further trial as far as Derby. But if we do not meet with better encouragement by that time I'll propose a retreat myself."

Elcho held the same opinion. As he pointed out, they had not set out to put a king on the throne of England without the consent of the people of England or against their will. They had had enough difficulty already in recruiting a few hundred vagabonds in England to prove that consent was lacking. But, like Lord George, he advocated going on as far as Derby—the Prince might be readier then to listen to reason.

But during the day the army spent at Manchester, Charles got no hint of what was in the minds of his officers. His high spirits persisted, and as usual he was out of bed in the morning before anyone else and getting matters in train.

Macclesfield was the next objective, and Charles led his division by Stockport while the second took the road to Knottesford. He found the bridge at Stockport broken down, and immediately plunged into the river, wading across over the waist in water. As he clambered up the far bank a group of people came forward to greet him—Jacobite gentlemen from Cheshire. With them was the venerable Mrs. Skyring, a zealous partisan of the Stuarts who had been held up in her mother's arms to witness the return of Charles II to London in 1660. Since 1688 she had laid aside half of her income each year and sent it anonymously to the exiled court abroad. Now, learning of the Prince's approach, she had sold her jewels and other valuables, and had brought the money with her in a purse.

As the tall and handsome youth came ashore, she threw the purse at his feet. He stooped and picked it up with his instinctive courtesy and, deeply moved, extended his hand.

The old lady seized it and covered it with kisses. Charles, greatly heartened, continued his march ; the old lady, her generosity and zeal thus rewarded, returned home to await news of his success ; but the news she got was more than she could bear, and a few weeks after the incident she died, heart-broken.

Meantime the second division had found the bridge at Knottesford also down, and so threw over temporary bridges of poplar trees laid lengthwise with planks across. The horse and artillery made for Chedleford, where they crossed safely, and that evening the whole army linked up again at Macclesfield.

§

Charles, studying the latest intelligence reports, discussed the situation with Lord George Murray.

The Duke of Cumberland, who had assumed command of Ligonier's army, was on his march northwards, and

The old lady seized his hand and covered it with kisses.

at present quartered at Lichfield, Coventry, Stafford and Newcastle-under-Lyme.

" Our road to London is by Derby," Charles pointed out. " But my cousin could easily get astride our route."

Lord George nodded. It was too soon yet, he saw, to talk of retreat ; the Prince was in great spirits, full of optimism, eager to meet his cousin on the field and completely convinced of the result. But as his main object was to reach London he was quite prepared to avoid a battle and keep his gallant little army intact for the descent upon the capital. The difficulty was how to avoid Cumberland, since a battle would give Wade the chance of coming down on Charles's flank.

Lord George smiled. In tactics he was supreme. With his resourcefulness, his instant grasp of the military situation and his bold and determined enterprise, he knew that he could outwit any general among the opposing forces. Calmly he made his proposal.

" I will take my division to Congleton," he suggested. " It is on the direct road to Lichfield, and when Cumberland learns of my movement he will immediately concentrate his forces there. That will leave the road to Derby open."

It was a daring move, and Charles, who for all his suspicions of Lord George Murray the politician had nothing but the liveliest respect for Lord George Murray the soldier, eagerly agreed.

Next morning he stood watching the division march. It made a brave show, ragged and footsore as it was, and the men were enthusiastic. Every face was lighted with eagerness to meet the enemy, and as well as grim determination there was supreme confidence there. None doubted the issue of a battle with the redcoats.

Later, Charles took the road for Derby by Gawsworth, and as he entered Leek a handful of men came out to greet him—Lord George's men. They had remained behind to report that the division had marched at great speed to Congleton, and that Lord George had sent Colonel Ker on with a mounted party at night towards Newcastle-under-Lyme, to get intelligence. The Duke of Kingston, who had been in Congleton with his regiment of horse, had retired as soon as he learned of the approach of the Highland army.

Ker, riding hard, had got to a village only three miles from Newcastle-under-Lyme almost in time to surprise a party of dragoons. They had fled as he entered the village ; but he had succeeded in laying hands on a spy, who was dragged back as he was trying to escape out of the window of a house. He was a man called Weir, who had been at Edinburgh all the time the Prince was there and had been seen hovering near the army on its southward march.

Cumberland, hearing of the Prince's approach, had promptly retired to Lichfield, where he concentrated his entire force in expectation of an encounter—a force nearly double that of the Highlanders.

Lord George, satisfied that he had completely outwitted the more ponderous and slow-minded German, had left Congleton next morning, turned left through Leek and had gone on to Ashbourne. The road to Derby lay wide open.

Charles, well pleased with his general's success, halted only briefly in Leek. It was dangerous to keep the army divided when the Hanoverian forces were so near, and at midnight the orders went out, the troops, rested and refreshed, fell into their ranks, and the march continued. He entered Ashbourne to join Lord George Murray early in the morning.

The Secretary reported on the case of Weir.

" This man has been recognised, your royal highness," he said. " He was employed as a spy in Flanders last year, and is well known to many here. The intention is to hang him immediately. He richly deserves it, and in any case it will prevent him from doing further mischief."

He almost added : " In case we fail . . . " But he restrained himself in time.

Charles glanced up sharply.

" Certainly not ! " he exclaimed. " I will not permit it."

"But, your royal highness, the man is a notorious spy—there is no manner of doubt—— "

" Certainly not," Charles said again. He had an instant vision of the gibbet, the wretch ignominiously dying before the assembled crowds, and the picture revolted him. This was no barbarous war, it was an honest, noble and just effort to drive out a usurper. He would never countenance any act that might sully the honourable character of the campaign.

Murray readily gave way. He was quick to retract, for he had always studied to suggest to the Prince only the line of action he knew the Prince himself wished to follow. But others objected. If the enterprise failed, Weir could be a very dangerous man. His evidence would be enough to hang them all—and their enemies would certainly not show any nicety of feeling or any trace of compassion. But Charles was obstinate. He had never agreed to stern measures, he had always insisted on sparing his enemies when they fell into his hands, and he persisted in that to the end.

" The man is not, properly speaking, a spy," he declared. " He was not found in the army in disguise. He was captured when that village was entered—— "

" But, sir, he was instantly recognised. That is why he was captured—— "

" But he was not in disguise among our troops. He must be released."

There was nothing for it but to let him go, and he went—not with any gratitude to the Prince who had saved his life, but with the intention, as soon as the chance offered, of turning his knowledge of the Jacobite movement to the best account. His testimony would certainly be well rewarded.

§

On the 4th of December the army was on the march
once more. The Duke of Devonshire, who had been
posted in Derby with 700 militia, discreetly left the town
in good time, and at eleven o'clock in the forenoon a
party of thirty horsemen came clattering in. They
ordered quarters for 9,000 men.

At three o'clock Lord Elcho appeared with the life-
guards, in their gay blue uniforms faced with red, with
scarlet waistcoats trimmed with gold lace. A con-
temporary account says of these cavaliers that " being
likely men," they " made a good appearance," and the
citizens of Derby turned out to see the show, and to
cheer, not because they favoured the Prince but simply
because they enjoyed the spectacle.

Later in the afternoon they heard, for the first time
in their lives, the skirl of the pipes, and the first companies
of infantry appeared, swinging along eight abreast
behind the pipers. They bore their standards, white
with red crosses, and the gold cross of St. Andrew on a
blue field, and soon the Market Place was filled with
white cockades.

The army arrived in separate detachments. It was a
simple ruse to prevent any accurate estimation of its
strength, and at dusk the citizens were electrified by the
sight of a tall and gallant looking youth, in Highland
dress, marching at the head of a detachment of picked
clansmen, head erect and lean face alert and eager. They
noted his long, tireless stride, his splendid physique, his
high spirits. They noted, too, that he brushed aside the
reception that had been prepared for him and went
straight to the Duke of Exeter's house, where he was to
spend the night.

That impressed them. This young man was in a
hurry. He had no use for empty show, he had sterner
business on his hands.

The men with him impressed them too. They had

heard plenty of rumours, they had been assiduously fed with propaganda these last few weeks, and those who could had fled with their wives and families, leaving their servants to be massacred by the savages from the north. Those who could not escape remained, waiting in fear and trembling for the awful things that were about to happen to them. Some even believed the stories that the Highlanders were cannibals and would eat their babies. Everyone was convinced that his wives and daughters would be raped, his house plundered and himself probably murdered. The Hanoverian government, which had introduced the art of propaganda into its efforts to discredit the Stuarts, had plied its propaganda well.

The men dispersed to their billets. Terrified householders bowed obsequiously before them, grovelling in their eagerness to placate these strange outlandish people, and the puzzled Highlanders, mildly asking for bread and cheese, took bundles of straw to make their beds on the floor. They smiled, they made friendly gestures, the few who knew a little English tried to talk to their unwilling hosts, and, as they sat down to their bread and cheese, they took off their bonnets and raised their eyes devoutly and murmured their Gaelic grace.

This was too much for the gravity of at least one English gentleman. The idea of savages saying grace seemed to him wonderfully comical. Other gentlemen wrote—afterwards, when they had got their courage back—what they thought of the Prince and his army—" like so many fiends turned out of Hell to ravage the Kingdom," said one, quite ignoring the fact that these same fiends behaved with perfect civility and courtesy and injured no one.

The cavalry, said another, were " fierce and desperate ruffians," and the clansmen " a parcel of shabby, lousy, pitiful-looking fellows, mixed up with old men and boys, dressed in dirty plaids and as dirty shirts, without breeches and wore their stockings made of plaid not

much above half-way up their legs, and some without
shoes or next to none, and numbers of them so fatigued
with their long march that they really commanded our
pity more than fear."

Mr. Henry Bracken of Warrington described them in
a despatch to the government in London as a most
despicable crew, undersized, of a wan and meagre
countenance, stumbling along as though hardly able to
bear the weight of their weapons ; he forgot to explain
how it was that these same men had outmarched and
outmanœuvred three English generals, had smashed one
English army in less than ten minutes, had captured
several important English towns and got within 127
miles of London in spite of being out-numbered by more
than six to one.

As for their behaviour in Derby, the worst crimes
that their enemies were able to allege against them were
that one of the " fierce and desperate ruffians " had
commandeered " a very good horse belonging to young
Mr. Stanford," while a few of the lousy, pitiful-looking
fellows had stopped well-shod citizens on the street and
made them change shoes with them ! As for the women-
folk of Derby, they were treated with a courtesy and
respect that must have been a new experience in their
lives, and the bread and cheese that the Highlanders
asked for after their long hard march can hardly have
put a strain on any larder.

Meantime, news of their appearance in Derby was
travelling south, and consternation and terror travelled
with it. In London the reaction was what might have
been expected. There was immediate panic, a rush on
the bank, a vast trek of scared citizens out to the south—
a trek given impetus by the example of the most
prominent citizens, who promptly retired to their country
houses.

The government, astute as ever, directed the feelings
of the mob. This was no Jacobite movement, it was
something much more alarming than that—the Scots

were invading England ! All the shops put up their shutters, the trained bands paraded through the streets, the Archbishop of Canterbury composed a special prayer for the occasion, and the King, who had chosen to adopt an attitude of contemptuous indifference in public, privately gave orders for his yacht to be got ready at Tower Pier to carry him and all his belongings to safety.

The newspapers, developing their traditional style in propaganda, clamoured unanimously a single slogan, as newspapers have always done since. On this occasion it was, " No Popery, no arbitrary power ! " It would, of course, have been high treason to mention the fact that the Prince and his father had given categorical assurances of religious tolerances and constitutional government, or that Charles, while in Scotland, had attended the Protestant church. Misrepresentation being the life-blood of politics, the truth must be excluded.

Charles and the majority of his supporters—particularly the Highland chiefs—were a century behind the times. They were an anachronism, and as such doomed to extinction ; they still believed in honour, clemency and fair dealing.

§

Charles sat near the window of his room, awaiting the arrival of the council of war he had called. It was the morning of Thursday, the 5th of December, and, thoroughly refreshed by a sound sleep and a hearty breakfast, he was in the highest spirits.

The future lay open and assured. It had been a long hard road, a road that had demanded all his determination, his diplomacy and tact, his enthusiasm and boyish eagerness. It had made, too, the sternest demands upon his own physical powers.

Since leaving Edinburgh, he had walked every inch of the road, marching at the head of the clans. He had waded through rivers, stumbled through mud and marsh, toiled over mountains in deep snow, and he had never once shown fatigue or distress. He had kept himself in magnificent physical condition, setting an example to his Highlanders which they readily understood and appreciated. He had been strictly abstemious, so that the wine bills—which have been preserved—are the most modest ever known in the history of an army's march. He ate nothing all day while on the march, seldom touched spirits.

In just over four weeks he had brought his army to within 130 miles of London—less, in fact, since he had sent off an advance party along the London road to take possession of Swarkstone Bridge, six miles beyond Derby. The Highlanders, travelling with their usual speed, had got there in time to prevent its destruction, and so were in possession of it with a free road thence to London.

The only obstacle on the way was Cumberland. The levies encamped on Finchley Common could be disregarded—they would disappear like a morning mist in summer sunshine long before the Highland army came to grips with them. Cumberland was the real danger. But Cumberland had been outwitted. He was even now sitting stolidly at Lichfield, hopelessly deceived by Lord George Murray's brilliant move, and it was an absolute certainty that however fast he might march the Highlanders could reach London a clear day ahead of him.

And to reach London was to achieve complete and final victory. Charles could guess, accurately enough, the effect upon London of the news of his entry into Derby. That news did not, in fact, reach the capital until the following day, which went down in history as Black Friday because of the pandemonium and panic that marked it, but Charles knew enough, and had seen enough already, to believe that his appearance in London would produce the same reaction as elsewhere—obsequious citizens hastening to declare their submission, militiamen hurrying to get rid of their arms before they were called upon to use them, and the regular troops floundering far in the rear.

In London Jacobitism was strong. In London the Prince would find many powerful adherents and little opposition, with the government paralysed, the king fled, and many leading noblemen aligned on his side. But how far his view was correct can only be a matter for conjecture. The government, by representing the affair as a Scots invasion, by spreading the wildest rumours about the Highland army, knowing that a gullible populace would swallow the most fantastic and blood-curdling tales, had inflamed public feeling to such a pitch that anything might have happened.

Yet to Charles the situation was crystal clear. By a magnificent feat of physical and mental exertion he had reached Derby ; in less than a fortnight he could be in London. That fortnight's march was a mere matter of routine ; and, travelling as he had always done with the troops, mixing with his soldiers, supping and often sleeping among them, he knew their temper. They were fired with a zeal that matched his own. They talked now only of London, that great city so much more huge than anything they had ever seen, so rich, so wonderful. They saw themselves swinging to the music of the pipes through the thronged streets of London, guarding their Prince and setting him firmly in St. James's. They saw victory within their grasp, and even now, sitting near the window, he could hear their excited voices as they crowded outside the doors of all the cutlers' shops, taking their turns to have their claymores and dirks sharpened, even quarrelling over matters of precedence on such an important occasion.

Pipers strutted in the streets of Derby. Singing men gathered in groups, collected outside the Prince's head-quarters and cheered and cheered. Never had an army been in such high fettle, never surer of victory. Charles, listening to them, smiled to himself and made up his mind. He would go and meet his cousin Cumberland.

He had no trace of doubt of the result. The Duke might have at his command overwhelming superiority of numbers. He had not the one thing vital to victory— the *élan*, the spirit of the Highlanders. It would carry them through the ranks of the redcoats like a scythe through corn ripe for the cutting ; and in that Charles no way exaggerated.

His officers began to arrive.

At the back of his mind there had been a faint uneasiness, a sense of being cut off from these men by some secret barrier. He had noted their glum looks, their lack of elation at their success. Now, seeing one gloomy face after another as the council of war filed into the room, he felt a sudden chill.

Lord George Murray, who had carried out that manœuvre against Cumberland with such dash and skill ; the gallant Duke of Perth, simple hearted, direct and brave as a lion ; young Lord Elcho with his slightly supercilious silences ; the gentle Lochiel, grave and care-worn ; Keppoch, fiery and proud ; MacPherson of Cluny burning with zeal and loyalty now that he had thrown in his lot with his Prince ; Mr. Secretary Murray, looking uncomfortable and distraught ; Sheridan and O'Sullivan failing to meet his eyes as they took their places. . . . Charles sat up with a jerk and surveyed them keenly.

Lord George Murray rose. "Gentlemen," he said gravely, "I can only advocate an immediate retreat."

Thunderstruck, the Prince stared at him, listening to his voice droning on, stating his reasons deliberately, flatly, and evenly.

" In spite of our success in every action, and the ease with which we have penetrated so far into England, our moral failure has been complete. We confidently expected an enthusiastic reception in the south, and a great increase of our strength. The response has been negligible. The Manchester Regiment—that is all that we have gained. Not upwards of three hundred men.

True, we might easily reach London before the Duke of Cumberland, but he is to-day reported to be at Stafford and will follow close upon our heels. We should have at most a single day in London before he came up with us. Then everything would depend upon the London mob. What evidence have we of their support ? The people in every other town have been completely apathetic. If the mob was against the affair, 4,500 men would not make a great figure in London. But thirty thousand regular troops, well trained and experienced in war, would be converging upon us from all sides. We should be hopelessly trapped, and not a man among us would escape."

He looked from face to face and Charles, a spark of anger kindling in his eyes, also looked around, and felt the chill that had gripped him turn his heart to ice.

" In fact," Lord George concluded, " I am in some doubt of our ability to break into London at all, and my conclusion is that we should go back and join our friends in Scotland, and live and die with them."

Through the open window came the sound of voices, of the pipes, of men laughing and singing. Confident and elated, they awaited the order to march. They hoped it would be against the Duke of Cumberland, so that once more they could show the redcoats what a Highland army could do to the best disciplined mercenaries in the world. But at least they took it for granted that the order would be to march to the south, to march on London. And here, in this room, at this moment their general advocated ignominious retreat. . . .

The Prince sat listening. What did Lord George Murray, or any of these officers, know of his army? He knew them. He had lived with them, learnt their language, talked with them every day, marched with them, shared all their hardships, their privations, their successes. They would follow him, through fire and flood to the very gates of hell. They would follow him to London. But . . .

" The Scots," declared Lord George, significantly, " have now done all that could be expected of them."

He sat down ; and Charles roused himself. He turned to the Duke of Perth and demanded his opinion. The Duke concurred with Lord George. He turned to Lochiel. The chief lowered his eyes and nodded. He too agreed. One by one the council gave their opinions—and these opinions were unanimous. Charles began to realise the truth. This was no spontaneous meeting. This had been arranged. Behind his back, while he talked to the men and the junior officers, his senior officers had been meeting and talking among themselves. They had come to an agreement. For once, for the first time, they felt alike, there was no dissentient voice, no argument.

" Sir Thomas Sheridan ? " he said sharply.

Sheridan, avoiding his eyes, nodded his head also.

" General O'Sullivan ? "

He too, averting his glance, nodded. Charles rose.

He began to speak, and as he spoke emotion seized him, words poured from his lips in a growing flood. He turned upon one after another, rallying them, railing at them. With flashing eyes he challenged them to uphold their manhood and live up to their faith.

" As my cause is just, it will prevail ! " he cried passionately. " How can men confront us ? Was our victory won by the broadsword alone ? No British troops will fight against their rightful Prince. When the moment comes, there will be large defections, and my cousin will find only his foreign mercenaries to support him. And how could they withstand the claymores of the clans ? "

But Lord George interposed.

" We are few, our enemies many. If we meet Cumberland and—as I do not doubt we should—defeat him utterly, we shall then have to face about and meet Marshal Wade, with more than 10,000 men under his command. Even if our losses in a pitched battle against the Duke were in proportion, we should count on losing perhaps a thousand men. How can an army of our size survive so heavy a loss? Our victory would be our complete undoing. Besides, Lord John Drummond has lately landed in Scotland from France, with his own Royal Scots and the pick of all the Irish regiments, fifty men from each. France will send other forces soon, may even plan a descent upon the coast of England. But if we are cut off our cause is lost. Your royal highness's person is essential for success."

Charles rounded on him, blazing.

" I have never counted my personal safety for a single moment ! "

" That is well known, your royal highness. But there is a price upon your head. Your capture means your death—and the end of all our hopes. If we go on now, we leave our enemies in control of our rear, our retreat is cut off, we have no escape . . . "

The Prince burst into another passionate plea, his voice shaking with emotion as he brought up every argument his tortured mind could conceive, for he was fighting for something more than mere existence.

He could feel that his words were taking effect, that the downcast eyes were filled with anguish and shame. They had marched with him, fought with him, triumphed with him. Surely they could not desert him now !

But there was no question of desertion ; only the cold hard logic of fact, the bitter certainty of failure ahead. It was not these men who were deserting him ; they had done all they could, they had done infinitely more than any of them had believed possible, without assistance from anyone else. If they failed, it was because they had no friends in the south, the English Jacobites had betrayed them utterly, either by their promises or by the falsely optimistic reports they had sent to him in France.

The Duke of Perth, that simple-hearted, direct soul, listened to his impassioned arguments and gave way.

His voice at least was raised in support ; but however well liked he might be he carried little weight, and the council remained unshaken.

They rose, and one by one they left the room, left the Prince sitting by the window, abject and alone among the ruins of his hopes. He had no illusions now about the future. Some of his officers might suppose that all was not yet lost, that in Scotland they could hold out until the tide changed ; not so the Prince. It was now or never, all or nothing with him, and the urgency that had driven him on since boyhood, that had made possible the magnificent feat he had performed, convinced him that he faced the ruin of all that life held for him.

He sat by the window, listening to the cheerful clamour of his army in the street, hearing nothing of it, hearing only the voice that reiterated in his mind the cold and bitter truth—" All is lost."

§

Sir John MacDonald, the Irishman, had dined heartily. He was, like several of the Men of Moidart, an old man, and a fiery one. Walking, perhaps a little unsteadily, out of the dining-room he encountered three men, standing together in a group, talking in low, wretched voices. They were Lord George Murray, Lochiel and Keppoch.

At sight of them his anger flared up, and he came over. He looked Lord George in the eye.

" Retreat ! " he exclaimed. " Retreat when success is in our grasp, when London lies open to us ! Retreat ! It is damnable heresy. It is rank cowardice, it is the act of craven men ! "

Silenced, the three made no reply. Perhaps they respected his age, perhaps they had no desire to quarrel with a man in his cups. But Sir John was not finished with them. He turned and buttonholed Keppoch.

" What," he shouted. " A MacDonald turn his back ! " He swung towards Lochiel.

" For shame ! " he cried. " A Cameron run away from his enemy ! Go forward, gentlemen—and I'll lead you ! "

They hung their heads. There was nothing to say ; but Lord George reflected that Sir John held a commission in the French army, that he had only to surrender to the English to be sure of honourable treatment as a prisoner of war. Theirs was a different case. They could only be certain of being hanged for treason.

Sir John turned about and marched away in disgust, knowing well that he voiced the opinion of the whole army, the men in the ranks and all their junior officers, who as yet knew nothing of the council's decision.

Another of the Seven Men of Moidart had yet to hear of it—old Tullibardine, who had been too ill to attend the council. When he learnt what had been decided he was stunned and shocked. Then he rose in fury, declaring he would never agree. But the others, crowding round him, urged their arguments afresh, and could thank his illness, in the end, for their victory over his spirit. But they had to plead long before he would give way.

Charles read his latest despatches, his heart contracting with pain and misery and a helpless rage. Lord John Drummond had eight hundred picked troops with him in Scotland—and precise orders from Louis XV forbidding him to cross the border into England until all strong points in his rear had been reduced.

George Kelly—that other of the Seven Men—wrote from France. Large reinforcements were being got ready, would soon sail. Prince Henry expected shortly to be at Calais to superintend the embarkation. Great things were planned. " But," added Kelly earnestly, " I wish you may be able to stand your ground, since a retreat must be fatal."

How well Charles realised that ! But the affair was out of his hands. He had no authority to issue orders to the army that was, he knew, heart and soul his own.

He glanced up as a servant announced two visitors—
Murray of Broughton and Sir Thomas Sheridan. They
came together on the same errand.

"Your royal highness, we wish to say that we have
changed our minds. We have seen how wrong we were.
We voted for the retreat only because it seemed to us that
with the Scots officers so opposed to an advance there
could be no hope of success. But we feel as you do, that
retreat will be fatal and that we should go on . . ."

Charles looked at them both ; but there was no spark
of warmth in his eyes now, no welcome for this change
of tune. He had seen through them both at last. He
remembered how eagerly they had advocated retreat,
how convinced they had been in that opinion, how
plausible and eloquent. He could value their change of
heart at its true worth. They sought only to ingratiate
themselves, so that, if disaster came, they could repudiate
any blame for it.

"Thank you, gentlemen," he said quietly, and
dismissed them.

But he did more than that. He summoned Lord
George and the others again. He proposed a march
into Wales, where all were agreed he would find great
support. Cumberland—all England, in fact—feared just
that, and assumed he would march in that direction, and
descend upon England again with an army doubled in
strength—and almost exclusively Celtic in character, an
army whose moves would be unpredictable and whose
passionate zeal would make light of overwhelming
enemy strength.

The council refused to consider the project, and Charles
then declared that the council was no longer unanimous,
that certain gentlemen at least felt as he did. Lord
George put a stop to that.

"Let those who disagree with us put their disagreement in writing," he said sharply, "and we shall then
discuss their proposals."

Sheridan and Murray of Broughton, seeing their bluff

called, remained silent, and dropped their eyes before the
Prince's contemptuous glance.

Charles made a gesture of finality.

"Very well," he said. "I withdraw my opposition to
the council's decision. The march northwards may
begin to-morrow."

Lord George spoke up.

"Then, sir, may I offer to command the rearguard
in person, at least as far as Carlisle?"

The Prince accepted the offer. He knew that it was the
only hope he had of keeping his army intact. Whatever
he thought of Lord George, he did not doubt his super-
lative ability.

The council broke up. Charles shut himself in his own
apartments and saw no one for the remainder of the
day. Let his staff deal with routine matters, with all
the detail of this retreat that had been forced upon him.
He had no heart for that work. He had played his great
gamble. He knew now that he had lost.

CHAPTER THIRTEEN

NORTHWARDS

THE ARMY was astir before dawn.

The men filled their haversacks, looked to their weapons, fell into their ranks. An issue of powder and ball was made, and spirits rose with a bound. They were going to meet the enemy at last ! Laughing, excited, exultant, they formed their ranks and never questioned when the order to march was given. In the darkness, the citizens of Derby awoke to the steady tramp of marching feet, peered out of their windows to behold an army on the move, keyed up and itching to fight.

A body of horse, under orders from Lord George, clattered off in the direction of Swarkstone Bridge, which was still held by a party of Highlanders. They galloped over the bridge and made towards Lichfield. But the army, all sense of direction lost in the streets of Derby, swung out on the road to the north and did not guess whither it was bound.

Dawn came, with a soft lightening of the heavy darkness. Keen eyes began peering about, and presently a man touched his neighbour.

" That clump of trees," he said. " I have seen it before."

Others looked. They recognised here a house, there a wall or a plantation, a bend in the road, a hollow or hill.

They looked at each other in blank amazement ; and then the word ran down the files, and startled eyes questioned each other, uncertain voices called to the junior officers.

Where are we going? Why are we back on this road? Why are we marching *north* ? And the junior officers, knowing nothing, could only echo the bewilderment of their men.

Now a murmur rose from the great host, cries broke out, men shouted at the senior officers. Tell us where we are going ! Tell us why we are marching north !

There was no response ; and the singing that had lightened their steps, the piping that had put a spring to their strides were silenced. A moaning like that of a wounded beast swelled from the marching ranks, and a rage of frustration laid hold upon them. Tears poured down bearded faces, heads hung dejectedly, feet dragged in the dust as they went on and on. All the gaiety, the high spirits, the elation and the *élan* had departed. Bewildered, confused and wretched the clansmen marched, with anger growing in their hearts, and shame, and bitter despair. Never before had they been asked to turn their backs upon their enemies. Never before had the honour of the clans been thus sullied. They would have died gladly, gone to their deaths singing, against the most impossible odds, if they had been allowed to advance. But to retreat—it was worse than death.

The rearguard waited, outside the Prince's head-quarters. The army had already had more than three hours' start, yet there was no sign of the Prince. Sitting their horses, glancing sometimes nervously towards the south, looking about the streets and wondering just how much the citizens of Derby understood of the situation, they curbed their impatience and wished that he would come.

At last, through the open door, they saw him striding. No longer was he the gallant youth in Highland dress whom they adored. Here was a man bitter and withdrawn and silent, in riding kit, who glanced at them briefly without a smile, without a greeting, threw himself upon his horse and rode away. They fell in behind him.

He rode swiftly. Soon he had overtaken the straggling rear of the army, an army defeated not in battle but in the council chamber. He pushed past, rode on without turning his head. The clansmen lifted their faces, longing for some sign, some word of hope. He rode past in silence, chin on breast.

He did not draw rein until he had reached the van, and fell in there to ride alone. None dared to speak to him, to go near him, and when he rode into Ashbourne he sought his quarters and shut himself up in his own room, making it clear that he desired no conversation with anyone.

§

Leek, Macclesfield, Stockport, Manchester—the familiar names succeeded each other as in a dream. The men marched sullenly, in silence, with the scuffling of dejected feet instead of the steady tramp of an army marching with a springy stride and heads held high ; and, emerging from his quarters each morning hours after the march had begun, the Prince would spur past the trudging columns to the van, and speak to no one.

There had been rioting in Manchester. Believing that the Highlanders had been defeated by Cumberland, crowds of people collected in the streets, armed and ready to deal with the fleeing remnants. But at sight of the van, still preserving order in spite of its dejection, the mob dispersed at once. Fortunately for Manchester, the citizens had more wisdom than they had bravado ; for with the army in its present temper, if it had found sudden relief in action the result must have been a massacre. As it was, the Highlanders occupied Manchester once more without fuss or incident.

It was given out that reinforcements collected in

Scotland were on their way south, and that the army was marching to effect a junction, which might take place at Preston or Lancaster. Spirits rose at once ; but the retreat still seemed inexplicable, and an air of sullen suspicion and grief hung over the trudging columns of men.

As the Highlanders went north—gaining a two-days' start on Cumberland by Lord George's skilful moves—news of the retreat began to travel south. It reached the Duke at Lichfield, and he promptly put himself at the head of a thousand cavalry and mounted infantry to start pursuit. It reached London, and Black Friday in reverse followed. Men who have been badly scared are always ready to bluster when the tables are turned—and London had been badly scared, from king to commoner. Instantly there was an outcry for the bloodiest reprisals, and a savage hatred for the men who had thus terrified them—at a distance of 127 miles—received fresh impetus from the politicians. Horace Walpole, who had been scared almost to the point of clearing out of his town house, gave the lead : " Can rigour be ill-placed against banditti, who have so terrified, pillaged, and injured the poor people in Cumberland, Lancashire, Derbyshire, and the counties through which this rebellion has stalked ? " A horse commandeered, a few citizens compelled to change shoes, some bread and cheese to eat and bundles of straw to lie on . . . it was a strange sort of pillage that Mr. Walpole described. But a frightened man is an angry man.

London, thirsting for vengeance, already began to savour triumph. Cumberland was close on the Prince's heels with nearly twice his strength ; Wade, with more than three times the rebel army, had only to make a swift march westwards to cut off their retreat. Together, these two commanders had in the field almost as many cavalry as Charles had soldiers. It could only be a matter of days before the rebels were brought to a halt and cut to pieces.

But they reckoned without Lord George Murray. He had outwitted Cumberland and so had gained a two-days' start ; he had given Wade the impression that he had plenty of time—and Wade had moved too slowly. His cavalry entered Doncaster on the 8th of December, and the aged Marshal himself reached Wakefield two days later—only to realise that he was far too late ; so he sent his cavalry off to join Cumberland's, and retired to Newcastle.

As Charles came into Manchester, Lord Elcho, commanding the advance guard, waited to speak to him. He had found a young soldier of the vanguard lying murdered in the road, and in a cottage nearby a woman and her son hiding, with their garments stained with blood. It was as clear a case of murder as could be found. Plainly there should be a summary trial, and the hanging of the murderers. But Charles, rousing himself from his apathy, frowned and shook his head.

" The evidence is not conclusive enough," he said shortly. " I cannot agree."

The murderous pair were allowed to go.

In the forenoon on the 10th the army marched again, reaching Wigan that night. As they were leaving Manchester a shot rang out. The bullet whistled close to O'Sullivan's head, and some of the life-guards rushed forward and seized the man who had fired the shot. He was a Whig fanatic who had mistaken the Irishman for Charles.

The Prince spoke sternly.

" No one has been hit. There must be no reprisals. Let the fellow go."

They grumbled ; but they obeyed. His magnanimity, always so marked, argued a dangerous indifference to his own safety that troubled them. But they respected his wishes.

Gradually, on the long road north, a new change came over the army. Lord George had had to order one officer of each regiment to remain with the rear-guard, in order to whip up stragglers ; but as the countryside became more hostile there was no longer need for this. It was dangerous to fall behind, and presently the High-landers, footsore and weary, began commandeering horses to help them on their way. They took them from the plough, and often as many as three or four Highlanders would bestride one of these plodding patient sturdy animals.

The whole of the 12th of December was spent at Preston, from which Charles sent the Duke of Perth ahead with 100 horse to meet the reinforcements that were expected from the north. Next day the army was back in Lancaster, and Lord George, going to his quarters, discovered that the Prince had given orders to halt there the whole of the next day. Alarmed, he went to see Charles early next morning.

Charles greeted him with a quiet obstinacy.

" I have resolved to stand and fight my cousin," he said simply. " I desire you and General O'Sullivan to reconnoitre the ground and choose a field of battle."

Murray of Broughton, who had been one of those to advise the Prince to this step, sat watching Lord George's face, waiting for him to raise the expected protest. It did not come.

" Then, sir," Lord George said immediately, " as the ground suitable for regular troops might not answer so well for the Highlanders, may I suggest that some Highland officers should also inspect the field ? Lochiel, will you accompany us ? "

The chief complied immediately, and, with an escort of cavalry, they rode out. Two miles south they found the ideal ground—and also a body of the enemy's scouts. The escort, clapping spurs to their mounts, rode forward and succeeded in cutting out three of these, whom they took prisoner and brought back to Lancaster.

Lord George interrogated them. The corps they belonged to, the Rangers, was at Garstang ; a great body of Wade's dragoons had left Preston a few hours after the Prince, and must now be very close. Lord George interviewed the Prince.

" If our numbers are sufficient, sir, I could not want a better field than the one we have found."

Charles looked up gloomily.

" I have changed my mind," he said abruptly. " We shall continue the retreat."

Lord George, biting his lip, felt that here indeed was a great change. The Prince they had always had to restrain was now the one to apply restraint. He went out, saddened and upset, to make arrangements, and on the morning of the 15th the retreat continued. The rear of the army was scarcely clear of the town when the bells were heard ringing and the mob huzza-ing as Wade's horse rode in. Word was passed forward, and the retreat was halted, the Highlanders forming in order of battle and suddenly galvanised by the prospect of striking a blow at last.

But the dragoons remained where they were. They had no mind to meet an enemy who turned at bay.

§

Lord George Murray found his troubles increasing rapidly. At Kendal he went to talk to the Prince, but found he had already retired, and so had to content himself with O'Sullivan instead. To him he explained that the carriages must be replaced with two-wheeled carts, that the whole army must be issued with a ration of bread and cheese for the long hard march over Shap, and the Quarter-Master General heartily agreed. But he sat on over his bottle of Malaga and made no move to give the necessary orders, and in the morning it was clear that no orders had been given. The staff officers, who had done their work well enough before, had lost all interest in the job. They were all of Murray of Broughton's choosing, and Lord George could do no more than protest.

Confusion spread through what had been an orderly, well conducted retreat. Ammunition waggons broke down, and the rearguard—on this occasion the Glengarry men—had to spend the night on the highroad in drenching rain. Never the most patient of mortals, they yet did all they could, and Lord George said afterwards that he " never was better pleased with men in his life."

Next day the main body reached Penrith, last lap before Carlisle ; but the rearguard and artillery could struggle no further than Shap. Moving out of Shap next morning, Lord George could see troop after troop of Cumberland's dragoons and mounted infantry riding two abreast against the skyline in the hills ahead. They had been cut off ! The rattle of kettledrums and the blare of trumpets gave the impression that Cumberland's whole force was coming up, and Lord George paused, irresolute.

Before he could make up his mind what to do, one of the officers of Lally's Regiment, Col. Brown, drew his sword and ran up the hill towards the enemy ; the regiment rushed after him, and Lord George signalled to the Glengarry men.

The claymores leapt from their scabbards, and the nimble-footed Highlanders, outstripping Lally's men, went racing up the hill and over the crest. They swept towards the enemy, to find only a small body of English light horse who promptly wheeled and galloped for their lives. Their gallant kettledrums and trumpets had very nearly been the death of them.

The march went on ; but suddenly there was a clatter and a shouting and two thousand of Cumberland's cavalry came thundering down upon the MacDonalds, who still brought up the rear. The Highlanders scattered behind the hedges and ditches and, as the horsemen came up, went in among them with their swords. It was an affair of moments ; the attack was repulsed, then the MacDonalds raced down the road to the waggons, turned again, and repulsed another charge. Again and again the dragoons, far outnumbering the clansmen, charged upon them as they retreated ; again and again the MacDonalds hurled them back, and so reached Clifton, two miles from Penrith, with scarcely any loss.

But now Lord George, looking back, could see a great body of mounted men drawn up on Clifton Moor, the local light horse in their green uniforms, Cumberland's dragoons and mounted infantry in scarlet. He sent a runner forward to Penrith, and Charles promptly sent back the MacPhersons, Stuarts of Appin, and Colonel Roy Stuart's Lowland Regiment. Thus reinforced, Lord George awaited the enemy's attack.

The ground was broken up by hedges and ditches, preventing a cavalry charge ; but Cumberland sent five hundred men, dismounted, and came forward in skirmishing order from hedge to hedge, keeping up an irregular fire as they came. Roy Stuart's regiment lay astride of the road with the Appin men on their left and the MacPhersons beyond them, while the Glengarry men held the right of the road. Lord George gave the order to hold their fire, allowing the enemy to creep closer and closer, emboldened by the superiority of their own fire. The light was failing, and as the dragoons found it increasingly difficult to see their sights they were suddenly electrified by a tremendous shout from both sides of the road. Lord George had given the order to charge.

Leaping the hedges, the Highlanders rushed forward and were on top of the dragoons in a moment. The claymores plied briskly, and the dragoons, breaking immediately, turned and ran. Lord George called his men back to their defensive line, and sat down to wait for darkness ; then, quietly, he carried out an orderly withdrawal undetected, for by then the baggage and artillery had got a good start on the Carlisle road.

They entered Carlisle on the 19th of December, a month all but one day from the time when they had marched out of Carlisle on the road to London.

§

Charles, waking up on the morning of the 20th, felt a sudden lift of his spirits. It was his birthday* ; to-day he was twenty-five. He was in magnificent physical condition, he had an army, still intact, at his back, his rearguard had fought a small but brilliant action in which once again the claymore had triumphed. His depression fell off him like a discarded cloak.

The men around him felt the change. He made his appearance full of vigour and keenness, but the bitter experiences of these last few weeks had led him to make one definite decision. No more councils of war ! Hereafter he would make his own plans, decide what he was going to do, and interview his officers individually afterwards in order to bring them round to his views, or to listen to their objections.

One of his first decisions was to leave a garrison in Carlisle. It was, in the event, a tragic mistake, for it meant sacrificing four hundred men ; but at the moment it seemed wise to keep a spring-board from which to renew the invasion of England. He did not doubt for a moment that this invasion would take place.

At Carlisle he had found letters waiting for him. They were of rather old date, but the news they contained was heartening. Lord John Drummond reported on his arrival from France with his own Royal Scots and the Irish pickets, and a train of artillery and engineers. He mentioned that King Louis was extremely anxious that the Prince should proceed with caution and avoid a pitched battle until the succours being prepared for him could arrive. These reinforcements, King Louis declared, would put the matter beyond doubt.

Lord Strathallan wrote that he had assembled a fresh army at Perth outnumbering the force Charles had with him, and in the highest spirits. It seemed simple

* Old style. By new style reckoning, Dec. 31st.

commonsense, therefore, to continue the retreat and join forces with these powerful additions to his strength.

He flung himself into the work with all the old vigour and enthusiasm, and by two o'clock in the afternoon the army had reached the Esk, on the Scots border. The river, usually quite shallow at the ford, was in spate, and rising rapidly. It would be dangerous to delay. A horseman, splashing in, found the water four feet deep over the ford.

Charles gave his orders. A body of cavalry was sent into the river above the ford, to break the force of the rushing water, while another body waded in and took station below, ready to rescue any of the infantry who got into difficulties. Charles himself went with this party. A few Jacobite ladies accompanying the army from Carlisle were the first to ride across the ford ; then the Highlanders waded in.

They came a hundred abreast, each man holding firmly to the collar of his neighbour, with Lord George Murray, in his kilt, at the head of the line. Soon there were as many as two thousand men in the water at one time, most of them up to their necks ; and as they scrambled out on the far bank the pipers struck up and the whole army began dancing reels to dry themselves :

> The Esk was swollen sae broad and deep,
> But shouther to shouther the brave lads keep ;
> Twa thoosand swam ower frae fell English ground,
> And danced themselves dry to the pibroch's sound !

> *Wi' a hundred pipers and a', and a',*
> *Wi' a hundred pipers and a',*
> *We'll up and gie them a blaw, a blaw,*
> *Wi' a hundred pipers and a' !*

Men lost their footing and were swept away ; but the horsemen were waiting for them, and seized hold of them and drew them safely ashore. The Prince himself,

seeing one man in difficulties, edged his horse over and, leaning down, snatched at him as he swirled past. He caught him by the hair, held on, and shouted in Gaelic—in itself sufficient indication of his presence of mind : " *Cobhear! Cobhear!* " (Help ! Help !) and another horseman forced his way against the stream to lend a hand.

Another Highlander, swimming desperately after he had lost his footing, came within reach, and Charles, getting a grip of him, dragged him up behind him on his horse and brought him safely over, the bedraggled soldier clinging to his waist. When he reached the bank, he was in time to help a third, who was crawling ashore exhausted, and him he picked up and placed in his own chair, which no one but himself had dared to use, since it was the King's chair.

Charles was happy again. He had re-established contact with the men he understood and loved—his loyal Highlanders ; and presently the whole army was over into Scotland, without a single loss.

§

Once more the army was split into its customary divisions, and set off on its march for Glasgow. But there was a marked difference now. The country they were passing through was not merely Whig ; it was

Covenanter country, with grim and bitter memories of Charles's ancestors, and in place of sullen indifference or frightened obsequiousness he met now only dour silence, glowering faces, and active hostility. It was a party of volunteers from Dumfries who had cut off his baggage train on his march south, so in Dumfries he gave peremptory orders to the provost, Mr. Crosbie. Dumfries would have to pay a fine of £2,000 for that exploit, and also supply 1,000 pairs of shoes. But only £1,000 was forthcoming, and Charles, who had no mind to linger here, simply carried off the provost and another prominent citizen, Walter Riddel, as surety for the remainder.

On the way north he slept overnight at the Duke of Queensberry's house Drumlanrig, at Douglas Castle, and at the Duke of Hamilton's palace ; and now, with Glasgow so near at hand, he decided suddenly to take a day off. He had almost forgotten his favourite pastime ; so for this one day he took his shotgun and, laying all care aside, enjoyed himself wholeheartedly for the first time since leaving Italy.

" He behaved," says Daniel, one of the very few Englishmen to join him in the south, " to the admiration and surprise of all present, killing or hitting everything he shot at, so that, without flattery, he was looked upon as the best marksman in the Army."

It must have done his spirits an infinite deal of good.

Next day, the 26th, Glasgow was occupied, and in the evening the Prince marched in at the head of the clans. His first care, in this great Whig city, was for his men, and he immediately summoned the provost, Mr. Buchanan, and ordered him to provide 12,000 linen shirts, 6,000 cloth coats, 6,000 pairs of stockings, 6,000 waistcoats and shoes and blue bonnets. As the city had raised volunteers to fight against him, he demanded a list of the subscribers; but Buchanan replied with spirit.

" Not one name will I give you, sir, except my own.

I was the largest subscriber, because I considered it my plain duty. You may do with me as you will."

Charles fined him £500 and left it at that.

He had taken up his quarters in a mansion belonging to a Mr. Glassford, situated near where the Trongate now stands, and here he dined twice a day in public, wearing the Highland dress and waited upon by some Jacobite ladies ; for although Glasgow was wholly Whig there were, as the Provost complained, certain ladies of Jacobite sympathies temporarily visiting the city.

One of these was Miss Clementina Walkinshaw, whose father had a town house at Shawfield. She came to pay her respects, and Charles, greeting her with his customary courtesy, felt a strange lift of his spirits as they smiled into each other's eyes. No woman had yet had the power to stir him ; but now he felt strangely drawn to this tall, plain girl with the quiet manner.

" I was born in Rome," she told him. " Your mother stood sponsor, and I was named after her. My father was your father's agent in Vienna at the time of the elopement. He helped the Chevalier Wogan. So you see . . ."

It was the first time his mother's name had been mentioned, the first time he had had any contact with her for a very long time. They talked of poor unhappy Clementina, of Rome, of life in exile ; and suddenly Charles knew that he had found a friend—someone who sought nothing of him but his friendship, who cherished no secret ambitions, who had no axe to grind.

It was a brief interlude in the stern business he was engaged upon ; but it had a lasting effect upon a young man who until then had been practically a misogynist.

Buoyant again, he determined to review his troops. No longer was there need to conceal the smallness of his numbers ; rather he felt inclined to display it to the whole world, so that people could see with how few men he had invaded England, thrown the country into a panic, and defied all the overwhelming forces brought against him.

So the Army was drawn up on Glasgow Green, and an amazing fact emerged. On the whole of the English expedition he had lost, in killed, in missing, and by desertion less than forty men ! Never had an army achieved such a feat, and indeed it had been a most amazing march, brilliantly planned, brilliantly executed ; had there been any strength in the repeated promises of the English Jacobites, it could not have failed to succeed.

But the populace of Glasgow, thronging to Glasgow Green to see the great parade, stood silent and unimpressed. Not a cheer was raised, not a face softened into a smile, not a handkerchief waved from a window. Charles, deeply mortified, declared that he had never seen a fairer city, and had never been in a place where he found fewer friends.

Glasgow provides an interesting sidelight on the Prince's habits, for the accounts of Gib, his master of household, show that no wine or spirits were ordered, and only four gallons of ale for the entire household during its week's stay. It was typical of an abstemiousness that was copied by his officers.

At Glasgow, too, Charles received some bad news.

Kinlochmoidart, journeying south to join the Highland army, had been seized at Lesmahagow by a party of local militia, and sent south to Carlisle, where—in fulfilment of his own prediction—he was summarily tried and hanged ; for Carlisle had fallen.

After a heroic resistance, Hamilton had been forced to surrender, and the gallant garrison received treatment very different from that which Charles had shown to the English garrison when he captured Carlisle. Most of the officers were sent south, and nine of them executed, while some of the soldiers were hanged forthwith.

It was tragic news, showing the Prince how badly he had blundered ; but he had clung to the hope of renewing the march on London. Now he must abandon that hope, and look forward only to a campaign in Scotland—unless France moved.

There was nothing to be gained by lingering in Glasgow ; but what was to be done ? He consulted his officers, and found many different opinions among them. But one opinion was strongest—that they should reduce the castles of Edinburgh and Stirling as soon as possible. Remembering the French siege artillery, remembering the French king's urgent orders to Lord John Drummond not to march south without taking every fort on his route, it seemed to Charles and his advisers politic to seize the two strongest points in all Scotland.

So on the 4th of January, 1746, the army marched again, and encamped near Bannockburn. There Charles made his headquarters at Bannockburn House, where that zealous Jacobite, Sir Hugh Paterson, was glad to entertain him again ; and Sir Hugh's niece, Clementina Walkinshaw, was among the guests.

On Sunday, the 5th, Stirling was surrounded, and called upon to capitulate. For a short time it held out, while the Highlanders and the French artillerymen were preparing the assault, and then, on Tuesday, the provost and councillors came to Bannockburn House to negotiate the surrender. The terms were generous—there should be no reprisals, no demands upon the town's revenues, and the town's arms should be sent into the Castle. Charles agreed, and next day the gates were opened and the Highlanders marched in. But the Castle held out.

§

The Prince reviewed his army again ; but it was no longer the gallant, tough little army that had marched to Derby and back. Nine thousand strong now, with ample reinforcements of fresh troops, it was drawn up on Plean Moor, two miles west of Bannockburn and only seven miles from Falkirk.

It was noon on the 17th of January. Charles, riding down the lines, saw that the regiments were drawn up, as always, in battle formation, and with full equipment. He turned to Lord George Murray with a smile.

" I said that there would be no more councils of war," he declared, cheerfully ; " but we will have one now."

It was called immediately, while the men remained in their ranks. But its deliberations were brief.

" Gentlemen," the Prince exclaimed, " the enemy is at hand. General Hawley has marched from Edinburgh with a force not over 2,000 more than our own. For us, these are simple odds. I have no doubt he proposes to attack us. I propose to attack him."

The council agreed enthusiastically, and Lord George, who had already drawn up battle plans, consulted with the Prince. A thousand men were left to maintain the siege of Stirling Castle ; back on the parade ground Charles, facing his troops, gave a simple order—not the " dismiss " they had expected.

" Right turn. Forward march ! "

The army moved off the parade ground—to battle.

Hawley had been sent to Scotland to replace the discredited Cope. He came full of confidence in his own ability and determined to lose no time in winning the laurels that had eluded his predecessor's grasp. He was typical of the army commander of the time, modelling himself upon the soldier princes of the German confederacy—ambitious, brutal, domineering, and coarse.

The Dutch troops in England had been recalled, since King Louis of France had made strong representations to Holland against their presence in England ; they were being replaced by 6,000 Hessians under King George's son-in-law, the Prince of Hesse himself, who had already sailed from Wilhelmstadt and were expected any day in the Firth of Forth. But Hawley refused to wait for this powerful reinforcement. He preferred to gain his laurels without their help.

His soldiers were mainly veterans, strengthened by Cobham's Regiment, newly returned from the Continent. He had no doubt of their ability to smash any Highland army to pieces at the first collision. His thirteen hundred cavalry alone could do that. So he prepared gibbets in Edinburgh for hanging the rebels who were going to fall into his hands, and marched forth with complete assurance, to deal with this wretched gang of ignorant mountaineers.

He had an initial setback that whetted his appetite for revenge and made him look forward all the more eagerly to using those gibbets. A vast quantity of stores had been collected at Linlithgow for the use of his troops— and the Prince had got to know about it. Lord George Murray left Falkirk at 4 a.m. on the 14th, with five battalions of the clans, raced to Linlithgow, and seized the stores. While the Highlanders were loading this rich booty into waggons word came that Hawley's cavalry was at hand. Lord George sallied out—and the cavalry retired at speed.

Hawley himself left Edinburgh that day, and installed himself at Callander House as the uninvited guest of the Countess of Kilmarnock. There news was brought that 1,000 Campbells had joined his army—and that the enemy had been sighted. Lord John Drummond, with a small body of horse and foot, had been sent to make the usual diversion while the army itself marched with its accustomed speed and secrecy to the chosen battle ground.

General Hawley was not impressed. But presently a countryman entered his lines with news that the Highlanders were almost upon them, and Lieut. Col. Howard galloped to Callander House with the news. Hawley grunted and told him to order the men to put on their accoutrements. He was still in no way impressed.

The Prince reached Dunipace, and so came out into the open to cross the River Carron. There was no longer room for doubt of what was happening, and another officer was sent for the General, now breakfasting in comfort with his unwilling hostess. Hawley, in sudden passion at this interruption, leapt up and strode out, flinging himself on to his horse in such haste that he left his hat behind. He would deal with these wretched Highlanders and their boy prince who played at soldiers !

He reached the scene in time to find that the Highlanders were already on the march on Falkirk Moor and making for the top of the hill. Instantly, without prospecting the ground, he ordered his dragoons up, and the infantry with fixed bayonets in support. The opposing sides raced to reach the heights. As they did so, halting within musket range of each other, a sudden change came over the scene. It had been a brilliant morning ; but now a storm blew up, and torrents of rain slanted down full in the faces of the dragoons. The Highlanders, peering through the thick weather, had wind and rain on their backs, and Lord George Murray, in command of the right wing, instantly realised the advantage. The army was drawn up in its usual formation, the first line, from right to left, consisting of the MacDonalds of Keppoch, Clanranald and Glengarry, the Farquharsons, the MacKenzies, Mackintoshes and Macphersons, the Frasers under the young Master of Lovat, the Stewarts of Appin, and the Camerons. The remainder of the army formed the second line, with the Prince twenty yards in the rear, in personal command of a body of horse and foot and joined presently by Lord John Drummond, who had returned from his successful feint.

So swift had been the march that the Prince's artillery was left far behind ; but, as it happened, this made no odds, for Hawley's had been hopelessly bogged at the foot of the hill and was useless.

Hawley, confident of his dragoons, gave the order to advance ; and almost simultaneously Lord George gave the same order. His scouts brought him word that

In a few minutes it was all over.

Hawley's infantry were not yet in position to support the dragoons—proof of the measure of their commander's supreme confidence—and Lord George took instant advantage of this oversight. He went down the lines himself, speaking to every company in turn.

" Hold your fire until I give the signal," he ordered, earnestly. " On no account open fire before me. When I fire, then deliver your volley."

The men understood, and Lord George, striding out in front of the line, waited calmly, with his target on his left arm to cover his body. The dragoons advanced. First a trot, then a canter, then full gallop—fifty yards, thirty yards, twenty yards. Still the Highland line remained silent. The dragoons, cheering, charged on. Fifteen yards. Lord George raised his musket deliberately and fired.

Instantly the shattering roar of the volley rippled along the line. The range was fifteen, even only ten yards. Horses plunged, riders were thrown, men fell. The charge was broken almost at the moment of impact. Desperately the dragoons reined in, wheeled, turned in a plunging screaming confusion of horses and men. A hundred fell at that first volley. Hamilton's and Ligonier's dragoons (formerly Gardiner's) suddenly reverted to form and galloped off. Only Cobham's, veterans as they were, pressed home their attack, and for a few minutes it was warm work as horsemen and clansmen became inextricably mingled.

No room now to wield the terrible claymore. The Highlanders threw themselves down, stabbed upwards with their dirks at the horses' bellies, leapt upon the riders as they were thrown. Others, seizing the dragoons by their clothes, pulled them from their horses and stabbed them as they fell. Clanranald, pinned under a fallen horse, saw one of his men struggling fiercely with a dragoon ; but the Highlander was the stronger, threw his antagonist and killed him before he could rise ; then he dashed over and dragged his chief clear.

The remnant of Cobham's dragoons, fighting their way out of the melee, set spurs to their horses ; but they had to ride the whole length of the front between the opposing armies in order to get clear, and many fell under the Highlanders' fire.

Through the drenching rain the clansmen saw the enemy infantry ahead of them now. It was too much for their discipline, and with wild shouts first one batch then another broke their ranks, and rushed forward to the attack. Lord George and their officers ran up and down ordering them back into their ranks, and the Keppoch men obeyed ; but it was too late to stop the others. They streamed downhill full in the face of Hawley's infantry.

One withering volley from the enemy, and the Highlanders, throwing away their own muskets, drew their claymores and charged. In a few minutes it was all over—as far as the right wing was concerned. The redcoats broke, turned, and ran from the field.

But out on the left wing one regiment stood firm, and in the midst of a scene of the wildest confusion a hard struggle went on. Where the Stewarts and Camerons had been able to get at their enemies they had crashed through them and sent them headlong in flight ; but at one point a wide ravine was interposed, and no charge was possible. For a short time an unequal musketry duel went on, but the Highlanders could not face the trained and experienced infantry, and were forced to give ground. The situation became acute.

The light was failing. The rain still poured down in blinding torrents, and the whole hillside was a swaying mass of men, inextricably mixed up, while in the distance MacDonalds and MacPhersons and Farquharsons raced after the running infantry, chasing them even into the streets of Falkirk. The Prince, advancing rapidly with his small force, wheeled past the ravine and found himself face to face with the still unbroken line of Hawley's right, who, unaware that their General had already galloped from the field, fought on convinced that victory was at hand.

Charles, displaying his standard, shouted to the Highlanders who straggled along the hillside, hopelessly lost and quite unaware of what was going on. As soon as they recognised him they flocked around him, and in a short time he had gathered a strong enough force.

" Forward ! " he cried, and the whole body advanced swiftly. At that moment Cobham's dragoons had rallied and were about to launch another charge. But at sight of the orderly ranks marching steadily towards them under the Prince's own orders they halted, began to retire. The infantry behind them retreated also, but in good order, and, in the increasing darkness, Charles had no need to order a charge. The field was left to him.

Jubilant, he sought out his officers. But they were scattered everywhere. Lord George Murray, who had now only 600 men with him, came down the hill seeking news, furious that he had not the strength to pursue the enemy. He encountered Lord John Drummond at the bottom of the hill, and a few moments later the Prince came up. He found them debating whether to retire to Dunipace or advance on Falkirk, and he settled the argument at once.

" To Falkirk, gentlemen," he said.

" Then we must send scouts," Lord George declared, and Strathallan's eldest son, accompanied by Oliphant, younger, of Gask, changed into the clothes of countrymen and went off to spy out the land. They came back presently with word that the fires they had seen did not mean that Hawley was remaining in camp. He had set fire to his tents and was hastening out of Falkirk on the Edinburgh road.

Charles, soaked through, tired but elated, sought shelter in a neighbouring house, while Lord George Murray, Lord John Drummond and Cameron of Lochiel set off with three separate columns to enter Falkirk by three separate routes. They found only a few stragglers in the town, and when word came back to the Prince he hastened off to join them. The victory, he saw, was complete.

But his men did not know that. Wandering about in the darkness, soaked to the skin, famished and weary, they sought in vain for their enemies ; but gradually their chiefs drew order out of chaos, and the word went about, four hours after the battle. Victory was theirs ! Lord Lewis Gordon and other officers had found shelter in the house of Mr. Primrose at Dunipace, and to them, late at night, came Lochgarry with direct word from the Prince. They were to join him in Falkirk at daybreak. The battle had been won.

Immediately recriminations started. Lord George complained bitterly that the left wing had been without a commander. The Prince had assumed that Lord John Drummond would take command ; he had given orders to that effect, but O'Sullivan, who as adjutant-general should have looked after the organisation of the left wing, had apparently neither passed on these orders nor taken command himself. In fact, he had not been seen on the field all day, and only appeared when the battle was over and won. What he had been doing meantime was never discovered.

Lord John, annoyed at the slight implied by Lord George's criticism, pointed out that Lord George had not acted so cleverly himself. In fact, he was perfectly correct, for Lord George, brilliant as he was when it came to manœuvring and marching, had made innumerable tactical errors on the field. He had chosen the ground, which he claimed to know well, without taking into consideration the ravine that had stopped the charge of his left wing. He had held back the MacDonalds when a concerted and organised charge with the claymore would probably have swept the entire field clear and have inflicted heavy losses. As it was, too few had broken out and charged to be able to deal with the great numbers of the enemy.

Still, it was a victory, this scrambling, confused affair on Falkirk Moor, and the official English casualty lists, showing 280 officers and men killed and wounded, were obviously false. Mr. Home, who was present, and who always made out the best case possible for the government side, reported that between 300 and 400 privates were killed ; Maxwell of Kirkconnel, who was also present, estimated the number at between 400 and 500, with several hundred prisoners, while the Chevalier Johnstone, always active in ferreting out facts and figures, put the number at 600 killed and 700 captured.

Whatever the figure may have been the Highland losses were never in dispute. They had fewer than forty men killed, and only double that number wounded. But they had one officer captured. He was Major MacDonald, a cousin of Keppoch, and like many others he had pursued the enemy from the field with more zeal than caution. Coming back to the battlefield, he had encountered in the dusk a body he mistook for Lord John Drummond's regiment.

" Gentlemen ! " he cried, " what are you doing here? Why don't you follow? "

Instantly there was a shout : " Here is a rebel ! Here is a rebel ! " He had walked into Barrel's regiment, retreating in good order.

General Huske, starting forward, bellowed an order.

" Shoot the dog instantly ! "

MacDonald found himself facing a line of raised muskets pointing at his breast. But at that moment one of the officers, Lord Robert Ker, leapt forward and beat down the muskets with his sword.

" For shame ! " he cried. " Is this the way to treat a soldier? "

MacDonald presented his sword. General Huske, livid with fury, turned away, refusing to accept it, and Lord Robert stepped forward again. Courteously he received the Major's surrender, and MacDonald pulled out his pistol to hand it over. Again Huske started forward. " The dog is going to shoot me ! " he yelled in terror ; but MacDonald, smiling slightly, flung back a dignified retort and handed the pistol to Ker.

His respite was short, however ; for he was carried to Edinburgh, summarily tried, and executed shortly after. General Hawley must have some justification for the gibbets he had erected before the battle !

Charles, sheltering in Hawley's headquarters, passed an uneasy night. Like all his men he had been soaked to the skin, he had gone hungry all day as usual, and even his magnificent physique had undergone a severe strain. But he was out in the torrential rain early next morning, personally supervising the work of burying the dead, with full military honours, particularly for the Highland officers in Hawley's army who had fallen. They were misguided subjects rather than enemies, brave men who deserved an honourable burial.

That done, and all the wounded cared for, he found he still could not relax. There was a decision to be taken. Should he now drive Hawley clean out of Scotland? Should he march south again with the laurels of this new victory still fresh, with his army in the highest fighting fettle and the enemy everywhere demoralised and panic-stricken? Or—and here spoke the voice of caution—should he obey King Louis's behest and reduce the enemy's strongholds in Scotland before proceeding farther?

M. Mirabelle de Gordon, artillery engineer and siege expert, settled the question. He could reduce Stirling in a matter of days ; Edinburgh Castle would follow in due course. So it was decided, and Charles went back to Bannockburn House—and Clementina, and a severe chill.

§

He was ill for some time ; but Clementina was there to nurse him, and those long hours of restful quiet must

have seemed very precious to them both ; for soon
they realised that they were in love. There, at her
uncle's house, she plighted him her troth.

" If your attempt fails in the end," she said, " you
need only send for me. Wherever Providence may lead
you, I will always follow at a word from you."

And Charles, knowing in his heart how little hope
remained to him, how meagre was his chance of success,
must have felt buoyed up and ready to face whatever the
future might bring ; for Clementina was sincere. She
might be no great beauty, she might not even have a
pretty wit to compensate for lack of looks, but she had,
as she was still to prove, a fund of strong devotion worth
more than a pretty face or a witty tongue.

CHAPTER FOURTEEN

CULLODEN

Was ever old warrior of suff'ring so weary?
Was ever the wild beast so bayed in his den?
The Southern bloodhounds lie in kennel so near me
That death would be welcome to Callum o' Glen.
My sons are all slain, and my daughters have left me,
No child to protect me, where once I had ten ;
My chief they have slain, and of stay have bereft me,
And woe to the grey hairs of Callum o' Glen.

NEWS came to Charles as he lay ill in bed. His cousin,
the Duke of Cumberland, had reached Edinburgh, taking
over command from the discredited Hawley. That
gentleman, in a raging temper, had not been idle. The
gibbets he had erected for the rebels must have their
victims, and he had been indulging in an orgy of hanging
his own soldiers on charges of cowardice. It was in
keeping with his reputation—the English soldiers had
nicknamed him the Lord Chief Justice, from his habit
of hanging or shooting his men at the least excuse.

But even the Duke of Cumberland, brought up in the brutal tradition of the German soldier princes, was abashed at what he found going on in Edinburgh. He put a stop to it at once.

In London the news of Falkirk had caused a fresh wave of uneasiness, but without any serious alarm. There was, at least, one happy man. Johnnie Cope, still smarting under his own discomfiture, had placed bets up to 10,000 guineas in the coffee houses of London that the next general sent against the Prince in Scotland would be beaten just as he had been. So Cope was 10,000 guineas the richer for the Battle of Falkirk. . . .

Cumberland acted not as a humanitarian but as a soldier. If his army was to fight the Jacobites its *morale* must be raised at once—and indiscriminate hangings did not help. He did something else, in keeping with his nature. Charles had released on parole a large number of English officers. Cumberland ordered them all to return forthwith to their regiments, informing them that he publicly released them from their parole.

A few had the spirit to refuse to countenance so dishonourable a proceeding, threw up their commissions and went home. The rest obeyed orders, and Maxwell of Kirkconnel commented bitterly : " The decay of virtue and honour in our island since the Hanoverian accession is very remarkable, but hitherto a gentleman's word has been looked upon as sacred." To Cumberland expediency, not honour, was the governing factor ; the German attitude to a " scrap of paper " was deeply rooted.

Charles, weighing up the situation, felt the burning need for action. His Highlanders were being kept idle at Falkirk, while the Lowland regiments and the French artillery besieged Stirling Castle with no prospect of success. The complete ineptitude of the great French expert was becoming daily more and more apparent. There was some resentment that the Lowland regiments should bear the brunt of the siege while the clans lay idle, and there was always the steady trickle of desertions. With their homes in many cases only a day's march away, with much booty already in their hands, the farms and crofts urgently demanding their attention, it was natural that many of the clansmen should slip away home. Charles, summoning Murray, sent him off to interview Lord George.

" Tell him," he ordered, " that I intend to go and attack the Duke of Cumberland when he advances as far as Falkirk."

He was getting rapidly better now, thanks to Clementina's nursing and his host's kindness, and the prospect of action cheered him. The Duke could not sit long in Edinburgh ; he would have to take the field soon— and Charles looked forward eagerly to that meeting.

Presently Murray came back. He brought with him new and improved plans for the forthcoming battle, for Lord George had received word of the Prince's decision with great enthusiasm and had set to work at once to check over the dispositions Charles proposed. That night, the Prince felt he could sleep content, for the long period of inaction was at an end.

He did not sleep. He was too restless, too excited and pleased ; so he was wide awake when, early in the morning, Hay of Restalrig, who was gradually taking over the duties of Secretary, came to him. He brought a paper.

" From my Lord George Murray, sir," he said, and handed it over. Charles, sitting up in bed, glanced at it quickly. Some new plan of battle, perhaps . . .

It was signed by Lochiel, Keppoch, Clanranald, Ardshiel, Lochgarry, Scothouse, the Master of Lovat, and Lord George himself. Charles, reading, felt himself go cold with shock. Their duty in this critical juncture, they wrote . . . lay their opinions, in the most respectful manner, before his royal highness . . . vast numbers of his troops had gone home since the battle of Falkirk

. . . this evil hourly increasing . . . could anticipate
nothing but utter destruction should the enemy advance
upon them before Stirling Castle was taken.

The Prince's startled eyes ran on. The only way to
extricate his royal highness, and those who remained
with him, out of the imminent danger which threatened
them, was to retire immediately to the Highlands . . .
be usefully employed during the remainder of the winter
taking the forts still holding out there—morally certain
they could keep enough men to prevent the enemy
following them, and in the spring would have an army
of ten thousand clansmen. . . .

Charles leapt out of bed. In an agony of bitterness
and distress he beat his head against the wall, and cried
out : " Good God ! Have I lived to see this ! "

Hay of Restalrig, averting his eyes, felt the moment of
tragedy. But the Prince recovered himself almost at
once, and sat down to write a reply. The chiefs had
pointed out the terrible fatigues and privations the army
had already suffered, the severity of the winter, the
possibility of a French landing in the early spring, which
Charles himself had always insisted would take place.
The Highlands would rise immediately in that event.
The only objection to retreat was the loss of the French
artillery. Better surely, they argued, to throw it into
the Forth than risk the loss of the flower of his army in
battle against overwhelming odds. . . .

Quietly, Charles penned his reply. It was dignified,
simple, and unanswerable. They were asking him to
throw away all that he had gained by his and their
exertions. They were . . . but indeed Charles knew,
in his heart, that they had never believed in success.
They had fought for him, not in the hope of victory
but solely out of loyalty. They were ready to throw
away their own lives ; but they had been brought up
to think more of the lives of their people. They refused
to throw these away uselessly.

Once more Charles could feel the fatal weakness of

this army of his. Had his troops been, like those of his enemies, mere mercenaries, to be pushed about like pawns on a board, sacrificed at will without thought, how different it would have been ! But no mercenaries in the world could have carried him to Derby—or back from Derby. One could not have it both ways.

He sent for Sir Thomas Sheridan, and despatched him to Falkirk to try to win over the chiefs ; but Sheridan came back, accompanied by Keppoch and several others, all determined to force him to agree to their plan. They brought one convincing argument. Patullo, the muster master of the army, reported that 5,000 men had deserted —nearly half the total strength !

Charles gave way. There was nothing else for it ; but his young, alert mind saw perhaps more clearly into the future than did the others. He knew that in agreeing he was signing away his last hopes of success, and he wrote, penning the final verdict on his great enterprise : " I know I have an army that I cannot command further than the chief officers please, and therefore if you are resolved upon it I must yield—but I take God to witness that it is with the greatest reluctance, and I wash my hands of the fatal consequences which I foresee but cannot help."

The retreat began almost at once.

§

Amazement, incredulity, consternation—these were the reactions of the clansmen when the word got about. Retreat? Why should they retreat? Had they not just beaten the enemy again? Were they not looking forward eagerly to another conflict with the same result? Out of consternation grew alarm. If retreat had been decided upon, there must be weighty reasons—there must be overwhelming forces of the enemy close at hand ! And here they were, encamped near Falkirk or scattered in billets, with no natural protection.

They did not wait for orders. It was " bundle and go " by the shortest route. Batch after batch of men crossed the Forth near Stirling, in small parties of the clans, leaving the carts and the cannon behind them. They had no use for such impedimenta. But as soon as they had crossed the Forth they stopped, of their own accord. What had seemed like panic was, after all, only the simple reasoning of men who, for all the drilling they had had, were still accustomed to thinking for themselves. With the river safe between them and the enemy they halted, preparing to hold the crossings.

The troops in Stirling, after spiking their cannon, did not wait for further orders either. They marched, in good order, to the Ford of the Frews and went across. Charles, leaving his headquarters, found he was almost alone, except for the chiefs and their bodyguards, and so the official retreat began.

It went on next day, the army straggling along the road to Crieff with little resemblance to the disspirited but still orderly force that had marched north from Derby. At Crieff, however, Charles took firm control. He ordered a halt—and a review of the troops. They were mustered, paraded—and Charles, riding along the lines, saw at once that he had been deceived. The army was less than 1,000 short of its former strength. He summoned the muster master.

" I was informed that 5,000 men had deserted," he exclaimed furiously. " It was for that reason alone that I consented to this retreat."

Patullo was nonplussed. But the chiefs came forward with their explanations. Many of their men had indeed gone home ; others had scattered in search of billets and so had been counted among the deserters. Still others, sick or recovering from wounds, had fallen far behind. Numbers of the deserters had been overtaken during the retreat, and had rejoined. There was no doubt that the army had been 5,000 men short at Falkirk.

Charles found it hard to believe. Bitterly he reflected

on how he had been deceived, and naturally his resentment centred upon Lord George Murray. Had he not enthusiastically supported the plan of attacking Cumberland—and a few hours later put his name to that statement of the chiefs, which had brought about the retreat?

He summoned a council. Sitting silent and glum, he listened to their wranglings, their animosities, their recriminations. Lord George, always haughty and quick to take offence, demanded the names of the men responsible for the precipitate retreat. Charles intervened.

" The entire blame for that is mine," he said curtly, and put a stop to the altercations. What mattered was to decide the future, not quarrel over the past.

So the decision was made. The army should march to Inverness in two divisions, the Lowland regiments and the horse by the coast route, the clans with Charles in command himself, by the Highland road. But there was still another quarrel, over the command of the first division. No one was willing to accept it, and Lord George himself, to settle the matter, undertook the job.

On the 4th of February Charles marched again, by Dunkeld and Blair Athole, where he halted until he received word that the first division had reached Aberdeen. Cumberland was far behind, his slower moving troops having no chance of overtaking the Highlanders ; but as they went north the Prince's men met a new enemy— the weather. Marching out of Aberdeen—where the local clergy had inveighed against them openly in the churches—Lord George Murray's division struggled through a terrible blizzard. It blew, snowed, hailed in their faces, so that they could not see ten yards ahead, and icicles formed on their beards and eyebrows. But they plodded on doggedly along the road to Inverness.

§

Charles, with a party of fifty men of the vanguard, rode up to Moy Castle.

The laird of Mackintosh was not present. Holding a commission in the 43rd Highlanders (afterwards the 42nd) he had taken his oath of allegiance to King George and felt bound in honour not to join the Prince. He had, in fact, done his utmost to restrain the clan, but had been ordered to Inverness to join Lord Loudon, who lay there with a considerable force of Lowland troops and the Whig clans—MacLeods under the Laird of MacLeod, Munroes, Sutherlands, Forbeses and others ; for the clans were widely split. Lord President Forbes had worked assiduously, winning over a number of chiefs against the Prince, so that there were MacLeods, MacKenzies, MacKays and other clansmen on both sides.

Lady Mackintosh, however, had her own views. A daughter of Farquharson of Invercauld, she was a zealous Jacobite, and as soon as her husband had gone she had raised the clan for Charles. Now she was to have the honour of entertaining him—and incidentally of saving his life.

Lord Loudon in Inverness soon learnt of the Prince's presence at Moy Hall, a bare ten miles away. Here was a marvellous opportunity, and he collected his troops and set off forthwith to surprise and capture the Prince. But he reckoned without Lady Mackintosh's mother, who lived in the town. Word of Lord Loudon's move came to her ears, and she summoned assistance. It came in the form of fifteen-year-old Lauchlan Mackintosh.

" Go at once to Moy Hall," she told him, " and warn the Prince that Loudon is coming."

The boy sped away. Cutting across fields, he soon had a sight of Loudon's men ; but there was no hope of reaching the road ahead of them undetected. So he hid behind a wall and let them pass, then left the road and took to the open moors and the mountains. Tirelessly he climbed and scrambled and ran, and at last reached Moy Hall and gasped out his story to Lady Mackintosh.

"Say nothing!" she commanded quickly, and slipped away. No need to disturb her royal guest—let the poor laddie sleep! There were two hundred Mackintoshes to guard him, and Loudon's fifteen hundred did not alarm her unduly.

She sent for the blacksmith, Fraser.

"Take four or five men and go down the road and keep watch," she ordered, and went herself to prepare the guards, posting them round the house. Fraser, grinning to himself, led off his little party, and as soon as they were out of earshot of their Lady told them his own plan. Some distance down the road they halted, and hid, three on one side, three on the other; and almost immediately they heard the tramp and clatter of the approaching army.

Fraser, peering through the darkness, saw the van approach—a body of 70 men under the Laird of MacLeod. He waited, tense; then, as they drew near, he leapt up.

"Here come the rascals that mean to carry off our prince!" he bellowed. "Fire, my lads! Don't spare them! No quarter!"

He fired. The other five did likewise, then all six leapt up and ran from side to side, shouting, clashing their swords, loading and firing again as they ran.

"Loch Moigh!" yelled one.

"Dunmaglass!" roared another.

"Chlanna nan con, thigibh an so 's gheibh sibh feoil!" shouted another—"Sons of the hounds, come here and get flesh!"—the war cry of the Camerons.

"Form on the right, MacBeans!"

"Fall on their rear, MacDonalds!"

The night air was reft with shouted orders to all the clans, and in that uproar and commotion Loundon's soldiers halted, stricken with terror. They had marched into an ambush! MacLeod could not even rally his men, for his piper, MacCruimen, had been shot dead at the start. In a moment pandemonium reigned. The MacLeods turned and fought their way back, the cavalry, in panic, wheeled their horses and rode down the infantry behind them. The road was a shambles, a milling swarm of terrified men, who broke through the mêlée at last to stream back along the Inverness road.

They did not slow down until the very gates of Inverness offered them sanctuary, and for hours afterwards weary and bedraggled officers came limping into the town to get their injuries dressed.

Fraser and his five companions marched back in triumph to Moy Hall, and the Prince, who had been aroused by the shooting and the commotion, roared with laughter when he learnt of their exploit. If only he could have been there ! How he would have enjoyed such a ploy !

Next morning, part of the main body of the clans having come up, Charles set out for Inverness. He was looking forward eagerly to meeting Loudon and settling the score. But Loudon did not stay to meet him. He collected his demoralised forces and retired discreetly northwards. Charles entered Inverness unopposed and summoned the castle of Fort George to surrender.

Loudon had left the MacLeods and the Grants to strengthen the garrison, and the Governor, Grant of Rothiemurchus, promptly rejected the Prince's summons. Like Grant of Grant he was anti-Jacobite, and now had a lively fear of the consequences. But the bold face he put on it served no purpose. The Prince's men proceeded to undermine the Fort, which they could do under cover of an adjacent hill, and within two days they were ready to carry the barrels of gunpowder into position. The Governor, faced with the choice of surrendering or being blown sky-high, did the sensible thing, and on February 20th Fort George belonged to the Prince. He had no use for it, however, and ordered the engineers to finish the job. It had cost his relatives in London £50,000, so there must have been keen satisfaction in seeing it disintegrate as the gunpowder was touched off.

§

There followed now a long uneasy spell of intermittent activity.

Lord Loudon had retreated across the Moray Firth, and, with the King's ships cruising in the firth to protect him, sat on the beach and kept watch. That direct and impetuous soldier, the Duke of Perth, itched to get at him, but every time he marched round the Firth Loudon simply retired to the hills—and came back to the beach when Perth withdrew. So one night the Duke collected a force of 1,800 men, embarked them in smallboats, and set off across the Firth. It was an intrepid and perilous undertaking, but the boatmen were skilled, dodged the ships successfully, and ran ashore unsuspected a short distance from Loudon's camp. A quick muster, that silent, orderly muster in the dark that the Highlanders excelled in, then the whole force fell upon Loudon's camp.

There was no fight. The surprise was complete, and the startled north country Whigs and their Highland auxiliaries woke up and took to their heels. By morning, Loudon's powerful force had melted away, dispersed in every direction beyond the wit of man to call together again. Loudon, discomfited, retired farther north.

Brigadier Stapleton, with the Irish and French troops and some companies of Camerons and MacDonalds of Keppoch, set off to capture Fort William and Fort Augustus. Fort Augustus fell quickly enough, but Fort William was a tougher nut and held out against him.

Cumberland had sent the Prince of Hesse with his mercenaries and a thousand Campbells from Argyll (whose chiefs had always been staunch Whigs) into Athole, and Lord George Murray received orders which delighted him. He was to lead his own clan and all the

Athole men into their own country and deal with the invaders. It was a job after their own heart, and they had soon mopped up all the Campbell garrisons and laid siege to Blair Castle. But without artillery they were helpless, and negotiation was impossible. Sir Andrew Agnew, blustering, choleric, and overbearing, was in command of the Hanoverian force which had seized Lord George's old home. He let it be known that he would hang anyone whom Lord George might send to discuss terms, and even when his lordship bribed a pretty serving maid to carry his terms to Sir Andrew, she had to pick up her skirts and run for her life. Lord George, defeated, gave up the attempt and retired.

Meanwhile Cumberland had reached Aberdeen on the 27th of February, just three weeks behind Murray, and in Aberdeen he remained for five weeks, while he received reinforcements by sea. There, too, he gave a foretaste of his methods. He was living in a Whig city, which had never supported the Prince and had, in fact, done much to help the Hanoverian cause ; yet he behaved with all the brutality he was later to show in the Highlands. He lodged in the house of Alexander Thomson, an advocate ; but whereas Charles had always punctiliously paid for his lodgings the Duke offered Mr. Thomson neither money nor thanks. He helped himself to all the provisions he found in the house, to coal and candles, and walked out of the place five weeks later without even the briefest acknowledgment to his host.

General Hawley was with him, and, seeking quarters, induced Mrs. Gordon of Hallhead to lend him her town house. He promised that the greatest care would be taken of everything in the house, and that he would bring all the linen and other necessities he required for his suite. She might lock up whatever she liked. She did so, and next day had a message from General Hawley demanding her keys and threatening to smash all the locks. She handed over the keys, and that evening Major

Wolfe, one of Hawley's aide-de-camps, presented himself and informed her that everything had been confiscated.

Mrs. Gordon, thunderstruck, begged at least to be allowed her small stock of tea, an expensive luxury in those days.

" Certainly not, madam," replied the gallant major. " It is very good tea—and we are short of tea in the army."

" Then may I have my chocolate? "

" Certainly not."

" Then at least allow me to collect my china and other things—— "

" No, madam, You have a great deal of china. It's very pretty, and the general and his friends are very fond of china."

And he took his leave. The good lady, in despair, sent a petition to Cumberland, who promised that she should have everything back ; but the promise was worthless, for the Royal Duke was hand in glove with his officers. General Hawley proceeded to pack up everything in the house and shipped it off to Edinburgh—to a total value of over £600, including all her husband's clothes and most of her son Bob's clothes as well. He stripped the beds, the cupboards, the linen chests—everything, even flutes and music books ; and in due course a Mrs. Jackson, who knew Mrs. Gordon's china well from many visits to her house, saw some of it in a shop in London. When she enquired how it had got there, she was told that the woman who had sold it to the shops had stated she had got it from the Duke of Cumberland.

The wolves had come back to Scotland, with a vengeance. . . .

Cumberland quitted Aberdeen on the 8th of April, on his way to Inverness, and all along the route he burned the Episcopalian churches and the houses of the gentry. Every house he and his officers spent a night in was sacked the following morning, and loads of plunder went south—Whig plunder as well as Jacobite, for these

Hanoverian gentlemen did not trouble to make a distinction when plunder was to be had.

On the 12th he crossed the Spey, and the pattern of what was to follow took shape. Here was the ponderous German efficiency at work, the patient gathering of overwhelming force, ensuring odds of three or four to one before a risk was taken ; and in face of that slow, resistless advance Lord John Drummond, with his tiny rearguard, could only continue to fall back.

§

Charles remained in Inverness and thereabouts until the 16th of April. Much of the time he was ill, suffering from a severe chill and a fever, but he managed to call upon Lady Mackintosh's mother to thank her in person for her timely warning of Lord Loudon's plan to kidnap him. He kept open house, gave a number of balls—at which he danced with all his old grace and charm—and had some happy days with his gun, shooting. But from the 11th to the 20th of March he was completely bed-ridden in a house in Elgin.

He saw few of his former advisers, and Murray of Broughton, Sheridan and O'Sullivan did all they could to isolate him. Hay of Restalrig, who was a willing adherent of their faction, took over Murray's work more and more, and when the Secretary fell seriously ill was appointed in his place. It removed one dangerously biassed councillor from the Prince's entourage, but the change was hardly for the better. Murray at least had been efficient ; Hay was the reverse, and it was not long before his mismanagement of the commissariat began to be felt.

Lord George Murray and the chiefs had pressed Charles to collect 5,000 bolls of meal, at Pitsligo's suggestion, in the neighbouring shires of Moray, Nairn and Banff, and to send these valuable supplies into the Highlands as a precaution in the event of a further retreat. The meal was collected, but brought instead to Inverness, a fatal error in the circumstances.

When he rose from his sickbed Charles, realising the urgency of the situation, tried to take urgent measures. The crossing of the Spey should be disputed, but where were the men to do that ? Lord George Murray was somewhere in the south with the Athole men, the Duke of Perth was chasing Loudon away to the north, Brigadier Stapleton and the regular troops were investing Fort William with no apparent success—and Charles had no money left. Cumberland crossed the Spey unopposed.

A change had come over the Highland army. The men were still confident of victory, still cocksure and eager to fight ; but the rot had set in. They had lost all confidence in the higher direction of affairs. They had won notable victories—and they had been ordered to retreat. They could win victories, but their officers could not exploit them ; they could see no hope of ultimate success, and thought with anxiety of their homes, already in part invaded by the enemy. They longed to meet Cumberland and destroy his army, if only to protect their homes and families. Inevitably, there were more desertions, mainly of men hurrying off to their own glens to deal with Cumberland's raiding parties and save their wives and children, their cattle and sheep.

They were no longer paid in cash for their services. All that Hay of Restalrig could offer them was a weekly ration of oatmeal. Charles, reviewing the situation, realised that it could not go on. Something must happen soon.

Cumberland moved steadily on. Lord George Murray, Stapleton and the Duke of Perth were recalled ; but Lord Cromarty was still in the north with some of the best regiments—the MacGregors, Mackinnons and MacDonalds. Cluny was in Badenoch, and half of the Frasers were still in their march to Inverness to join the Prince, so that 2,000 of the best troops Charles possessed were absent as the moment of crisis approached. Less than 6,000 could be mustered at Inverness, while all reports showed that the Duke had not less than 9,000 in his main body.

On the 15th of April the Duke was celebrating his birthday at Nairn, and Charles transferred his head-quarters to Culloden House, his army encamped on Culloden Moor. The decisive moment was at hand.

Lord George Murray came forward. He had a plan ready made to meet the situation. It was, as always, simple and ingenious, for Lord George had genius.

" The only means we have of offsetting our numerical inferiority," he pointed out, " is to attack. Cumberland lies at Nairn, celebrating his birthday. If we make a night march to Nairn we can fall upon his lines at dawn and inflict such heavy losses before he can recover that we may destroy him completely, or at least adjust the balance. I mistrust Culloden Moor as a battleground."

The Prince's spirits rose. He had grown of late despondent, convinced that the retreats that had been forced upon him had destroyed every chance of success. Now here was a plan after his own heart, action at last, attack instead of retreat. He greeted the suggestion with eager enthusiasm, and threw himself into the work of preparation with all the old verve and energy.

By eight o'clock that night the army was ready for its desperate adventure. Lord George was to lead the van, Lord John Drummond the centre, and Charles himself, with the Duke of Perth, the rear. They had only twelve miles to go. The order to march was given.

Lord George set the pace. His men were far from fresh, but he had the pick of them all, and they had recently had a meal—not much, but enough to give a spring to their step. In silence, they disappeared into the night. Lord John followed ; and the Prince put the rear in motion.

He marched on foot. He had recovered his spirits, the sheer joy of battle buoying him up. He knew how desperate this enterprise was, and its very desperation appealed irresistibly to all the love of adventure that had kept him from despair so long.

But he could not perform more than his men were capable of ; and drenched and cold and hungry, they plodded through the rain with stumbling feet, many of them so weak from weariness and lack of food that they could not keep pace. Slowly the rear fell behind, and towards one o'clock, with several miles still to go, Charles spoke to Perth.

" Go forward and inform Lord George that unless a halt is called we cannot bring up the rear in time."

As the Duke rode forward, he overtook Lord John and told him of his mission. Drummond agreed at once, and went on with him. Messages passed back and forth, and Charles, spurring his tired men on, felt a sudden alarm. At all costs the attack must be made, even with only a small body. Murray must not halt too long. He called O'Sullivan, bade him ride forward and urge Lord George and Drummond to go ahead. He would follow at the best speed possible and hope to be in time.

Lord George, listening glumly to Perth and Drummond, wiped the rain from his eyes and looked round with irritation as O'Sullivan rode up.

" His royal highness urges you to go on," the adjutant general told him. " The attack must be made."

Lord George pondered briefly. If Charles was so far behind, and the main body still some way off, what hope remained? A halt would destroy the whole essence of the plan, for dawn would come too soon. Once the alarm was given attack would be mere suicide.

Already the camp fires of the enemy were in sight— and the heavy darkness presaged the dawn. Lord George made up his mind.

" Give the order to retreat," he said harshly. " It is too late now."

Consternation greeted his words. The weary troops faced about, bewildered, frustrated, crushed. They had kept going only because soon they would fall upon the enemy. They had forced their unwilling legs to carry them forward because now they would settle accounts, now they would put an end to all this wearying campaign, dirk and broadsword would flash in one final, shattering blow, and their enemies would be destroyed.

In a sullen, uncomprehending silence they set out to retrace their steps. Hay of Restalrig, sent forward to find out what was happening, met them, and spoke to Lord George. He turned and spurred back to the Prince.

" Where the devil are the men going? " Charles demanded furiously.

" Lord George has ordered a retreat ! " Hay reported, and the Prince, thunderstruck, stared at him through the rain. Then, as the full implications dawned upon him, as he remembered the tired and hungry men, so heavily outnumbered, his restraint broke down.

" Lord George Murray has betrayed me ! " he cried passionately, and all the old suspicions, all the poison instilled into his mind by Murray of Broughton and his Irish cronies, surged up again. But he made a great effort to control himself, and hastened to see Lord George.

" Why have you done this, my lord? " he demanded passionately.

" There is no alternative. I could not attack alone. Before the centre and the rear could have come up the sun would have risen, we should have been too late."

Charles turned away. He rode towards the waiting troops, and in a voice choked with bitter emotion gave his orders.

" There is no help for it, my lads. March back to Culloden House."

The army marched again—weary, disspirited, drenched and cold and starving ; and the Duke of Cumberland slumbered on, entirely unsuspecting. Had the Highlanders gone on they would have found a sleeping encampment, they could have fallen upon it and cut the troops to pieces before they had shaken the sleep from their eyes. But Charles did not know that ; and had he known, he was now almost past caring. Throughout the whole campaign his authority, his generalship had been set at nought, he had never had effective control. Now, in his last extremity, the decision had been taken out of his hands again.

Staggering with fatigue, the army reached Culloden Moor. There was no food there—Hay of Restalrig had overlooked that need. The men, subsiding on the wet ground, wrapped their torn and drenched plaids about them and went to sleep ; and the staff that should have been sleepless—those nominees of Murray of Broughton and Sheridan and O'Sullivan—slept too.

A handful of Elcho's lifeguards, dropping with weariness, had tethered their horses and crowded into a barn to sleep. At least the straw was dry and they were out of the teeming rain. But they did not rest long. Within two hours a woman came from the neighbouring farm to warn them that the Duke of Cumberland's cavalry were in sight. The lifeguards rushed out, threw themselves into the saddle and galloped off towards Culloden House. But already another party of lifeguards had raised the alarm, and Charles was out assembling his army on the Moor.

It was a scene of the wildest confusion. Men drugged with weariness rose and fumbled for their weapons, stumbled about to find their comrades, drawing their belts tight to help forget the ache of hunger in their bellies. Shivering with cold, their hands raw and bleeding, they tried to fall into their ordered ranks, while the drums beat and the pipes wailed through the driving rain.

The Prince glanced over the battle-ground. It was badly chosen, far too cramped, and in the desperate hurry of rousing the exhausted men O'Sullivan had committed a terrible oversight. Along one side ran a stone wall, which ordinary common sense would have shown should be thrown down. It was left intact in spite of Lord George's protests ; and now O'Sullivan made a far worse blunder. He allowed the army to be drawn up in reverse order, with the Athole men and the Camerons on the right, then the Stuarts of Appin, the Frasers, the Mackintoshes, the Farquharsons, the MacLeans—and the MacDonalds on the left.

Never before had such a slight been offered to Clan Donald. Even bewildered and weary as they were, they realised the affront, and stood in their ranks in sullen silence. But it was too late now to rectify the error. Cumberland was close. No time left for marching or counter-marching. Battle was upon them.

In the second line the Highland horse occupied the right, with the Irish in the centre and Lord Lewis Gordon and Sir Alexander Bannerman on the left ; and the whole army did not number 5,000 men.

Some voices were raised, suggesting a retreat across the River Nairn to the hills, where Cumberland dare not follow. By night, reinforcements would have arrived, and they would be in a position to choose their ground and give battle to the best advantage. Somehow the plan, so sound and sensible, was not mentioned again. The end was at hand.

§

Charles rode out before his troops.

This was the decisive, the supreme moment. A few hours hence all uncertainty would be over. He would have won a final victory—or his cause would be defeated for ever. The crisis found him ready, for it was at such moments that he rose to his greatest heights. Gay and debonair as they remembered him in his triumphs, he appeared to them now, and the weary men straightened their drooping shoulders, wiped their eyes and loosened the claymores in their scabbards with a fresh upsurge of spirit. But there was desperation in these strained and haggard faces, a strange melancholy fanaticism in those burning hungry eyes. Death was close at hand.

Their Prince, gallant and upright, rode down the lines, then took his place with a body of FitzJames's horse, on an eminence behind the first line. Calm but anxious, he awaited the fateful decision.

Cumberland had drawn up his vast army in three lines, with his cannon mounted in the gaps between the regiments. At this moment he was supremely nervous, with galling recollections of Prestonpans and Falkirk, and he admitted later that he was keenly anxious about the issue. He had realised that greatly superior numbers were not enough to daunt the Highlanders. He had spent some time training his troops to receive a frontal charge with the broadsword, and he hoped they would stand firm now ; but he had his doubts. For that reason he had decided upon three deep lines, with strict orders that if the first line broke the second should open fire at once. He had given other orders too. There was to be no quarter. No prisoners, no wounded left alive. . . .

Lord Bury, one of the Duke's aide-de-camps, rode forward to reconnoitre, and as he came within gunshot the Prince's cannons opened up without orders. Bury retired, and little harm was done ; but now Cumberland's artillery replied. Some guns were trained upon the knoll on which the Prince and his party were placed, and suddenly Charles's horse shied, and began to prance and scream. A ball had grazed its knee. It became unmanageable, and Charles was forced to dismount and take a fresh horse. A groom close behind the Prince was shot dead as he sat holding the reins of a sumpter horse, and several cannon balls threw up mud that spattered the Prince's face. He sat unconcerned, waiting for some sign of movement.

Suddenly it was seen that a large body of the enemy had gone down by the river and were throwing down some walls of an enclosure. Lord George Murray tried to intercept them but was too late, and a strong force of

dragoons rode through the gaps and formed in the rear
of the Highland army. It was a menacing move, and
became more so when the enemy's infantry, who had
thrown down the walls, now lined the remaining walls
ready to pour in a flanking fire when battle was joined.

Colonel Ker sought the Prince, with a message from
Lord George. He wished to know if he should begin the
attack. The English cannonade, maintained without
pause, was decimating the Highland line, and the men
were clamouring to be led forward. The Prince sent
back his orders. The attack was to commence at once.

But an unhappy circumstance had befallen. The two
armies were not quite parallel to each other, so that the
Prince's left had far further to go ; and in any case the
MacDonalds, still disgruntled, had lost their customary
impetuosity. Lord George, hoping the Duke would
make a move, held back his men ; but suddenly, before
he could give the order to attack, there was a concerted
movement. The Mackintoshes, stung to fury by the
terrible cannonade and by their own inactivity, suddenly
broke out of their ranks and with a wild shout rushed
forward, straight at the smoke of the cannon. Lord
George, seeing the desperate situation, shouted an order
for the whole right wing, and led the charge.

At first a quick walk, then a trot, then at a run they
went. As they came within pistol-shot, a long line of
flame leapt from the English ranks, and the cannon
poured grapeshot into the advancing mass. Whole
ranks were mown down. Their comrades leapt over
them and ran on, halted briefly to discharge their muskets,
then threw these away and drew the claymore.

Mackintoshes, Camerons, MacLachlans and MacLeans
hurled themselves forward, behind the gallant figure of
Lord George. Sword in hand they fell upon the English
regiments, hacked their way through them, beat down
the bayonets and left over 200 soldiers dead or wounded
behind them.

They ran straight into the murderous fire of two

supporting regiments. But the impetus of their charge carried them right up to the bayonets, and they slashed their way through and swung to attack the left of Cumberland's second line.

A far heavier fire met them through the clouds of smoke and the rain—grapeshot and volleys of musketry that cut them down in droves. Yet they charged on, in desperation now, regardless of their lives.

The centre, too, had charged—the Athole men, the Stuarts of Appin, the Frasers and other regiments. Staggering with fatigue though they were, they drove through the English centre, charged on towards the second line, while they fell by the score under the terrible hail of grapeshot and musketry. But the second line stood firm. The unequal contest could not last. Broadsword and dirk against cannon and musketry—against overwhelming numbers of trained and veteran troops, against the solid wall of bayonets ; individual valour could achieve no more. The clansmen turned.

Behind them Cumberland's reserves had formed, hemming them in. They rushed upon them, hacked their way through, regained the open ground.

The left wing had moved at last. Advancing swiftly to within musket-shot, the MacDonalds discharged their pieces and prepared to charge ; but something seemed to go wrong. The withering fire from the English right swept their ranks—a fire that poured through clouds of smoke from an invisible enemy. The charge wavered, halted, broke. Keppoch, stung to fury, drew his sword and rushed on alone.

Suddenly he fell, with a musket-ball wound, and Donald Roy MacDonald, a former lieutenant in his regiment, now a captain in Clanranald's, rushed forward to him.

" You can do no more ! " he cried. " Let me carry you back to your regiment."

Keppoch staggered to his feet, wiping the blood away. " Never ! " he cried, " There is no retreat for Keppoch ! "

Stumbling, he ran again towards the enemy. He did not go far. Another shot brought him to the ground, and, still trying to crawl forward, he died.

Charles, watching the scene from the knoll, set spurs to his mount. He headed down to intercept the fleeing clans, to rally them, to make them face about. His second line was still intact behind him, stubbornly holding off the dragoons who had charged in pursuit. With tears streaming down his cheeks he rode down, while O'Sullivan and Sheridan went after him, urging him to come back. O'Sullivan, overtaking him, seized his bridle, wrenched the reins out of his hands, and turned the horse's head.

Once off the field, Charles rounded on him, and dashed to put himself at the head of the right wing, still retiring in such good order that the English cavalry could make no impression upon it. Then he gave orders for the army to separate, one division, consisting of the Lowland regiments and all the clans except the Frasers, he ordered to cross the Nairn and head for Badenoch ; the other division—the Frasers, Lord John Drummond's regiment, and the French picquets—he ordered to take the road to Inverness.

The Highlanders, crossing the river, passed within pistol-shot of the English dragoons who had got to the rear of the Prince's army ; but they made no move to interfere. The second division was less fortunate, for it had to pass over level ground, and Cumberland's dragoons, in great numbers, hemmed them in. The slaughter had begun.

/ Riding over the battlefield, they cut down every man they overtook. At the faintest sign of life among the heaps of dead they shot or sabred indiscriminately. They came upon numbers of townspeople and country-men who, attracted by the noise of battle, had been drawn to the scene. Thirsting for blood, they rode them down in cold blood, killing right and left. Remembering their disgrace at Prestonpans and Falkirk, the soldiers swarmed over the field ; remembering perhaps the Prince's clemency, the compassion the Highland army had shown them, they repaid it now in full, even their officers joining in the carnage. They stripped the dead, left them lying naked on the blood-soaked ground. They dragged out every man who, wounded and maimed, still breathed, and stabbed him to death or shot him in cold blood.

Wherever the dragoons found parties of fleeing men they followed up and hewed them down with their sabres. But one man whom they cornered at least sold his life dearly. He was Gillies MacBane, a giant of six feet four, terribly wounded but still upon his feet. Seeing the dragoons, he put his back to a wall and prepared to defend himself with target and claymore to the end. The dragoons crowded round him in a body, but the giant held them at bay. One after another fell under the terrible blows of the claymore, until thirteen lay piled at his feet. Some officers, riding up, impressed by his bravery, ordered their men to desist and let him go. But the dragoons, maddened and deaf to their orders, hurled themselves in fresh fury upon him until they bore him down.

All day the slaughter continued. The Duke himself, riding over the battlefield, caught sight of Charles Fraser, younger, of Inverallachie, lying severely wounded. At sight of the Duke he raised himself on his elbow and stared at him. Cumberland turned to an officer, Wolfe, who was riding beside him.

" Wolfe," he ordered, " shoot me that Highland scoundrel who thus dares to look on us with so insolent a stare."

The officer, appalled, drew back.

" My commission is at your royal highness's disposal," he retorted stiffly, and the other officers, heartened by this refusal, equally refused the order. The Duke, infuriated, summoned a common soldier, who promptly shot young Fraser before their eyes. His royal master, with a pleased smile, rode on to look for other victims.

Night came, and found Cumberland in Inverness,

where the French officers and Stapleton, surrendering
on terms, had at least some hope of honourable treatment.
But Cumberland did not rest.   Orders went out, and
many ladies of Jacobite sympathy were seized and thrown
into the common gaol.   At the same time an affray
developed between the Scots and English soldiers in the
Duke's own army.   A Highland officer named Forbes,
who had formerly seen service with the British Army,
was recognised among the prisoners in the town and
instantly hanged.   An English officer plunged his sword
into the corpse, crying out : " All his countrymen are
traitors and rebels like himself ! "   In a moment the
outraged Scots were up in arms, and Cumberland was
forced to intervene himself.

Next day word came that parties of wounded Highlanders were in hiding near the field, and the Provost of
Inverness, Mr. Hossock, who had rendered many services
to the government, called at Cumberland's headquarters
to intercede.   He found Generals Hawley and Huske in
the act of concocting orders to search parties for the
murder of these men.   He attempted to remonstrate
with them.

" As his majesty's troops have been happily successful
against the rebels," he urged earnestly, " I hope your
excellencies will be so good as to mingle mercy with
judgment."

Hawley, flying into a rage, leapt to his feet.

" Damn the puppy ! " he roared.   " Does he pretend
to dictate here ?   Carry him away ! "

Some soldiers rushed forward, and the unhappy
provost was kicked downstairs and into the street.   Then
the search parties went out.

Behind hedges, in ditches, in barns and outbuildings
they found their victims.   They dragged them out,
piled them on open ground, poured volleys into the heaps
of maimed and wounded bodies.   They searched the
houses, dragging out the men who had crept to shelter
there, and the young Laird of MacLeod, his stomach

turned by the terrible behaviour of the men on whose side he had elected to fight, declared that he himself saw 72 wounded men butchered in cold blood.

The soldiers approached a small hut, used for sheltering sheep and goats in winter. Looking in, they saw that it was crowded with wounded Highlanders. Instantly they secured the door, set fire to the hut in several places, and gathered round to listen to the screams of the forty wounded men burning to death inside.

A party of nineteen wounded officers was discovered in Culloden House, where they had lain for two days with no attention except from the Lord President's own steward, who at the risk of his life tried to succour them. The soldiers tied them with ropes, piled them into carts, and took them to the park wall a little distance from the house. Here they were hauled from the carts, ranged along the wall, and an officer promptly gave the order to fire at a range of two or three yards. Then he ordered the soldiers to club their muskets and dash out the brains of any that survived. One of these, John Fraser, received a blow which smashed his cheek and dashed out one of his eyes ; he was left for dead, but, being found some time later by the Earl of Kilmarnock's son, Lord Boyd, he was carried to a cottage where he lay concealed for three months. He afterwards escaped, to drag out a few more years an ailing cripple.

So it went on, a slaughter without mercy from which even the innocent bystanders could not escape. Their houses were plundered, their cattle stolen, their women-folk ravaged indiscriminately by the English soldiers and their German comrades, and all Scotland, Lowland and Highland, Whig and Jacobite, was shocked to the depths by this sudden display of savage depravity at the behest of the son of the man they called king.

The Jacobite cause was lost for ever—and all Scotland was won to Jacobitism. The clans had received their death blow ; and out of the carnage, and the terrible sufferings still to come, was born something new and enduring—the fusion of north and south, so that now, at last, ancient antagonisms were laid aside and from the Borders to Caithness the country became one and indivisible.

But before that happened Prince Charles was to share the sufferings of the people who had risked all for his sake—and had lost.

CHAPTER FIFTEEN

ROYAL FUGITIVE

A wee bird cam' to oor ha' door,
He warbled sweet and clearly,
And aye the o'ercome o' his sang
Was, " Wae's me for Prince Charlie ! "

O when I heard the bonnie bonnie bird
The tears cam' drapping rarely ;
I took my bonnet aff my head,
For weel I lo'ed Prince Charlie !

" LORD, what am I that I should be spared, when so
many brave men lie dead upon the spot ? "

That cry from the heart was the Prince's comment
upon the destruction of all his hopes, and now a different
sort of action lay ahead. He had crossed the Nairn in
good order at the ford of Falie, four miles from the field,
and after a brief consultation instructed the horse and
all but a few of his attendants to proceed to Ruthven in
Badenoch to await orders. He himself, with Sheridan,
O'Sullivan, Captain O'Neil, John Hay of Restalrig and
a few others, set off for Gortuleg, the home of Lord
Lovat's steward.

O'Sullivan, conscious perhaps of his own shortcomings, of the terrible neglect of his duty which had contributed so much to this disaster, did not let slip this golden opportunity.

" Lord George Murray is to blame," he told the Prince. " He betrayed us all." Sheridan added his voice. He realised the magnitude of the disaster, the dangers that lay ahead—and neither he nor O'Sullivan had anything to lose except their lives. They were agreed as to their course. The rebellion had failed. Very well, we have had our adventure, let us get back to France, where we shall be as well off as we were before ! They set about persuading the Prince.

It was not difficult. If Lord George Murray and the chiefs had brought this ruin upon their cause, what hope was there of carrying on the struggle ? As for keeping their forces together, so that a bold front could be displayed against Cumberland and terms demanded, the Irishmen were not interested. The Prince, distraught and wretched, listened gloomily, and all his old suspicions crystalised. He was torn between the high determination never to give in, but to carry on the struggle as long as any hope remained, and the feeling of utter despair that the men closest to him did their best to engender.

They reached Gortuleg at sunset ; and there they found Lord Lovat himself. As Charles, in answer to his anxious inquiry, bluntly told him the blunt truth, the enormous corpulent body of the aged chief of the Frasers was galvanised by an agony of despair. For a moment his nerve broke altogether, and he turned, with shaking jowls and staring eyes, upon his attendants.

" Kill me now ! " he cried passionately. " Cut off my head and have done ! Why wait for the headsman's axe ? "

The Prince, startled and dismayed, heard him and remembered all the insinuations of his Irish companions. But the paroxysm was brief, and old Lovat pulled himself together, made an effort to be calm, and sat down to discuss the situation with a common sense as surprising as his frantic outburst had been.

"I beg you not to leave the country, sir," he said earnestly. "Stay and gather your forces again. Cumberland can easily be held off until the summer in these mountains, and afterwards . . . "

The Prince seized upon this slender ray of hope, and one of his aide-de-camps, Alexander MacLeod, sat down and wrote a dispatch to Cluny MacPherson telling him there was to be a review of the troops at Fort Augustus next day, and requesting him to be present. Thereafter the party had supper, and at ten o'clock rode away from Gortuleg, which was too near the scene of the defeat to be healthy for the Prince. Discarding the well-known tartan short coat which he had worn at Culloden, Charles changed into other clothes, so that he should not too easily be recognised.

They rode hard. They passed Fort Augustus without pause, as if Charles had completely forgotten the dispatch to Cluny, and at four o'clock in the morning they drew rein outside Invergarry Castle.

The place was utterly deserted. All but one of the servants had left, and almost all the furniture had been removed—a natural precaution. The aged retainer who remained could offer them no cheer.

"Then we must sleep where we can," the Prince declared, and wrapping his coat closely about him lay down upon the floor. The others followed his example. Cold, wet, and exhausted by the long hard ride, they slept.

The Prince was up at daybreak; but there was no food to be had. But he was not alone astir, for Alexander MacLeod's servant, Edward Burke, was also awake.

"We must be finding food for all the young gentlemen!" cried Ned, a quick-witted South Uist man, and out he went from the castle. The Prince wandered after him, and watched. Ned looked about, and presently went running down towards the river Garry. He had caught sight of a net. He set to work, and soon, pulling in the net, he landed a couple of handsome salmon.

" A good dinner for the gentlemen ! " cried Ned, and turned cook for the occasion.

Fortified, the Prince spoke to his companions.

" I have made up my mind to return to France," he said, with decision. " Hay, you will proceed to Ruthven with a message from me to Lord George and the chiefs. O'Sullivan and O'Neil—you will come with me. And my good friend Ned. He knows the country well, and will be our guide. The rest of you must disperse and seek your own safety."

At three o'clock in the afternoon he set off, and that night slept at the house of Donald Cameron of Glenpean. But he did not rest, and spent the following night, the 18th, at Mewboll, where clean sheets, ample food, and a warm welcome awaited them. Next morning they set out for Glenbeasdale, which he had given as his immediate destination.

They rode down to Loch Morar-side, and sat down to wait for a boat to take them across. Ned Burke went scouting, but after several hours they gave up.

" We must go on foot to Glenbeasdale," Ned declared. " It is the quickest way."

He led them off, and soon they had to abandon the horses and take to the rocks. Ned went swiftly, accustomed to this wild country, and Charles, clambering after him, felt a strange lift of spirit in the clear keen mountain air. His gloom, his wretchedness fell from him, and he responded eagerly to the demands of this hard journey. Here was the sort of thing he knew he could do, here he excelled, and the mere physical exertion was a tonic.

It was a gruelling journey, and they spent the night in a little shieling among the mountains huddled together for warmth ; but next day, Sunday, the 20th, their guide pointed confidently down, and trudging on they reached at last the welcome haven of Glenbeasdale.

§

Hay of Restalrig found a dubious welcome. Lord George had collected nearly 3,000 men at Ruthven, including Cluny's MacPhersons, and confidently awaited the Prince's orders. It had not yet occurred to any of the chiefs that the rebellion was over, that no further stand was to be made. But they were in serious difficulties. The meal that Hay had collected had all been taken into Inverness instead of being sent, as the chiefs had requested, into the Highlands ; there was no food for the army. It would be impossible to keep the men together for more than a few days, and the man who was directly responsible for this state of affairs, arriving hot-foot with word from the Prince, found only sour looks and acute dislike.

His message was not calculated to improve matters. Lorg George was thunderstruck. So, too, were the chiefs, who saw themselves deserted now with the enemy on their doorstep—and who knew what the consequences must be. Desperately they discussed the situation together, appealing to Lord George ; but he himself had already written to the Prince, with greater forthrightness than ever before—and that letter was even now in the Prince's hands :

" May it please your royal highness :

" As no person in these kingdoms ventured more frankly in the cause than myself, and as I had more at stake than almost all the others put together, so, to be sure, I cannot but be deeply affected with our late loss and present situation ; but I declare, that were your royal highness's person in safety, the loss of the cause, and the misfortunate and unhappy situation of my countrymen, is the only things that grieves me, for I thank God I have resolution to bear my own family's ruin without a grudge. Sir, you will, I hope, upon this occasion, pardon me, if

I mention a few truths, which all the gentlemen of our army seem convinced of.

" It was highly wrong to have set up the royal standard without having positive assurances from his Most Christian Majesty, that he would assist you with all his force ; and as your royal family lost the crown of these realms upon the account of France, the world did and had reason to expect that France would seize the first favourable opportunity to restore your august family.

" I must also acquaint your royal highness that we were all fully convinced that Mr. O'Sullivan, whom your royal highness trusted with the most essential things with regard to your operations, was exceedingly unfit for it, and committed gross blunders on every occasion of moment. He whose business it was, did not so much as visit the ground where we were to be drawn up in line of battle, and it was a fatal error to allow the enemy these walls upon their left, which made it impossible for us to break them, and they, with their front fire, and flanking us when we went upon the attack, destroyed us without any possibility of our breaking them, and our Athole men have lost a full half of their officers and men. I wish Mr. O'Sullivan had never got any other charge in the army than the care of the baggage, which, I am told, he had been brought up to and understood. I never saw him in time of action, neither at Gladsmuir (Prestonpans), Falkirk, nor in the last, and his orders were vastly confused.

" The want of provisions was another misfortune which had the most fatal consequence. Mr. Hay, whom your royal highness trusted with the principal direction of ordering provisions of late, and without whose orders a boll of meal or farthing of money was not to be delivered, has served your royal highness egregiously ill. When I spoke to him, he told me the thing is ordered, it will be got, etc. ; but he neglected his duty to such a degree, that our ruin might probably have been prevented had he done his duty. In short, the three last days which were so critical, our army was starved. This was the reason our night march was rendered abortive, when we possibly might have surprised and defeated the enemy at Nairn ; but for want of provisions a third of the army scattered to Inverness, &c., and the others who marched had not spirits to make it so quick as was necessary, being really faint for want of provisions.

" The next day, which was the fatal day, if we had got plenty of provisions we might have crossed the water of Nairn, and drawn up so advantageously, that we would have obliged the enemy to come to us, for they were resolved to fight at all hazards at prodigious disadvantage, and probably in that case we would have done by them as they unhappily have done by us. In short, Mr. O'Sullivan and Mr. Hay had rendered themselves odious to all our army, and had disgusted them to such a degree, that they had bred a mutiny in all ranks, that had not the battle come on they were to have represented their grievances to your royal highness for a remedy. For my own part, I never had any particular discussion with either of them ; but I ever thought them uncapable and unfit to serve in the stations they were placed in.

" Your royal highness knows I always told I had no design to continue in the army. I would of late, when I came last from Athole, have resigned my commission ; but all my friends told me it might be of prejudice to the cause at such a critical time. I hope your royal highness will now accept of my demission. What commands you have for me in any other situation, please honour me with them.

" I am, with great zeal, Sir,
    " Your royal highness's most dutiful and
    humble servant,
       " GEORGE MURRAY.
" RUTHVEN, 17th April, 1746.
    " I have taken the liberty to keep 500 pieces, which shant be disposed upon except you give leave."

Plainly, it had never entered Lord George's head that the army might be disbanded and the whole rebellion called off, and Hay of Restalrig's dispatches was a severe shock. He immediately sat down and wrote a reply, pointing out that the Highlanders could make a summer campaign without risk of misfortune, that they could march through the mountains to Banffshire, Aberdeenshire, the Mearns, Perthshire and elsewhere by ways that regular troops could not have followed, and that Cumberland's forces could not have ventured into the mountains without serious risk and heavy loss. Further, the Highlanders would never have starved in their own country, so long as sheep and cattle were to be had ; they could march in three days a distance that would take regular troops at least five, and so they could fall upon the enemy's columns at will and cut them to pieces one by one : they could thus have gained time for France to move, and at the very least have forced Cumberland to agree to terms.

He sent Hay off post-haste with this ; but knew in advance that it would have no effect. With O'Sullivan at his elbow, the Prince, incensed as he must have been at Lord George's resignation, was not likely to listen to such arguments ; and indeed so it proved.

Perplexed and stricken, Charles did not know which way to move. Had he been betrayed ? Had he been badly served ? He had always fretted at the dampener the council had put upon his plans, at the way his natural ardour had been restrained. He had suspected treachery often—and O'Sullivan would not allow his suspicions to rest.

Word went back to Ruthven. The army must disperse and seek its own safety. So at Ruthven a tragic ceremony took place. The officers, drinking a toast for the last time together, did not hide their tears ; and outside, the clansmen, who had endured so much, wept bitterly, lamenting the loss of the cause for which they had given so much.

§

"When I came into this country," wrote Charles in a letter headed "For the Chiefs," " it was my only view to do all in my power for your good and safety. This I will always do as long as life is in me. But, alas ! I see with grief I can at present do little for you on this side the water, for the only thing that can now be done is to defend yourselves until the French assist you, if not to be able to make better terms. To effectuate this, the only way is to assemble in a body as soon as possible, and then to take measures for the best, which you that know the country are only judges of. This makes me be of little use here ; whereas, by my going into France instantly, however dangerous it be, I will certainly engage the French court either to assist us effectually and powerfully, or at least to procure you such terms as you would not obtain otherways. My presence there, I flatter myself, will have more effect to bring this sooner to a determination than any body else, for several reasons ; one of which I will mention here : viz. it is thought to be a politick (policy), though a false one, of the French court, not to restore our master, but to keep a continual civil war in this country, which renders the English government less powerful, and of consequence themselves more. This is absolutely destroyed by my leaving the country, which nothing else but this will persuade them that this play cannot last, and if not remedied, the Elector will soon be as despotick as the French king, which, I should think, will oblige them to strike the great stroke, which is always in their power, however averse

they may have been to it for the time past.   Before
leaving off, I must recommend to you that all things
should be decided by a council of all your chiefs, or, in
any of your absence, the next commander of your several
corps with the assistance of the Duke of Perth and Lord
George Murray, who, I am persuaded, will stick by you
to the very last.   My departure should be kept as long
private and concealed as possible on one pretext or other
which you will fall upon.   May the Almighty bless and
direct you."

Charles postdated the letter April 28th, and enclosed
it in another sent to Sir Thomas Sheridan on the 23rd,
urging him to conceal his plan of leaving the country.
The Navy was already out in great strength in the west,
and any ship attempting to run that blockade would take
serious risks ; but Charles had never hesitated to take
a risk, and meant to make the attempt.   It was common
wisdom, however, to prevent the government from
learning of it in time to double the strength of their
squadrons on the West of Scotland.

The letter dispatched, Charles relaxed.   He was done
now with all the wearisome business that had afflicted
him so long.   His course was clear, he could face the
uncertainties of the future, at last relieved of all intrigue
and animosities and vacillation.   He welcomed the
change ; and although he could not know it from that
moment, Prince Charles Edward Stuart ceased to exist,
and in his place was born that other lovable and high-
spirited character, Bonnie Prince Charlie.   The cause was
lost for ever ; in its place sprang up a legend that placed
him among the immortals.

§

Men came to Glenbeasdale—young Clanranald, Lockhart, younger, of Carnwath, Æneas MacDonald the
banker, and others.   They had one thought in mind—
to dissuade Charles from quitting the mainland.

" The Elector's cruisers are swarming in the Hebrides,"
they told him. " You will undoubtedly be caught if
you attempt to reach the Isles."

But O'Sullivan was clamorous. He dreaded remaining
here, he wanted to get away, to escape from the columns
already moving inexorably in pursuit ; and out of old
respect and affection the Prince gave way to him.

" There is far more chance of finding a ship for France
in the Isles," the Irishman argued, earnestly. " Let us
get away from the mainland at once ! "

But Charles first decided to seek protection. He knew
that both the Laird of MacLeod and Sir Alexander
MacDonald of Sleat had not only refused to implement
their promise of support but had gone over to the enemy ;
yet he could not even now bring himself to believe
that they would desert him utterly. So now, in his
perplexity, he made up his mind to appeal to them.
He sent a messenger to Kinlochmoidart to summon a
man he knew he could trust—old Donald MacLeod, who
had been in Inverness, shipping a cargo of meal to Skye,
when Charles was there. Donald had gone off with
Æneas MacDonald the banker to Barra to fetch over a
sum of £380 that was lying there, and Æneas could vouch
for him.

Donald did not hesitate. He set off for Glenbeasdale
at once, and as he came near, taking a path through a
forest, he came upon a young man wandering aimlessly
alone among the trees. The stranger ran forward to
greet him.

" It is Donald MacLeod of Gaultergill, is it not? " he
cried, and the old man, with a sudden startled excitement,
recognised the youth.

" Yes, sir," he replied quietly.

" Then you see, Donald, I am in distress," the Prince
exclaimed. " I throw myself into your hands. Do with
me what you like. I hear you are an honest man, and
fit to be trusted."

The aged Highlander shook a troubled head.

" I doubt I can be of little service to your excellency,"
he demurred ; · but Charles was insistent.

" I want you to go to Skye, and appeal to the Laird
of MacLeod and Sir Alexander MacDonald to give me
refuge."

Donald was thunderstruck.

" After the way they have betrayed their promise
already ? " he cried. " They have taken part against your
excellency. They will but betray you again. I cannot
carry such a message."

The Prince looked gloomily into the honest old eyes,
and nodded at length.

" Ah, well, Donald," he said, in a melancholy voice.
" No doubt you are right. I have few friends left."

" You have many friends, your royal highness,"
Donald replied firmly ; and together they went on to
Glenbeasdale.

The next few days were an anguish of indecision. At
the last moment Charles could not bear the thought that
all was lost. He sent some of Clanranald's men to seek
intelligence ; they returned with no good news. The
clans were dispersing to their homes. Many had given
up their arms, and the army, obedient to the Prince's
last behest, had melted away. Lord Loudon was on the
point of crossing over to Arisaig with a large body of
militia to search for the Prince, and Cumberland was
reported—falsely, as it happened—at Fort Augustus.
There seemed nothing for it but to leave.

§

It was Donald MacLeod who found a boat—a stout,
eight-oared craft.

" I hear, Donald," the Prince had said to him, " that
you're a good pilot and know all this coast well, and
therefore I hope you can carry me safely through the
islands, where I may look for more safety than I can
do here."

Donald, still active and strong at 68, took this for an order and found not only the boat but seven reliable boatmen. Charles had been by then four days in the district, staying in the house of Angus MacDonald of Borrodale, where he had been so hospitably received nine months before. Mrs. MacDonald gave him a new Highland dress to wear, and Donald put four pecks of oatmeal into the boat. He also had the forethought to bring a large pot for cooking their meals, and thus equipped the Prince and his party clambered on board. O'Sullivan, Captain O'Neil, Allan MacDonald—a priest belonging to Clanranald's family—and the faithful Ned Burke made up the party.

Donald was none too happy about it.

"There is a storm will be blowing up this night," he told Charles, anxiously. "I do not like the look of the sky. Better we wait till it blows over."

But the Prince would not listen. Even four days, after the terrible exertions of the journey to Glenbeasdale, had seemed too long to lie idle, and he itched to be on the move. So Donald gave the order, the boatmen dipped their oars in unison, setting up a slow, lilting chant, and Charles sat down in the sternsheets at the pilot's feet.

They thrust out of Loch nan Uamh into long steep seas under a lowering sky. Ahead lay the narrow passage between the islands of Eigg and Muck, and then the open sea, with a stiff wind blowing across the Little Minch. Inside an hour, Donald's prediction was proved accurate, for the wind increased to gale force, and, as night drew on, spray pattered on their clothes, broken water slumped over the gunwales and swilled along the bilges, and the boat, struggling on athwart the seas, plunged and staggered drunkenly.

The boatmen set their sail to try to steady her, and darkness came. A roaring, heaving, sodden darkness, for the lowering skies poured a driving deluge down to hiss upon the frothing seas. It tasted sweet on the lips

after the salt tang of the spray and the spindrift. The
wind shifted to the east, and Donald, that consummate
old seaman, let her run before it, nursing her along.
A fresh slant of the wind added a new anxiety. They
might be driven upon the island of Skye, where their
enemies swarmed in numbers, where the Laird of
MacLeod's men were in arms for the government and
the Prince's life would soon be forfeit.

A sudden vivid flash lit up the struggling boat and
the wan, tense faces of the men crouching in her. Then
the thunder crackled and roared overhead, and flash after
flash in blinding succession split the pitch darkness and
glistened on the frothing wave crests. The Prince,
feeling himself at last wholly free, gloried in the storm
in this primitive battle with the elements, and raised his
voice in a favourite Gaelic song. The men joined in ;
but in time even the Prince's gallant voice was silenced.
The storm redoubled its fury, and the boat, scudding
before it, shipped green seas, staggered under the weight
of the blows that succeeded each other in relentless
procession, and but for Donald's expert hand and steady
nerve as he held the tiller she must have been swamped
or smashed.

The hours passed, in a nightmare of crashing thunder
and flickering lightning and the roar of wind and sea,
and as the horizon behind them lightened and the old
pilot, wiping his eyes, peered ahead there was a cry of
uttermost relief.

" The Long Isle ! It is her that is ahead ! "

By seven o'clock in the morning Donald was bringing
the boat towards the rocky shore of Rossinish, a point
of land on the north-east side of Benbecula. It was
tricky work, but Donald was equal to it, and the boatmen
were alert and agile. As the prow surged in they vaulted
into the water, Charles and O'Neil and Burke after them,
and laying hands on the boat dragged her clear of the
pounding surf. They carried her up to safety, and by
great good luck discovered a little hut near by. In a

few minutes the men had a fire kindled, and they wrung out their sodden garments and stamped about to warm their cramped limbs. Then Charles sallied out.

There was a croft near by, and an old woman with a quick smile for the young stranger.

" Will you sell me a cow, good wife? " asked Charles. " You see, I and my companions have been driven ashore by the storm."

She agreed willingly and the Prince pulled money from his sporran, paid her, and proudly led his purchase back. Ned acted slaughterman, and soon an appetising fragrance filled the hut, and the drenched and famished voyagers, crowding round the fire, sat in the steam of their sodden clothes and ate a hearty breakfast.

§

Of them all, gayest and most carefree seemed the Prince. When O'Sullivan spoke of their wretched plight he laughed lightly, clapped him on the back, and set him an example by spooning up his porridge or munching his hunk of beef with keen enjoyment. He had loved the fripperies and refinements of society and courts ; he loved still more the homely fare, the old sail for a bed on the floor of the hut, the feeling of self-reliance and of freedom.

When old Clanranald, who owned the island, came calling, he found a Prince remarkably cheerful and in no way dejected. He would not talk of the past. Like all the Stuarts he had one rare quality—he was a good loser. But he was completely convinced that by next summer he would be back, and not, this time, unaided. France would be compelled to move at last, and the cause would yet triumph. Meantime, all he thought of was the moment, and a ship to take him to France. Danger he disregarded, although the seas between swarmed with English ships. These last few days had renewed his faith in his destiny.

Clanranald was distressed. He knew that great bodies of regulars and militia had been landed in different parts of the Hebrides, that the Prince had many enemies in Lewis and in Skye. He suggested that Charles should see his brother, Boisdale, in South Uist.

It was an affecting meeting. Both remembered vividly that other meeting, when Boisdale had predicted disaster for the Prince. But the older man did not recall his words now. His loyalty had never been in question, and all he thought of was the Prince's safety.

" My advice to you, sir," he declared, after some discussion, " is to go to Stornoway. Give out that you and your company are the crew of a merchant ship from the Orkneys, wrecked on the island of Tiree. Hire a vessel to carry you home, and so you may escape to France."

It was sound advice, and on the 29th of April, two days after their arrival at Rossinish, the men put their boat in the water again, and the Prince set sail.

It seemed that the elements were ever at war with the Stuarts, for almost at once a south-westerly gale overtook them and Donald, knowing these dangerous waters well, turned the boat's head for shelter towards the isle of Scalpay, half-way on their voyage. In the dark, he found the shore in safety, and they landed about two hours before daybreak on the 30th.

" I have a friend here will help us," Donald declared, and led them off across the island to a farmhouse, where they knocked up the farmer. He came out buckling on his kilt and cried out at sight of MacLeod. They wrung each other's hands, and then the old man made his introductions.

" My friend, Donald Campbell—these gentlemen are merchants shipwrecked on their way to Orkney. I am carrying them to Stornoway to hire a vessel to take them home. This "—he pointed to O'Sullivan—" is Mr. Sinclair, and this "—he pointed to Charles—"is his son."

Campbell shook hands heartily.

"Welcome you are, gentlemen, to my house, for as long as you care to remain my guests."

It was an unpretentious place, but Charles had never been more hospitably entertained. Next morning old Donald borrowed a boat from his friend and went off to Stornoway in search of a ship, and on the 3rd of May a message came from him. He had been successful, and requested the Prince to hasten to Stornoway.

Next morning they embarked again, and once again storm drove them out of their course. There was nothing for it but to run into Loch Seaforth and land there, many miles from their destination. Allan MacDonald, the priest, took leave of the Prince here, and went off by himself, while the rest set off for the north.

There was no road, not even a track, but Burke was confident, and they trudged on through the night, in a steady downpour of rain ; but long before morning Ned was forced to admit he had gone astray. They were lost, and he had no idea where they were. They huddled together on the heather for warmth until daybreak, and it was noon before they came near the town.

Charles deliberated.

"It is late in the day to risk going into Stornoway," he said. "Had it been dawn, we might have been safely on board and no one the wiser."

"I will go and see Donald, your excellency," Ned proposed, and set off. He was back fairly soon, he and the old man bringing a welcome supply of bread and cheese and brandy, and they found Charles and his two companions standing patiently on the moors near the Point of Arynish, wet to the skin and drooping with fatigue. Donald cried out in distress, and led them at once to the house of Mrs. MacKenzie of Kildun, nearby, where the good lady sent the Prince to bed at once. He fell instantly asleep, and did not stir until Donald wakened him with news.

He had been into Stornoway again, and had had a very unpleasant experience. He found the town in commotion, with upwards of 200 men under arms, and all manner of rumours flying about. Boldly he had walked into the room in the inn where the gentlemen who had appointed themselves officers had assembled, and there Donald had demanded to know what was going on. For answer, the whole room rounded on him and abused him bitterly for bringing the Prince and his followers to Lewis.

Startled, Donald demanded to hear more of this, and it transpired that the Presbyterian minister of South Uist had sent word that Prince Charles was on his way to Lewis with 500 men to burn the town of Stornoway, carry off all the cattle, and force a vessel to take him to France. So the Lewismen were gathering to protect themselves !

Donald took a bold line.

" It is true the Prince is here," he told them. " But he has only two companions with him. And yet," he added, with sudden passion, " let me tell you further, gentlemen, if Seaforth himself were here, by God he durst not put a hand to the Prince's breast ! "

The company shuffled their feet and looked at the floor, until one of them spoke up.

" We have no intention of doing the Prince the slightest harm," he declared. " The only thing we require of him is to leave the island."

" That he will do at once," Donald promised instantly. ". But you must give us a pilot."

" No, we cannot do that."

" I would pay him liberally," Donald persisted ; but they refused, and Donald left them and hastened to the ship he had hired. But her master had changed his mind. He had heard the rumours that were going about, and was not going to be deceived into running so deadly a risk as was involved in a voyage to France with such dangerous passengers.

" We should take to the moors," O'Sullivan suggested anxiously, but the Prince shook his head.

" They would only come after us," he pointed out.

" Whereas while we are here they will leave us alone and give us time to depart."

So they remained overnight, and Mrs. MacKenzie gave them a cow for their food. Donald offered to pay for it, but she would not hear of that. He persisted, however, and in the end forced the money into her hand. He had no mind to have it said that the Prince cost people who were kind to him any undue expense.

Ned Burke acted as cook again ; but suddenly he was thrust aside.

" I'll show you how to cook, Ned ! " cried a laughing voice, and the Prince set to work. He prepared oatmeal and mixed in the brains of the cow, then baked his bannocks on a flat stone in front of the fire. They were excellent bannocks.

At daybreak next morning they embarked again, carrying a small stock of beef and oatmeal and abundance of sugar and brandy.

" Steer for Bollein in Kintail," Charles ordered ; but the boatmen refused.

" It is too long a voyage in an open boat. And besides, there are the English ships everywhere."

So instead they steered south, and very soon a cry of alarm went up. Two ships were sighted, steering north directly towards them. Donald promptly altered course, and ran in to the little isle of Iubhard, just north of the isle of Scalpay. They went ashore and climbed to the top of a little hill to watch the ships.

" They are French ! " Charles cried, with sudden excitement.

" I think not," O'Sullivan replied. " They are English."

The others agreed ; but Charles was convinced he was right ; and indeed so he was, for had he but known it they were frigates from Nantes which had reached Loch nan Uamh the very day after his departure from there. They had landed fresh supplies of money and arms and ammunition, and were now returning to France.

§

At first sight Iubhard seemed deserted. The handful of inhabitants, imagining the Prince's boat to be a press-gang cutter, had fled from their homes and hidden themselves, leaving their latest catch of fish drying on the rocks. The Prince and his friends helped themselves to some of the fish, and characteristically Charles pulled out money to leave on the rocks in payment. But the others protested. Such a gesture would only arouse suspicion that he was not just a common wayfarer, and might lead the bloodhounds too closely on his tracks.

For four days they remained on Iubhard, huddled into a wretched hovel they found, whose leaking roof they patched with the sail of the boat. They lay upon the bare floor without any covering, and kept watch by turns, the Prince standing his trick like the rest.

On the 10th Charles decided to go back to Scalpay and pay Donald Campbell a visit, so they embarked again. But Campbell was gone. He knew well who his guest had been, and word had got about that others also knew, and that he would be seized and imprisoned, perhaps shot, for helping the Prince; so he had fled from the island until the affair blew over.

There was nothing for it but to carry on, and as the wind had dropped the boatmen had to row, hour after hour until, at daybreak, a fresh breeze came and they hoisted sail again, scudding down the coast of Harris. Their only food was oatmeal now, and they had no fresh water on board; but the ever-ready Ned mixed the meal with sea-water and made it at least edible. The Prince ate this *drammach* heartily, and helped it down with a dram of brandy, pouring a dram from his bottle for each of the others.

Crossing the mouth of Finsbay, they sighted an English ship less than two musket-shots away. She instantly started in pursuit, and for three leagues followed them close; but Donald held his course calmly, and then

turned and headed in among the rocks off the point of
Rodil, where the ship dared not follow. But they had
no sooner shaken off one pursuer than another was after
them, coming out from Loch Maddy in North Uist and
giving chase. But their luck held, and Donald ran ashore
on Benbecula a short distance ahead of the two English
ships, which had joined company on the chase. Just then
a shift of wind came to their rescue and drove the ships
off the coast, so that for the moment there was no fear
of immediate pursuit.

It was extreme low water when they landed, and one
of the boatmen promptly took advantage of this fact,
searching the rocks for shellfish. Charles, ever eager for
any new ploy, had followed him to see what he was up
to, and now the boatman let out a whoop of triumph
and held up a large crab. Charles waved back to him,
went to the boat for a pail, and came running to join
him. Busily they searched the rocks and the little pools,
and soon the pail was full of crabs. The Prince took
hold of it triumphantly.

" Your royal highness," cried Donald, distressed, " you
must allow me to carry the pail."

" Certainly not ! " retorted Charles. " You and the
others can carry the baggage. *I'm* carrying the
commissariat ! Why, I caught most of them, didn't I ? "
And laughing like a boy he strode up to the hut they had
found for shelter. It was a mean, low structure, into
which they had to crawl on hands and knees, and was
probably used mainly for sheltering sheep in winter.
But it served, and sitting on the ground Charles scribbled
a note to old Clanranald to tell him he was back in
Benbecula.

The chief arrived in haste in answer to the note, to
promise all the help that lay in his power, and a servant
brought a welcome present from old Lady Clanranald—
half a dozen shirts, some shoes and stockings, wine and
brandy and other comforts.

After a few days in the hut, Clanranald advised a shift

to South Uist, but before he left Benbecula Charles sent the faithful old Donald MacLeod off to the mainland in Campbell's boat, with letters to Lochiel and Murray of Broughton, asking how affairs stood with them and requesting a supply of money and brandy. Then on the 16th of May he moved to South Uist, where he found shelter in the house of one of Clanranald's tenants at Coradale. It was known as the Forest House of Glencoradale, remotely situated and therefore fairly safe ; but it was in bad repair, and two cow hides had to be rigged on sticks over the Prince's bed to keep him dry while he slept. Compared with previous lodging places, it was palatial, and Charles was well content.

Every day he went out with his gun, for the island abounded with game, and once more he displayed that almost legendary prowess of his, startling his companions by bringing down birds on the wing with complete ease. He never pulled a trigger but he scored a hit ; and when the bag was sufficient there was always another diversion to be had. He would go out in a boat with hand-lines and catch lyth, a small Hebridean fish of inferior flavour but good food nevertheless.

Twelve stalwart men were in attendance, at Clanranald's orders, to act as guides and guards, and for a while at least the Prince enjoyed every moment of his days, forgetting the disaster that had overwhelmed him and the terrible tragedy being enacted not so far away.

But the net was drawing closer. More than fifteen hundred men had been landed on the Long Island to search for him, every beach was guarded, and the seas were infested with English ships. More than a hundred people in South Uist knew his hiding place—and knew also that £30,000 would be paid to anyone who gave information. But no one spoke.

Donald MacLeod arrived back from the mainland. He had met Lochiel and Murray of Broughton at the head of Loch Arkaig, and they had given him letters for the Prince, but he brought back only gloomy news. The redcoats were in all the glens, plundering, murdering, burning. Everywhere they went they shot the men on sight, raped the women and drove them with their children naked out on to the bare hillsides. They rounded up their cattle and sheep, they pillaged the houses and burned them to the ground. Swarms of English cattle dealers had come to Inverness, buying cattle from the English soldiery at a few shillings a head. All over the Highlands—Whig as well as Jacobite, fire and sword were devastating the land, leaving misery and starvation and death behind them. It was a terrible tale of wanton savagery, and nothing could be done to stop it. Droves of black cattle—often more than 2,000 in a drove—were going south while the Highlands, stripped of their wealth, their livelihood, lay smoking and desolate. Bands of soldiers, avid for blood, would rush into the hamlets, and when the women and children ran screaming for the hills they would shoot them as they ran. . . .

Lochiel could give no help, no reassurance, and no hope.

As for Murray of Broughton, he showed up at last in his true colours. He had, he declared, no money to spare —only sixty louis d'or which he proposed to keep for his own necessities. Charles could whistle for help from his former Secretary.

In the middle of June more alarming news arrived. The military had landed on Eriskay ; he must be on the run again.

He left with his four companions in Campbell's boat on the 14th, and landed on the little isle of Wiay, where he stayed four nights ; then, leaving O'Sullivan and Donald MacLeod on Wiay, he went on with O'Neil and Burke to Rossinish. After two nights there, word came that the militia were landing in Benbecula, and he resolved to return to the shelter of Coradale.

MacLeod, who had also had word, anticipated the design, and he and O'Sullivan brought the boat to Rossinish overnight. Storm again attended them, and the gale, driving torrential rain before it, forced them to

land among the rocks at Uishinish point, where they hid
in a cleft of the cliffs. Ned Burke went scouting, came
back to report their enemies less than two miles away,
and in the darkness they set sail again, steering for
Loch Boisdale. But they soon encountered another boat,
and turned about to seek refuge among the rocks again.

They reached Loch Boisdale next day, and instantly
heard alarming news. Boisdale had been arrested. For
a moment only Charles was dismayed, for he had depended
upon Boisdale for guidance to some safe hiding place ;
but, thrown on his own resources, he recovered his
spirits at once and led his little party off to skulk about
the shores of the Loch. At intervals, Lady Boisdale
managed to send them food ; and all the time they had
fresh food for thought. The Minch was alive with
warships. At one time Charles counted fifteen sail in
sight together, and when two of them entered the Loch
he had to abandon the precious boat and take to the
hills.

For two nights they slept in the fields, using the sail
for a tent ; then they moved higher up the inlet for the
next two nights, and word was brought of approaching
danger. Captain Caroline Scott, almost as notorious as
General Hawley and others for his savage cruelty, had
landed with 500 regulars and militia within a mile and
a half of their hiding places.

"We must separate instantly," Charles decided.
"O'Neil, you will come with me. The rest must shift
for themselves. God speed you, gentlemen."

He rose to take leave of them. For a long moment he
and Donald MacLeod looked into each other's eyes ; and
as they shook hands the old Highlander turned his head
away, to hide the tears that streamed down his wrinkled
cheeks.

§

O'Neil was a cheerful companion. Young and active

like Charles, he was prepared for any risk, and the two set off at speed for Benbecula. It was hard going, but they were both fit and strong, and inured by now to any hardships. The Prince, at least, need not control his impatience and slow his pace to that of older men. He could stride out at his best speed, and at midnight they were well to the north and approaching a little dark cottage.

" I will go ahead, sir," O'Neil offered, " and see what chance brings."

Charles waited outside, and the Irishman disappeared. He seemed to be gone a very long time, and Charles, listening intently, could hear voices arguing earnestly. Then at last he reappeared and beckoned the Prince. He led him indoors.

A young woman rose at his entry, and in the candlelight the Prince saw that she was pleasant to look upon, with kind eyes and a smiling, vivacious face. He knew instinctively that he had found a friend.

She dropped a curtsey, and O'Neil performed the introduction.

" Your royal highness, may I be permitted to present the Lady Flora MacDonald of Milton, in South Uist? Miss MacDonald, this is his royal highness, Prince Charles Edward Stuart."

The Prince bowed; the lady curtsied again; and suddenly Charles held out his hand.

CHAPTER SIXTEEN

FLORA MACDONALD

Far over yon hills of the heather sae green,
An' doon by the corrie that sings to the sea,
The bonnie young Flora sat sighing her lane,
The dew on her plaid and the tear in her e'e.
She look'd at a boat with the breezes that swung
Away on the wave, like a bird on the wing,
And ay as it lessen'd she sighed and she sung :
" Fareweel to the lad I shall ne'er see again !
Fareweel to my hero, the gallant and young,
Fareweel to the lad I shall ne'er see again ! "

THERE was a sparkle about young O'Neil as he performed
the introductions. He had met Miss Flora recently at
Clanranald's house, Ormaclade, where the Prince had
been too much taken up with shooting and fishing and
enjoying the gipsy life to be interested in the society of
the young ladies of the island ; and O'Neil made no
secret of the fact that he had fallen in love.

Flora, the daughter of MacDonald of Milton, had been
left an orphan when only a year old, and her widowed
mother had later married MacDonald of Armadale, in
Skye. Now she was twenty-four, of middle height,
lovely and vivacious. The hut where O'Neil had so

324

providentially discovered her belonged to her only
brother, Angus, with whom she had made her home.

O'Neil, reminding her that she had often said she
would do anything she could to help the Prince, had
promptly suggested she should dress him up as a woman,
pass him off as her maid, and take him to Skye. At
first she refused. Her stepfather was in South Uist, in
command of a company of the Skye MacDonalds whom
Sir Alexander had raised in the government service, and
through him she knew that there were MacDonald,
MacLeod and Campbell militia roaming all over the
Long Isle in search of Charles. There were guards at
every ferry, and no one could leave the island without a
passport. The Minch swarmed with ships, and there
was no hope of getting across unperceived.

O'Neil knew something about women. As Flora was
determined in her refusal, he played his trump card, and
called Charles into the hut.

Sheer pity of the Prince's plight would alone have
been enough to change her mind ; but besides that, she
had been brought up a confirmed Jacobite, and the
stirring story of the rebellion and of the Prince's escape
had fired her imagination. The poor lad was worn and
thin and exhausted, yet he summoned a cheerful smile,
greeting her with all the charm and dignity and courtesy
of his Holyrood days, and in an instant she was conquered.
In face of such fortitude and courage as she read in his
eyes she could not refuse her help.

" I will go at once to Clanranald," she promised, and
set off immediately with her servant, Neil MacEachan,
who, incidentally, was the father of that distinguished
soldier, Marshal MacDonald, Duke of Tarentum. Charles
and O'Neil settled down to wait.

They had to wait until four o'clock the following
afternoon, when a messenger arrived.

" All is well," he reported simply, and the pair decided
to go at once. But the messenger shook his head. " Both
the fords between South Uist and Benbecula are strongly

guarded," he told them. " You will not get across."
" Then what are we to do ? " O'Neil demanded.
" Wait you," replied the messenger. " I will see."

He disappeared, and presently returned with a local
man who would row them over to Benbecula. They
started at once, and the passage was made in safety.

" Go on, and meet us at the far side of the island,"
Charles ordered the boatmen as they pushed off, and he
and O'Neil set out on foot. A few minutes later they
realised that something had gone wrong. They were
cut off. They had landed on a rocky islet and not upon
the mainland. They hallooed after the boat, but it was
out of earshot, and they went back to study the situation.
How the mistake arose could not be known. Perhaps
the boatmen had been frightened, wanted to get rid of
their dangerous passengers as quickly as possible ; perhaps
in the heavy weather they had made a genuine mistake.
But Charles pointed out that it was now high tide.

" When the tide goes out we may be able to wade over,"
he suggested ; so they sat down to wait. Hours passed—
and the narrow turbulent stretch of water separating
them from the land was still impassable. For a moment
his spirit might have quailed, for they were marooned
on a desert islet from which there seemed no escape ;
but Charles had never yet given way to despair, and it
was in difficulty that he showed up best. He left O'Neil
to ponder, and started a vigorous exploration of the whole
islet, until he found a place where he believed he could
cross over.

They were soaked and famished, weak from privation
and fatigue ; but Charles plunged into the water boldly
and struck out. O'Neil followed, and soon they were
trudging over the now familiar moors towards Rossinish.
They arrived about midnight, and Charles, going ahead
to reconnoitre, saw a body of militia stationed close by.
They turned and retraced their steps some distance, and
then Charles found shelter among the rocks and lay down
while O'Neil went off to Ormaclade.

Charles watched him go and sat for a while, thinking. Then, shivering with cold and wet, he got up and began walking in a circle, and stumbled upon a deserted hovel. He crawled into it, pulled his sodden plaid tighter round him, and went to sleep.

But he did not sleep long.

Hunger gnawed at him, he was chilled to the bone, and soon he sat up, took a swig of brandy to give him strength, and sallied out. He must have food. He found it—a sheep which he captured dexterously and carried off to his hut. A fire was the next requisite, and he went out to collect driftwood and tinder, whittling away the wet outer wood with his knife. Soon the wretched little hovel had become a home, with a fire blazing and mutton roasting on a spit, and the Prince, all else forgotten, settled down to enjoy these luxuries in solitary splendour. His steaming clothes dried by degrees, and although he had to go frequently to the door to keep watch, the danger only added extra spice to a situation in which, finally, he had to rely entirely upon himself. He enjoyed those hours immensely.

§

Next day, the 27th of June, his alert ear caught a soft whistle in the distance, and he took a quick look out of the door to see a party approaching. Then he went back to his work. So when O'Neil came in, leading Flora and MacEachan and Lady Clanranald and another lady, Mrs. MacDonald, they stopped in amazement at sight of their Prince calmly squatting on the floor roasting the heart, liver and kidneys of a sheep on a wooden spit. He jumped up at once and the ladies were introduced, and cried out in distress at finding him in such a situation.

Charles laughed.

"A man must eat," he cried gaily. "And a prince ought to be able to do everything better than any of his subjects. Let me give you some recipes, Lady Clanranald!"

His boyish high spirits won their hearts. Was not this a prince to serve at any risk or trouble? Presently he rose again and bowed to them.

"Mesdames, messieurs, dinner is served."

He placed stools for them, Flora on his right, Lady Clanranald on his left, and solemnly they ate the meal he had prepared. Then Flora told of her adventures.

On the way to Ormaclade she and MacEachan, not having passports, had been seized by the military and locked up until the next morning. Then they had been brought before the commanding officer, whom Flora had greeted with a quiet smile.

"Good morning, Father . . . " It was Captain Hugh MacDonald of Armadale himself. Amazed and upset, he had offered her his deepest apologies, and Flora took advantage of the situation with quick-witted perception.

"I want to go to Skye," she told her stepfather. "May I have passports for myself and Neil and my maid, Betty Burke?"

Captain MacDonald agreed readily. He was fond of Flora, and glad that she was to be out of the way while the Long Isle was filled with the military. She would be safe with her mother in Skye. He promptly wrote a letter to his wife:

> "I have sent your daughter from this country lest she should be any way frightened with the troops lying here. She has got one Betty Burke, an Irish girl who, as she tells me, is a good spinster. If her spinning pleases you, you may keep her till she spin all your lint; or, if you have any wool to spin, you may employ her. I have sent Neil Mackechan along with your daughter, and Betty Burke to take care of them.
>
> "I am your dutiful husband,
>
> "HUGH MacDONALD.

"June 22, 1746."

Charles, hearing what his next job might be, roared
with laughter.

Flora also explained that she had hired a six-oared
boat for the journey to Skye, and it was to be ready
next day.

After dinner, they started to dress Charles for his part.
The clothes Lady Clanranald had provided were suited
to his new station in life, and besides the flowered linen
gown, the light-coloured quilted petticoat and white
apron, she had thoughtfully included a mantle with a
hood in the Irish fashion. They could take no risks with
the Prince's disguise.

For the moment they forgot how deadly serious this
game was, and the little hovel was filled with roars of
laughter as Charles, striding back and forth, tried to
shorten his steps and mince along convincingly. There
was one difficulty that had not occurred to any of them.
It was not going to be easy to keep a straight face while
Betty Burke was about ! She persisted in bursting into
stifled guffaws, making large, mannish gestures, and
cursing her petticoats.

The ladies left to return to Ormaclade, attended by

MacEachan, and in the evening they all met again on the shore, about a mile from the house, for supper in the open air. They had no sooner started to eat than a servant came running. General Campbell himself with a large party of soldiers and marines was at Ormaclade House ! Lady Clanranald hurried off home to allay suspicions, enduring a long interrogation with complete calmness. She had, she declared, been visiting a sick child.

The others went down to the beach where the boat lay afloat, and Charles kindled a fire on the rocks to warm them ; but suddenly four boats appeared, crammed with soldiers and making directly towards them. They smothered the fire and hid among the rocks, but the boats went on and landed about a gunshot away.

" We must wait until evening," the Prince decided, and the party remained hidden among the rocks until dusk. Then, at eight o'clock on the 28th, they embarked. Charles and O'Neil shook hands, and for a moment the Prince's spirits sank very low. He was taking farewell of his last remaining companion, a man whom he could trust implicitly.

But Flora had been firm. The passports were only for herself and two servants ; she could not risk taking a fourth into the boat.

The boatmen pushed off. It was a serene and lovely evening, and when they hoisted sail only a gentle breeze, rippling over the smooth water, wafted the boat along ; but the weather could never treat a Stuart in this way for long, and soon clouds began banking up, and they had gone less than three miles when the wind rose and one of the sudden terrible Minch storms was upon them.

> Speed, bonnie boat, like a bird on the wing,
>   Onward, the sailors cry.
> Carry the lad that is born to be king
>   Over the sea to Skye !

Loud the winds howl, loud the waves roar,
  Thunderclouds rend the air.
Baffled, our foes stand by the shore,
  Follow they will not dare !

Charles sat completely calm. He had lived through tempest before ; it had no terrors for him. But the rest, perhaps knowing better than he the full danger, soon became alarmed. It would take all their skill to keep afloat, and the little craft staggered on into the seething, plunging darkness, with men bailing desperately as the seas broke over her. Charles began talking, quietly, telling them stories of Italy, of his childhood, of the campaign. Amusing stories that caught their attention, that compelled their laughter. Then, when the stories began to pall, he sang, in his pleasant, well-trained voice —Gaelic airs mostly, which he had picked up on the campaign, and also a spirited tune composed on the occasion of the restoration of Charles II.

Eventually Flora, tired out, fell asleep, and the Prince, moving close to her, protected her from the broaching seas and saw that she was not disturbed. When daylight came, the boat was out of sight of land.

" Where are we ? " Charles asked ; but the boatmen shook their heads. The wind had shifted several times during the night, and they had had to keep before it. They could not tell where they had been driven during those terrible hours of storm. But suddenly one of them pointed.

" Vaternish ! " he cried, and soon they were running close to the point.

A musket-shot cracked, and then a whole fusillade followed, and voices called to them in Gaelic. It was a party of MacLeod militia.

" Put in to the shore and be examined ! "

They held their course. The militia fired again.

" Don't be afraid of those fellows," Charles told the boatmen.

" We are not afraid for ourselves, sir," one of them retorted. " Our only fear is for your highness."

" No fear of me ! " he replied with a laugh, and turned to Flora.

" Lie down in the bottom of the boat, Miss MacDonald," he begged her. " You will be out of the way of the bullets then."

Smiling, she shook her head.

" I am here to preserve the life of my prince. I will never degrade myself by attending to my own safety while my master is in danger. I beg *you* to lie down, your royal highness."

Charles shook his head in turn ; but as the fusillade grew more intense—and less erratic—he pleaded with her again. Flora remained obstinate, and at last Charles cried :

" Very well, then we will *both* lie down ! "

By then they were almost out of musket-shot, and soon they had passed that danger. The boat headed for a small creek, where they went ashore and, after easing their cramped limbs, rowed on again to Kilbride. They landed only a short distance from Sir Alexander MacDonald's house, Monkstadt, near the north end of the island.

It seemed a highly dangerous proceeding, for Sir Alexander MacDonald was even then with the Duke of Cumberland, and had called out his whole clan against the Prince ; but his wife Margaret, a daughter of the Earl of Eglintoun, was a staunch Jacobite. Charles had already written to her, under cover of a letter from Hugh MacDonald of Balishair, in North Uist, to his brother, Donald Roy, in which Hugh said that Charles would seek refuge on the little isle of Fladdachuan near Trotternish, and requested Donald Roy to keep strict watch for him, and supply him with necessities when he arrived.

Flora set off at once with MacEachan to visit Lady Margaret. It was fortunate that the Prince stayed

behind, for an officer of the MacLeod militia was at
Monkstadt at the time, and he immediately interrogated
Flora closely about her journey. Her ready answers
satisfied him completely, but Lady Margaret, who had
guessed the truth, was highly alarmed for the Prince's
safety. Her presence of mind saved the situation, and
she played up to Flora's inventions with remarkable
quickness of wits.

Her husband's factor, MacDonald of Kingsburgh, was
in the house, and she drew him out into the garden to
discuss the situation privately. She also sent for Donald
Roy, who promptly saddled a horse and rode over, to
find the pair walking up and down in earnest
conversation.

" Oh, Donald Roy, we are ruined for ever ! " Lady
Margaret cried at seeing him ; but she already had a
plan. The Prince should be taken to old Raasay, who was
himself in hiding with some friends, and until that
could be arranged he should stay at Kingsburgh.

Meanwhile Charles was still sitting on the shore, in
the guise of Betty Burke. MacEachan was sent to warn
him that Kingsburgh would visit him, and urged him
to leave the shore and hide behind a hill. But when
Kingsburgh arrived at the spot there was no sight of
Charles, and he searched for him in vain. He was on
the point of going back when he saw a suspicious movement among a flock of sheep, and hurried over, to find
a large ungainly female squatting on the ground. The
female leapt up and strode towards him cautiously,
grasping a large stick. Kingsburgh smiled.

" I am MacDonald of Kingsburgh, come to serve your
royal highness."

Charles wrung his hand, and listened eagerly to Lady
Margaret's plan.

Meanwhile Flora was doing her part. The MacLeod
officer, satisfied with her answers, was for sallying out
on a tour of inspection of the neighbourhood, and it
took all her invention to keep the conversation going

so that, out of politeness, he could find no opportunity
to excuse himself and escape. Finally dinner was
announced, to their great relief, and the ladies prolonged
the meal to its utmost. In the end, Flora rose to go,
but Lady Margaret pressed her to stay, saying that Flora
had long promised to visit her and now was an excellent
chance. The officer, listening to this feminine chatter,
was wholly deceived, and felt very sympathetic when
Flora declared she must go to her mother, who must be
very anxious and worried with her husband away with
his militia.

Flora took her leave, going off with Neil and a Mrs.
MacDonald, who was accompanied by two servants, a
man and a woman. The party went on horseback, and
soon overtook Charles and Kingsburgh, who were, of
course, on foot. Mrs. MacDonald's maid, staring at
Charles, exclaimed to Flora :

" I've never in all my life seen such an impudent
looking woman as that one that Kingsburgh's walking
with ! I wonder who she is ? Either she's one of those
terrible Irish women, or else it's a man in disguise ! "

" You're quite right," Flora replied readily. " It's an
Irishwoman. I've seen her before."

" Bless me ! " cried the maid, " what long strides the
jade takes, and how awkwardly she manages her petticoats ! "

Flora merely nodded, and touched her mount, setting
the whole party into a canter so that the maid's attention
was distracted ; and Charles and Kingsburgh, leaving
the road, cut away across country and reached the house
an hour before midnight. Flora and MacEachan arrived
immediately after, and a maid went up to announce to
Kingsburgh's wife, who had gone to bed, that her husband
had arrived with guests. A moment later Kingsburgh's
little girl burst into the bedroom and announced :

" Father's back, and he's brought the most odd muckle
ill-shaken-up wife I've ever seen, and taken her into the
hall too ! "

Mrs. MacDonald sat up ; and next moment her husband strode in.

" You must dress, my dear," he told her, " and get supper for our guests."

" But who are they ? " she exclaimed, protesting.

" No time for explanations now," her husband flung back at her, striding out. " But make haste."

Mrs. MacDonald got up.

" Go and fetch my keys from the hall," she told her daughter, but the little girl came back immediately, shaking with fright.

" I c-couldn't go into the hall, mother," she sobbed. " That awful woman is walking up and down there."

Mrs. MacDonald went down herself ; but at sight of the strange female her own courage failed, and she called to her husband to get her keys.

" Fetch them yourself, ma'am," he called back, and, trembling a little, Mrs. MacDonald ventured into the room. The large female had sat down ; but at sight of her leapt up and strode forward and kissed her on both cheeks, in the Highland manner. The good lady, shocked by the roughness of a male chin when she had expected something very different, fled incontinently and demanded of her husband who his guest was.

" My dear," he said quietly, " the person in the hall is the Prince himself."

" The Prince ! " she gasped. " Then we are all ruined. We'll all be hanged now ! "

" Hoot," said her husband, " we can die but once, and if we are hanged for this we'll die in a good cause, doing only an act of humanity and charity. But go, make haste with supper. Bring us eggs, butter, cheese, and whatever else can be got quickly ready."

" Eggs, butter, cheese ! " cried his wife. " What a supper is that for a Prince ! "

" Ah, wife," Kingsburgh replied, heavily, " you know little how this good Prince has lived of late. This will be a feast to him. Besides, to make a formal supper would make the servants suspect something. The less ceremony the better. Make haste, and come to supper yourself."

But at that Mrs. MacDonald demurred.

" *I* come to supper? I know not how to behave before majesty ! "

" You must come," her husband told her. ", The Prince will not eat one bit without you ; and you will find it no difficult matter to behave before him, so obliging and easy is he in his conversation."

So it proved. As before, Charles placed Flora on his right, and his hostess on his left. He ate a hearty supper, drank a bumper of brandy to the health and prosperity of his host and hostess, and afterwards smoked a pipe. He had taken to smoking recently, because it relieved a toothache that was plaguing him, and this new habit had, oddly enough, been the occasion of displaying the ingenuity he always had in devising makeshifts and contriving things for himself. The stems of the clay pipes were fragile and often broke, but Charles would take quills and, forcing one inside another, lengthen the broken stem enough to ensure a cool smoke.

§

To her great alarm Mrs. MacDonald learnt that Flora had sent the boat back at once.

" The boatmen will be taken and made to betray the Prince ! " she cried ; and so it happened. Seized as they reached home, they were carried off by the military and questioned closely. They refused to speak.

" Take them out and shoot them," the officer ordered, then changed his mind. " By God, I'll make the dogs talk ! "

He succeeded. Under torture one of them eventually told all he knew ; but by then the danger had been foreseen.

A good bed was something that Charles had been a stranger to for many weeks. Three or four hours' sleep at a stretch was all he had had since the start of his wanderings, and now he almost slept the clock round. He was wakened by Kingsburgh, at Flora's urgent request, and as soon as he had dressed the ladies came to tie his apron and cap. Mrs. MacDonald, in Gaelic, begged Flora to ask for a lock of the Prince's hair ; she refused, so the good lady applied to him herself, and at once Charles laid his head in Flora's lap, and bade her cut off the lock of yellow hair, which she divided in two.

The two men then left, Kingsburgh carrying a large bundle, and once clear of the house Charles threw off the garments of Betty Burke, kicking them aside with infinite relief and a humorous comment, and put on the new Highland dress his host had brought for him. There were new shoes as well, and picking up the Prince's old, worn-out brogues Kingsburgh cried :

" I will faithfully keep them till you are in St. James's. I will introduce myself by shaking them at you, to put you in mind of your night's entertainment and protection under my roof."

The Prince laughed.

" You must keep that promise, Kingsburgh ! " he exclaimed, and, embracing his host, he thanked him with deep feeling for all he had done. Then, with a boy called MacQueen for guide, the Prince set out across the hills. Flora went on along the Portree road on horseback to spy out the land ahead.

Donald Roy had gone to Portree in search of young Raasay, who had taken no part in the rising. When he heard of the Prince's dilemma, he at once offered to send word to his father, who was skulking in Knoydart, but he strongly advised against the Prince's going to the mainland. The best place, at the moment, would be Raasay itself ; but how were they to get him there ? They could not trust a Portree crew, and in this quandary young John of Raasay sought out his brother, Dr. Murdoch MacLeod, who had been wounded fighting on the Prince's side at Culloden.

" I'll risk my life again for my Prince, and gladly ! "
Murdoch declared. " There's a little boat lying at Loch
Fada. It's two miles from there to the sea, but we can
manage it."

There were no men they could trust, but Murdoch
found some women to help, and together they dragged
the boat up from the loch, over the hills and the moors
and the bogs to the precipitous shore. It was a terrible
journey, but they persisted, lowering the boat down the
precipices to the beach, and rowed it over to Raasay at
night with the help of a boy.

Young Raasay's cousin Malcolm, a captain in the
Prince's army, was then hiding on the island, and when
he heard their news he offered to help at once.

" But," he added to young Raasay, " you must not
run the risk of being involved in this. You were not
out, the government cannot touch you, and so the estates
are safe. But if you go to the Prince now you may lose
everything—— "

" I'll go to the Prince, even if it cost the estates and
my head as well ! " young Raasay retorted vehemently,
and Malcolm gave way.

" In God's name then, let us go," he cried, and brought
two strong boatmen to row them back to Skye. When
they came to the beach the boatmen hesitated.

" Not a step do we go into the boat," they declared,
" until we know where it is you want us to go."

Malcolm looked them in the eye.

" We are going to Skye to save the Prince," he told
them simply, and they nodded.

" In that case we are your men."

It was Monday evening, the 30th of June, and they
landed soon not half a mile from Portree. Malcolm left
young Raasay and his brother at the boat with one of
the men, John MacKenzie, while and he the other,
Donald MacFriar, made their way towards the inn.

Flora had arrived there with MacEachan, and had met
Donald Roy, who had given her the news of Raasay and

then gone out to look for the Prince. He had not found him, and, fearing the wound in his foot, still open since Culloden, would fester in the torrential downpour, he had to go back to the inn. Meanwhile Charles was plodding over the hills with the boy MacQueen, and presently came down towards the village.

" Go ahead," he said to the boy, and young MacQueen hastened off. He spoke to the landlord, MacNab, who found Donald Roy and brought the boy to him.

" There is a gentleman waiting a little above the house to speak to you," MacQueen told him, and Donald Roy hastened out.

Charles greeted him in silence, embracing him in his arms, and the pair went to the inn. The Prince, soaked to the skin, called for a dram, and started to change into a dry shirt ; but before he could dress again the roasted fish and bread and cheese that Donald Roy had ordered for him arrived. Still in his shirt tails, Charles flung himself into a chair and began to eat ravenously.

Donald Roy, sick at heart to see his Prince brought to such a pass, attempted a joke.

" That will no doubt be the English fashion ! "

" What fashion? " asked Charles, astonished.

" Why," said Donald Roy, " they say that when the English eat heartily they throw off their clothes."

Charles laughed.

" A good idea, too," he replied. " Because then there is nothing to get in the way of your hands when they are at work ! "

Presently, his first hunger appeased, he asked for a drink.

" There is nothing in the house but whisky and water," MacNab replied, mournfully. " Not even a glass of milk ! "

" Then water it must be," said Charles. But there was no jug in the room—only an old battered pail MacNab used for bailing his boat. It was full of fresh water, and Donald Roy, taking a drink himself, handed it over.

Charles looked at Donald, and Donald looked at Charles then whispered rapidly :

" For God's sake, sir, drink, whatever the pail be like ! "

The Prince, taking the hint, put the pail to his head and drank. Then as soon as the landlord was gone Donald Roy urged him to dress and get away.

" Man, it's teeming with rain, and it's dry and warm in here," Charles protested ; but Donald Roy was firm.

" There is no safety here—and the boat is waiting."

The Prince gave way, and calling for the landlord, demanded some tobacco.

" Only roll or pigtail," MacNab told him.

" Then that will serve," retorted Charles, and when the tobacco was weighed out handed over a sixpence. MacNab counted out three halfpence in change, and Charles was for waving it away ; but Donald Roy cut in impatiently:

" Take it, man, take it. In your present pass you may yet find three bawbees useful ! "

Charles slipped the money into his sporran.

" Come with me to Raasay, Donald Roy," he begged. " So long as I have a MacDonald with me I feel safe."

The other man shook his head.

" My wound festers, I am but a lame man," he replied. " I could be of little use to your royal highness when walking is in it. I can be of more use here in Skye, gathering news, and I will see you soon. I will come to Raasay when I can."

They went to join Flora, waiting to say good-bye. For a long moment neither spoke ; then the Prince, trying to cover his distress, put a hand into his sporran and pulled out some money.

" I borrowed a sum of you recently," he told her, " and I must pay my debts."

Silently she took the money, the exact amount she had lent him. There was another pause ; then he pulled out a miniature of himself.

" I beg you will keep this, Miss Flora, to remind you of me, and of all you have done for me."

She accepted it, and her eyes were blinded with tears. Then suddenly he took her in his arms and kissed her on both cheeks.

"From the bottom of my heart I thank you," he said quietly, and added after a moment, with a gallant smile : "Perhaps we shall yet meet in St. James's !"

He turned away, and wrung Neil MacEachan's hand. Neither could guess then that Neil was yet to accompany him into exile. Then he picked up the whole of his belongings—a bottle of whisky he had bought from the landlord, which he tied to his belt at one side, a bottle of brandy, four shirts, some sugar and a cold fowl which Kingsburgh had given him, which he made up into a bundle and tied at the other side, and thus equipped he went out into the pouring night, with Donald Roy at his heels.

CHAPTER SEVENTEEN

BROKEN MEN

Come o'er the stream, Charlie, dear Charlie, brave Charlie,
Come o'er the stream, Charlie, and dine wi' MacLean !
And though you be weary we'll make your heart cheery,
And welcome our Charlie and his loyal train !
We'll bring down the track deer, we'll bring down the black
    steer,
The lamb from the breckan, and doe from the glen ;
The salt sea we'll harry, and bring to our Charlie
The cream from the bothy, and curd from the pen !
          MacLean's Welcome, from the Gaelic.

It was still dark, the early morning of the 1st of July.
MacNab, watching him go, showed surprise at this
strange departure, and Donald Roy promptly led him
off in the opposite direction from the beach till they
were out of sight, when he cut across country towards
the boat. As they walked, they met Malcolm MacLeod,
and Donald Roy said good-bye. He went back to the
inn and stopped for a casual word with the landlord.

"That was Sir John MacDonald, poor man. An
Irish gentleman and a brother rebel, may God help him !
He has got free of his enemies and has been in hiding
with his kinsmen, the MacDonalds here. Give me your

word, MacNab, that you will not betray the poor man."

"I will never do that, your honour," the landlord replied; "you may depend upon it. But to my mind the gentleman looked more like the Prince in disguise. There was something very noble about the man."

Young Raasay received the Prince with fervent allegiance. It was by no wish of his that he had not been "out" in the Forty-Five. But the chiefs had been cautious ; so far as possible they had seen to it that one member of the family remained behind who could not be accused of complicity in the rising if it failed, and who therefore might keep the estates intact ; and young John had been chosen for this inactive role. But the Prince's dire need absolved him, he thought, from family duty now, and he took the risk lightly.

Charles managed to sleep a little in the boat, and they reached Raasay at daybreak without mishap. They landed at Glam, a distance of only ten miles from Portree, and sought shelter at once in a hut some shepherds had recently erected. There, while young Raasay went home, the rest kindled a fire and ate breakfast —oatmeal bread and whisky, for Charles had set himself a rule. He would never touch wheaten bread or brandy so long as the native oatmeal and whisky lasted—" my own country's bread and drink," he called them.

Young Raasay knew that he could trust his own people implicitly, and he placed guards to keep watch for any sign of suspicious movement across the sound. He visited the prince often, always bringing food with him, and for a while the fugitives lay in perfect safety. But they became alarmed by the sight of a stranger, a packman who had landed a fortnight before from Skye. He had sold all his wares, but instead of departing he remained on the island, wandering aimlessly about, and Malcolm, seeing him approaching the hut, raised the alarm. The three MacLeods were for killing him at once, to be on the safe side, but Charles would not hear of it.

" God forbid we should take away a man's life who

may be innocent, while we can preserve our own ! " he cried angrily, whereat John MacKenzie, the boatman, muttered to himself in Gaelic, which Charles did not catch :

" Well, well, the man must be shot. You are the king, but we are the parliament and we'll do what *we* choose ! "

The other smiled, and Charles, suspicious, demanded to be told what John had said. When he heard it, he laughed heartily, but repeated that the stranger must not be shot. Luckily the matter did not go further, for the unsuspecting packman wandered away in the other direction and disappeared. It transpired later that he was himself a fugitive from Culloden, disguised as a tobacco vendor.

There was only one relief from the monotony of idleness—talk ; and the four sat and talked interminably. Charles repeatedly asked about Dr. MacLeod's wound, caused by a ball which had entered at one shoulder and ploughed its way across to the other. When the MacLeod's tried to get him to give an opinion about the different Highland troops, he refused to be drawn.

" I do not like comparisons among brave men," he said. " They are all of them the best."

But now a new trouble afflicted the Prince. Hitherto he had been too much on the run, kept too busy with his plans and movements, to give thought to what was happening elsewhere. Now the plight in which he had left the loyal Highlands pressed more and more upon his thoughts, and, sitting in enforced idleness, he brooded upon the terrible consequences of the rising. Malcolm MacLeod overheard him often in his sleep, talking in Italian or French or English, and often he would cry out, in the anguish of his dreams : " Oh, God ! Poor Scotland ! "

Tortured thus, he could not rest, and after only two days in Raasay was impatient to be gone, as if seeking escape from his thoughts in action. His friends could do nothing with him, and that evening the whole party set off in the leaky old boat, landing about midnight at Nicolson's Rock near Scorobreck, in Trotternish. It had been a wild crossing, and several times the others had begged Charles to put back to Raasay ; but he refused to listen. Danger from the sea meant nothing to him, and after the fifteen turbulent and arduous miles he was the third man to leap out of the boat into the heavy surf, and seized hold of the gunwale to help carry her up on to the shore.

The only shelter they could find was a cowshed belonging to Nicolson of Scorobreck, and here they crowded in and had a meal. It consisted only of some oat-cakes that had mouldered down to crumbs, and some hard cheese. Thereafter Charles, still sitting in his wet clothes, fell asleep from sheer fatigue ; but the constant soakings, the long spells of fasting and frequent exposure had begun to take toll of even his tremendous vitality. Several times he started to his feet, wild-eyed and desperate, as if to defend himself ; then he would sink down again in a dazed way and fall into an uneasy slumber.

The effect of this troubled night lingered with him, and in the morning he found himself eyeing his companions with a new alertness, almost a suspicion. He became obsessed with the need to cover his tracks completely, to confuse the issue so much that no one, however loyal, should know what his plans were, and with this in mind he spoke to young Raasay and his brother, Murdoch.

" I want to get in touch with Donald Roy," he told the young chief. " Will you go and look for him? "

Young Raasay agreed with alacrity, and Charles turned next to Murdoch.

" I want you to go on ahead to Cammistinawag, and I will meet you there later on."

Murdoch nodded, little suspecting a fool's errand, and Charles presented him with a case containing a silver spoon, knife and fork.

" Keep this for me until we meet again," he begged him, and Murdoch, thanking him, went off with the two boatmen.

Charles sat down again, still feverish and uneasy, but at seven o'clock in the morning he suddenly picked up the bundle that contained all his possessions, walked out of the cowshed and started off. Malcolm followed. Without a word he took the bundle out of the Prince's hand, and after a while, seeing that Charles was taking a dangerous direction, he drew level and said, mildly:

" Will your royal highness please to tell me where we are going? I am afraid we shall fall into the hands of the military if we keep on this road."

Charles halted, passing a hand over his eyes in a weary gesture. He seemed to realise for the first time what he had been doing, and said, in a gentle tone :

" Why, MacLeod, I throw myself entirely into your hands. Do with me what you please. Only I want to go to Strath, Mackinnon's country. I hope you'll accompany me, if you can lead me safe enough to Strath."

" I'll go with your royal highness wherever you please. But to get to Strath we must go by sea. It is too dangerous by land."

The Prince shook his head. "Every way is dangerous," he said. " I mean to go by land."

Malcolm gave way, and the Prince, pulling himself together, at once took charge again.

" I will become your servant. Call me Lewis Caw. Poor young Lewis Caw was a surgeon in my army. Now he's skulking somewhere in Skye. He will not mind if I borrow his name. And here—— "

He stripped off coat and waistcoat.

" This," he said with a smile, holding up the waistcoat, " is a finer one than yours. Look at the gold twist buttons ! That's no waistcoat for a servant. Take it and give me yours."

Next he threw the bundle over his shoulder ; but Malcolm spoke in his turn.

" If you are my gillie you must walk behind me," he pointed out, laconically and Charles obediently fell to the rear. Malcolm struck off into the mountains, walking hard ; but he had all he could do to keep a suitable distance between himself and the Prince, for Charles was still tireless and swift in his stride. Malcolm, toiling ahead, said afterwards that he had never known anyone who could walk so fast or keep going so long with so few traces of fatigue. He remarked on it, over his shoulder, and the Prince laughed.

" Let me once get out of musket-shot," he said, " and I have no fear of English soldiers. There's none could ever catch me. But," he added less confidently, " I'd be more doubtful if I were chased by Highland militia. What shall we do if we meet anyone in the mountains? "

" That depends on their numbers," Malcolm replied. " If there are only four of them, I'll engage to manage two."

" And I'll engage to manage the other two ! " Charles cried gaily, almost welcoming the idea of an encounter.

" And if we meet any English soldiers," Malcolm asked, " what then? "

" Fight, to be sure," said Charles.

" And if we do fall in with anyone," the Highlander said next, " it's likely I may be known. If you see me stop to talk, you must sit down a little way off, and wait."

It was wise advice, for as they walked they had a few encounters with country people. Each time Malcolm would stop to exchange a few words, and Charles would sit down on the ground humbly and wait, springing to his feet and touching his bonnet whenever Malcolm spoke to him. He had entered into the spirit of the adventure with a will, and meant to carry it through.

They had brought no food, and all that remained of Charles's small stock was a bottle of brandy. Trudging through the rain, floundering through peat-bogs, scrambling over rocks, they soon were cold and famished, and the bottle was their only solace. Eventually, halting to rest, they found only one glass left.

" Take it, MacLeod," Charles urged. " You need it more than I."

" I will not ! " Malcolm retorted. " You must drink it yourself. It is yours, and you have carried it all the way."

" Not a drop for me," the Prince persisted. " Take it, man, and drain the bottle."

Malcolm, conscious of increasing fatigue and growing doubtful if he could finish the journey, hesitated no longer, but drank the brandy and hid the bottle. He found it three years later, and treasured it the rest of his life. He might yet take it with him one day to St. James's !

As they trudged on, Charles kept close enough behind to talk. They talked of many things, and at length the name of Lord George Murray cropped up.

" His lordship misconducted himself," the Prince declared. " Whether from ignorance or with a view to betraying me I cannot say. He disobeyed orders. Particularly for three or four days before Culloden he did nothing I desired him to do."

Malcolm listened glumly and made no comment ; but presently he started to tell Charles of the many atrocities committed after the battle. The Prince, who had heard none of this, was astounded and deeply shocked.

" Surely," he cried, " that man that calls himself the duke, and pretends to be so great a general, cannot be guilty of such cruelties ! I cannot believe it."

" It is true, nevertheless," Malcolm told him bluntly, and for a while they walked in silence, while Charles was sunk in bitter thoughts. But he roused himself later on.

" Don't you think, MacLeod," he asked, " that God Almighty has made this body of mine for doing some good yet? When I was in Italy, very often the sweat would be coming through my coat with the heat, and now that I'm in a cold country, where the climate is more trying, and I'm exposed to different kinds of fatigues, I really find I agree equally with both. I've had this kilt on for some days, and I find I do as well with it as any of the best breeches I ever put on. I hope to God, MacLeod, to walk the streets of London with it yet."

The long hard journey was nearly over.

" We are getting into the Mackinnon country now," Malcolm said. " I am afraid you may be recognised by some of Mackinnon's people who were out in your service. I think, sir, you should disguise yourself still more."

Charles promptly pulled off his wig and stuffed it into his pocket, then took out a dirty white napkin which he made Malcolm bind round his head close to his eyebrows. He tore the ruffles off his shirt and took the buckles from his shoes, which he tied up with string.

" Now do you think my friends will recognise me? " he demanded.

" I'm afraid they will," Malcolm replied gloomily, and Charles smiled ruefully.

" I have so odd a face that no man that ever saw me once but would know me again."

The one thing that no disguise could hide was, as Malcolm had observed, his bearing. There was something indefinably majestic about it, so that no matter how ragged and unkempt the Prince might look, one glance was enough to see that here was someone very much out of the ordinary.

There was nothing to be done about it, however, except hope for the best ; and Malcolm's fears were soon justified. They were in Strath now, and presently they encountered two Mackinnons, who had been out in the rebellion. They looked at Malcolm's gillie with only a passing glance—and knew him at once. Both burst into tears at the sight of him, and Malcolm spoke to them earnestly.

" Compose yourselves," he begged them. " You will betray us otherwise. You must show no sign of grief or others will guess our secret."

He whipped out his dirk.

" Swear that you will tell no one ! "

Each bent and kissed the naked steel with his lips, and Malcolm and the Prince went on.

" Do you wish to see the laird ? " Malcolm asked presently. " We are within two miles of his house."

" By no means," the Prince replied. " I know Mackinnon to be as good and honest a man as any in the world, but he is not fit for my purpose at present. You must conduct me to some other house."

Malcolm led the way to Ellagol, near Kilvory, where his brother-in-law, John Mackinnon, lived. He went forward alone to see his sister, who assured him he would be safe there. He mentioned he had a servant with him, a surgeon called Lewis Caw, also a fugitive, who had fallen sick, and Mrs. Mackinnon immediately offered him hospitality. So Charles came into the house, with his bundle on his back. He bowed and sat down quietly in a corner by himself. He and Malcolm had just walked thirty miles.

" Poor man," said Mrs. Mackinnon to her brother. " I pity him. At the same time, my heart warms to a man of his appearance ! "

Soon an abundant breakfast was on the table, and Malcolm called to the Prince:

" There are no strangers in the house. Draw near and share with me."

The Prince, starting to his feet, stood fingering his bonnet.

" Oh, no, sir," he stammered. " I know better how to conduct myself than to sit at the same table with my master."

" Come, do as I say," Malcolm retorted sternly, and Charles came forward, made a profound bow, sat down —and attacked the food without more ado.

While they ate, a servant girl brought hot water to wash Malcolm's feet, which were caked with black mud from the peat-bogs. When she had done, he asked her, in Gaelic, to do the same for " that poor sick man there."

" I hope you'll wash his feet too," he urged. " It will be a great charity, for he has as much need as I have."

The maid bridled and tossed her pretty head.

" No such thing ! " she cried indignantly. " Though I wash the master's feet I'm not obliged to wash the servant's. What ! He's but a low country woman's son. I will not wash his feet indeed."

Charles, still busy eating, caught none of all this ; but Malcolm entreated, and the girl grudgingly agreed ; so the Prince's feet were washed as well. But not too gently, and Charles had to ask Malcolm to implore her not to rub so hard !

After breakfast, bed. Charles threw himself down in his clothes, and slept soundly for a couple of hours. Malcolm slept much longer, and when he woke up was astonished to find Charles out of bed, dandling Mrs. Mackinnon's baby and singing to it. He looked as alert and clear-eyed as if he had slept all night.

" I'm hoping, MacLeod," he cried gaily, " that this youngster here, Neil Mackinnon, will one day be a captain in my service ! "

Presently Mrs. Mackinnon, who had been keeping watch outside, came in to say her husband was approaching, and Malcolm went to meet him. A brief exchange of greetings, and Malcolm knew he could trust his brother-in-law with the secret. He begged him to be careful in front of the servants, but Mackinnon, at sight of Charles, was so overcome with emotion that he burst into tears and had to leave the room quickly. His wife found pretexts to send all the servants away on errands, so that they could meet safely and discuss the situation.

Charles was insistent that the old laird should not be involved ; but Mackinnon, meeting his chief, found it impossible to deceive him, felt in honour bound to disclose the Prince's presence here, and the aged chief at once promised to provide a boat. Presently he came to Ellagol, to do homage to the royal wanderer and to lead him to a cave where Lady Mackinnon had laid out a meal of cold meat and wine.

Malcolm spoke privately to Charles.

" You are now in Mackinnon's hands," he said. " It would be an offence for me to interfere, so now I must leave you, sir. You are in good hands."

Charles tried to dissuade him. These niceties of Highland etiquette seemed out of place ; but Malcolm was firm on the point.

At eight in the evening they went down to the boat. Two men of war were standing in towards the island, before the wind, and Malcolm urged the Prince to put off his departure ; but it was Charles's turn to be stubborn.

" I've no fear of being caught, MacLeod," he declared. " The wind will shift in my favour soon."

Suddenly he remembered, with remorse, his treatment of young Raasay and his brother, and he begged Malcolm to convey his apologies, and wrote a note for Murdoch :

" Sir,

" I thank God I am in good health, and have got off as designed. Remember me to all my friends, and thank them for the trouble they have been at.

" I am, Sir,

" Your humble servant,

" JAMES THOMSON.

" Ellagol, July 4th, 1746."

Then he and Malcolm smoked a pipe together, the Highlander snapping his gun and igniting some tow by means of the flash in the pan. At parting, Charles put his arms round his loyal companion, kissed him on both cheeks, and pressed ten guineas into his hand. At first Malcolm refused, seeing the Prince's purse was meagre enough already, but Charles laughed.

" I shall get more where I am going, and you are a fugitive like myself. You may need the money as much as I."

Then, towards nine o'clock, the party set out—the Prince, the old laird, and John Mackinnon of Ellagol. Malcolm, climbing a hill to watch them out of sight, noticed that the wind shifted almost at once, driving the two English ships away. The boat sped eastwards towards the distant mainland, and gradually faded from sight in the gathering dusk.

§

Charles lay in the heather.

For three days and nights they had skulked by the shore, afraid to venture farther because of the parties of militia searching everywhere for him. The stormy thirty-mile voyage across had been uneventful—they had met only one boat, full of armed militia, but had not been challenged—and they had landed at Mallaigbheig, about a mile east of Mallaig. Now the old laird and one of the boatmen had gone off to seek a hiding-place, and presently John Mackinnon rose.

" We must go up the Loch," he declared, and led the way to the boat. They put her into the water and clambered in—Charles, and Mackinnon, and the remaining three boatmen, who took the oars at once. As they came round a point they almost collided with a boat tied to a rock, and there was an immediate shout. A party of militiamen had just landed.

" Boat ahoy ! " they yelled. " Who are you? Where are you from? "

" From Sleat," John called back.

" Then come ashore at once."

Mackinnon signed to his men, and they put their backs into their work, while Charles, who had slipped down into the bottom of the boat, grinned up at John enquiringly.

" They're after us," the Highlander whispered.

He bent down and spread his plaid over the Prince, who spoke from under this cover.

" How are things now? "

" They are not gaining an inch. Keep at it, lads."

" Now? "

" Gaining a little. Keep your muskets handy, lads. But don't fire until I do. We may escape them yet."

Charles lay waiting impatiently, and presently he pulled the plaid off his face as he heard Mackinnon give fresh orders :

" Take good aim, there's nothing to fear. We'll manage these rogues all right."

" For God's sake, Mackinnon," the Prince exclaimed, " don't shoot if you can help it. I want no blood spilt on my behalf."

" I'll not shoot unless I have to," Mackinnon replied crisply. " But if it comes to the bit, not one of them will escape alive to give us away. . . . Pull towards that wood there."

Charles looked up again.

" Let me go over the side and get ashore," he suggested. " I can easily give them the slip, and you will get away."

" No, sir. We stick together. Now . . . up with you!"

The boat's prow grated on shingle. Instantly Charles was up and out, with Mackinnon and one of the boatmen after him, and they raced for the wood and went up the steep hillside through the trees to the open summit.

" They have given up," the Prince said, simply, pointing to the militia boat, rowing away. " This is as safe as anywhere, and when you are safe you should sleep. There may not be another chance for long enough."

He lay down at once and fell sound asleep.

Three hours later they made their way down to the Loch again, where the boat still waited, and crossed over to a small island near the far side. Scothouse was not far away, and there was word that Clanranald was there, so Charles sent Mackinnon over to ask for sanctuary. He came back almost at once with a definite refusal from the old chief, and so they returned to Mallaigbheig, where the old laird of Mackinnon was waiting for them.

It was eight miles to MacDonald of Morar's house, and they set off at once. The Prince resumed his disguise as a servant, and at two shielings on the way they were given a draught of milk to stay their hunger. They also picked up a guide, for the night was dark and the path difficult to follow, and so they came to a ford.

Mackinnon turned to the guide, and pointed to Charles.

" Will you be so good as to carry this poor sick fellow across the water? " he requested ; but the guide indignantly refused.

" The deil be on the back he comes, or any fellow of a servant like him ! " he cried. " But I'll gladly take *you* on my back, sir, and carry you safe across."

" Not at all," said Mackinnon. " If the lad must wade, I'll wade along with him."

It was heartening to know that their guide had no suspicions of Mackinnon's tall servant.

§

They stood, just before daybreak, surveying what had once been Morar's mansion. It had been burnt to the ground ; but the chief, who had been a lieutenant-colonel of Clanranald's regiment, was living in a hut nearby, and came out to offer them a royal welcome. He led them to a cave, where they should be safe, and went off at the Prince's request to try and find young Clanranald. He came back to report failure.

" I must put myself in your hands," said the Prince.

But Morar was not prepared for that. The responsibility was more than he could manage, and for the first time Charles gave way to bitterness.

" When fortune smiled on me, there were people ready enough to serve me ! " he exclaimed. " Now that fortune frowns, and I have no pay to give, they forsake me in my necessity ! "

But Morar remained obstinate, in spite of the angry protests of old Mackinnon and his clansmen, and Charles turned away.

" I hope, Mr. Mackinnon," he said, " you will not desert me."

The old chief, with tears in his eyes, replied simply :

" I will never leave your royal highness in a moment of danger."

" No, no, sir," Charles exclaimed. " That is too much for your great age and your infirmity. You have done enough already. It was to John here, a stout young fellow, that I was speaking."

" Well, then," said John, " with the help of God I'll go through the wide world with your royal highness, if you desire me."

Borrodale seemed the most hopeful move, for there they might find the faithful old Æneas MacDonald, and Morar went so far as to offer the services of his young son as guide, and so they set off. But the Navy had been before them, and Borrodale's house was a heap of ashes. Borrodale himself, however, was living in a hovel nearby, and received John Mackinnon and his news with joy.

" I'll lodge him so secure," he vowed, " that all the forces in Britain shall not find him."

He was as good as his word, and John Mackinnon, having done his part, took his leave and made his way home in time to be arrested and sent to London in company with his aged chief, who had been caught in Morar the day after the Prince had left for Borrodale.

After a few days in a forest hut, the Prince was taken to a cave four miles to the east, to await a reply to a letter he had sent by one of Borrodale's sons to MacDonald of Glenaladale. Two days later, on the 15th of July, Glenaladale arrived, and the following day a letter came from his son-in-law, Angus MacEachan, who had been a surgeon in Glengarry's regiment. A rumour had got about that the Prince was hiding at Borrodale. It was time to move, and he had prepared a safe hiding-place for him in Morar.

Borrodale and his son John went with Charles and Glenaladale. On the way they met Borrodale's son-in-law bringing word that Clanranald, too, had prepared a hiding-place for the royal fugitive ; but it was late in the evening and Glen Morar was close by, so they continued on their way.

Borrodale went ahead. When he came back his face was grave. Several men-of-war, filled with troops under General Campbell, had anchored in Loch Nevis ; Captain Scott, with a strong force, was in the lower part of Arisaig. Borrodale had left two men to watch the ships and had hurried back. The English commanders, it seemed, were certain that the Prince was on one of the promontories between Loch Hourn and Loch Shiel, so Clanranald's country had been completely hemmed in, with a chain of posts, thirty miles long, whose sentries crossed each others' beats. At night, huge fires were lit all along the line.

The hounds were closing in. It seemed only a matter of time before Charles would be taken, for there could be no escape. Large numbers of ships lay off the whole coast waiting to intercept any boat that put out, and in addition to the chain of sentries large parties of military roamed about, combing the ground.

" We are too large a party," Charles decided, and took leave of Borrodale and his son-in-law. He had no wish for men to risk their lives, and with only three companions—Glenaladale, his brother John, and Borrodale's son—he set out early in the morning of the 18th.

His wanderings in the Isles had been strenuous enough ; but they were light compared with what lay ahead. To men born and bred among these mountains the route they chose perforce was a gruelling one ; but Charles, for all his gentler upbringing, had long ago hardened himself and was inured to any fatigue. Now he set the pace, and it was a hard one.

Midday found them on the summit of Sgur Bheag, at the eastern end of Arisaig, and Glenaladale's brother went off to Glenfinnan to pick up two men he had left there to keep watch. Charles, unable to rest, went on, and by ten at night had reached the top of Sgur nan Coireachan, in Lochiel's country, a few miles west of Loch Arkaig. After a short rest they went down and crossed Glen Pean and Glen Dessary and climbed the 2,800 feet to the summit of Fraoch Behinn. Glenaladale suddenly touched the Prince's arm. There was movement nearby, and as they stopped and listened and watched they made out a herd of cattle moving.

Glenaladale went forward cautiously. He came back almost at once. The people of the glen were driving their cattle away into the inaccessible mountains to save them from a force of seven hundred soldiers who had reached the head of Loch Arkaig.

" We'll have to take a different route," Glenaladale decided, and sent a man down to Glenfinnan, only a mile or so away, to recall his brother and the two scouts. He sent another messenger off to Donald Cameron of Glenpean, to learn the dispositions of the troops from Fort Augustus. While they waited, they found a hiding place, and slept.

In daylight, one of the women with the cattle came forward. There were tears in her eyes at sight of the chief in such desperate straits, and she had milked a cow to offer him some nourishment. The Prince, wrapping a cloth over his head to hide his face, passed as a servant with a headache, and was given his share of milk.

The man sent to Glenfinnan came back. He had not found Glenaladale's brother, but he had seen a company of a hundred Argyll militia at the foot of the mountain ! Charles and his companions waited only for sunset and started off again.

They travelled at great speed until eleven o'clock, when

Glenaladale again gave a warning. They were in a narrow steep glen, and he had caught a rattle of stones and knew that someone was approaching. Charles and young John dropped behind some rocks while Glenaladale went on alone. He came back in a few moments leading the stranger, and Charles, in a flood of thankfulness, found himself grasping the hand of Donald Cameron of Glenpean himself. He had brought his news in person, and, knowing the country so well, had guessed the way to intercept the Prince.

"I'll undertake to guide your royal highness safe past the guards," he declared. "There are roads no stranger would think passable even by day. But follow me, and you will pass safely through the chain."

The night was dry, and here in the high mountains it was never wholly dark. Cameron led off swiftly, and by four o'clock on the 19th they stopped to rest on the summit of Mam Nighean Callum, in the braes of Loch Arkaig. As they peered down, they picked out a camp of the enemy less than a mile away.

"This hill was searched yesterday," Cameron declared. "We should be safe here for a while."

So they lay down to rest, taking turns to watch, and at ten in the morning the alarm was raised. Someone was coming. Cameron slipped away to intercept him, and came back with Glenaladale's brother, who was searching for the Prince.

All day the party lay on the top of the mountain, and it was nine in the evening before they moved. They had almost no food, but Charles seemed not to care. Rest was all he needed, and when he rose to go on he was fresh and fit as ever. By one o'clock next morning they were on Coire nan Gall, on the border between Loch Arkaig and Knoydart, where Cameron hoped they might find some of the glen people with their cattle.

"We most forage for provisions," Glenaladale declared, and sent his brother and another man off. They slipped past the sentries and reached a group of shielings, only to find them empty and deserted, and when they came back empty-handed the party set off in a body towards Loch Naigh. At the top of a hill above the Loch they rested again, while the foraging party went off once more on its perilous quest. There was a considerable enemy camp within a mile of them.

Charles slept. Glenaladale and Borrodale's son took turns of standing guard, but there were no alarms, and dawn found all three peering down upon the enemy's camp at the head of the Loch. The day, warm and sunny, dragged its slow hours, until at last two figures could be seen, creeping expertly up the mountainside. The Highland passion for deer stalking, a sport in which they excelled, once more proved its value. Unseen, they passed the soldiers and came on. But they brought only two small cheeses—and bad news. A hundred soldiers were marching up the opposite side of the mountain, searching for some country people who had fled with their cattle. The people would, of course, be shot, the cattle stolen. That was what Cumberland had meant when he told Lord President Forbes that the only law he would enforce in Scotland was the law of his army.

The men looked at each other in silence, the same thought in each mind. Discovery was certain now, and Charles, thinking of the brave men whose lives would be forfeit, felt the old inclination to break out, to draw off the chase himself. But they dared not budge. They were completely surrounded.

The Highlanders chose a hiding-place, lay quiet in the heather, their plaids mingling with the ground colours in perfect camouflage. The tramp of heavy boots came close, the rattle of arms, the occasional bark of an order. The soldiers were beating the mountain top. Holding their breath, the fugitives waited for the moment of discovery. But it did not come. Gradually the sounds of search died away, and at eight o'clock at night Glenaladale crept closer to Charles.

" They have gone. The whole mountain has been

under observation all day. They must think we are not here. It should be safe to move."

So they started off again, heading north, and climbed the steep slope of Druim Chosaidh, where suddenly they came upon the glow of a camp fire straight ahead.

" We must go on," Cameron whispered. " We dare not lose our direction in the dark."

So, in perfect silence, they crept towards the fire. As they drew near they could hear the soldiers talking, grumbling and cursing or exchanging stories of their prowess in hunting rebels and plundering their homes and herds. The fugitives slipped past, undetected.

The mountain pitched steeply down, and here a little stream, spreading out, had made the ground damp and treacherous. Charles felt his foot slip. He fell, and went slithering down, shooting past their guide. Cameron snatched at him, caught him by the arm, and, flinging himself back, laid hold of a tuft of heather with his left hand. The Prince, half over the edge of a precipice, clung to the sleeve of Cameron's coat and waited, quietly, for help. Glenaladale started down at once, and dragged them both to safety in the darkness.

It had been a near shave, but only a quick handclasp thanked the Prince's rescuers, and they went on, picking their way cautiously down the precipitous mountain side behind their sure-footed guide.

They crossed the stream in Glen Cosaidh and toiled up the steep slope of Sgurr a' Claidheimh to look down upon another camp directly in their route.

" I'll go down," Cameron whispered. " If I succeed, and return safe, your royal highness may venture, and I'll conduct you."

The others sat down to wait. Soon Cameron was back, smiling to report his success, but as they set off he paused, and scratched his nose.

" My nose is itching," he told the Prince. " I misdoubt it is a bad omen."

" We can't stop now for an itching nose ! " cried

Charles, and the Highlander conquered superstition and led on. Turning a little to the westward, he took them down to a small brook, and crawled into it. The others followed, and on hands and knees they made their way down the stream until they were close to the line of sentries. Cameron reached back and touched the Prince's shoulder, giving it a slight pressure, and they raised cautious heads. They had reached a point opposite which two of the sentries met and passed each other.

They waited, with held breath. The sentries crossed, faced about, passed each other ; and when thus they had their backs to each other Cameron rose and ran swiftly between them, his brogues silent on the heather. He vanished, and Charles went after him, crouching low.

A few moments later all four were safely past, and lying in the heather out of earshot.

" Well, Donald," laughed the Prince, " how does your nose do now? "

" It is better now," Cameron replied. " But it still itches a bit."

" Aye, Donald, have we still more guards to go through? "

But Donald was not prepared to trust his nose so far, and he led the way down into the deep valley between Loch Quoich and Kinloch Hourn, and up by the stream of Coire Sgoir-adail to the top of the hill, where they sat down at last to eat.

There was only cheese and oatmeal ; but Charles did not wait to be shown what to do. He cut himself a slice of cheese and spread the dry oatmeal upon it, and ate a hearty meal, helped down with water from the crystal clear stream beside them.

They remained in hiding until eight at night, when the Prince announced that he wanted to go into Wester Ross. He had hopes that a French ship might get through to Poolewe, and in the North there might be news. But they had no sooner left their hiding-place than they discovered they had been lying up within gunshot of a small military camp. They watched some soldiers driving a flock of sheep into a hut for slaughter, and they waited a little before setting out to slip past this camp.

Again they travelled hard, climbing, scrambling, striding out wherever the ground permitted, and at three o'clock of the morning of the 27th they were in Glenshiel, in Seaforth's country.

Seaforth himself had been won over by Lord President Forbes, and had raised part of the MacKenzies for the government, so there was danger here ; but the clan, like others, was widely split, and the MacKenzies had paraded in strength in the Prince's army at Culloden.

Poolewe seemed the next point to aim at ; but they could find no guide, and the news from Wester Ross was bad. However, a Glengarry man, on the run after the soldiers had murdered his father, joined them and cheerfully offered to act as guide to Strathglass or Glenmoriston.

Cameron of Glenpean turned to the Prince.

" You are now in country that is strange to me," he said, " and I fear I can no longer be of service. So if your royal highness will give permission I will leave."

Charles wrung his hand, embraced him, and thanked him for all that he had done ; then, after a short rest, they set off again through Glenshiel overnight. But they had not gone over half a mile when Glenaladale clapped his hand to his side and cried :

" The devil take it, I have lost my purse."

The Prince commiserated with him ; but at the same time it seemed to him that a mere purse was not enough risk to delay for. However, Glenaladale retorted that it contained forty guineas, all the ready money he had, and he meant to get it. Borrodale's son went back with him to look for it.

They had scarcely disappeared when Charles heard footsteps, and dropped behind a rock. Peering round, he saw an officer and two privates going along the path that Glenaladale had just taken. There was no way of giving a warning, and Charles waited in acute suspense. But five minutes later his two companions reappeared. They had found the purse, and come back by a different route.

" A mercy I went back ! " Glenaladale cried when he heard the news. " But for my purse we should have walked straight into the arms of the soldiers."

Charles laughed.

" Glenaladale," he cried gaily, " I can see my time is not come. I believe I'd not be taken even if I had a mind to it ! "

All night they walked on, until at dawn they went into hiding on a hill above Strath Chluaine, where they rested until three in the afternoon of the 28th. When they moved on, they had not gone far before they heard firing, and looking down into the glen Charles had his first taste of what defeat meant to the ordinary people of the Highlands.

A party of troops, having burnt the cottages, had driven the people out in terror on to the bare hillsides. Some of the women had been stripped, and as they ran and clambered up the slope, dragging their children by the hand, the soldiers amused themselves by shooting at them. A woman fell ; then a child, then another woman. It was good sport for the conquering heroes from the south, and the Prince buried his face in his hands. At that moment he may have remembered all his own high principles, his own unfailing clemency, the strict orders, the scrupulous obedience of those orders that had marked the whole of his campaign.

This, if nothing else, should have marked the end of all his hopes. He had found himself in keenest sympathy with his Highlanders. Emotional and unstable as they were, he had understood them. They could be savage enough ; but that was always in the heat of battle. An emotional temperament cannot bear the sight of suffering in cold blood, and they had been quick to succour their enemies once their rage was spent. But a new spirit was stalking the country now—the ponderous, slow-witted, cold-blooded ruthlessness of Teutonic ideology, which used calculated brutality as an article of policy.

The horror he felt was to live with him for the rest of his life, spurring him on to new efforts, leaving him no peace.

§

The weather had changed. Heavy clouds scudded low among the glens, and rain slanted upon them in a relentless downpour. They found an open cave above Glenmoriston, and took refuge there ; but they could not lie down or sleep, they could find no fuel for a fire even had they dared to light one, and they were drenched to the skin and shivering with cold. Charles smoked his pipe, for the sake of the little warmth it gave.

At three o'clock on the morning of the 29th they started off again, hoping to find a guide for Poolewe, and sending a man off in search of one. He came back to say that he had encountered seven broken men who were living in a cave on the side of Coire Mheadhoin and would give them shelter.

Glenaladale and his brother went to prepare the way, while Charles waited with the other two MacDonalds. They found the seven men—a mixed band, MacDonells, Chisholms, a MacGregor, a Grant and a MacMillan—on the point of dining on a sheep they had killed, and they received a hearty invitation to sit down and eat.

" I have a friend outside," said Glenaladale, " in greater need than I."

" Who is he ? " one of the seven asked.

" Young Clanranald."

" Then fetch him in ! We'll be honoured to entertain him. He is very welcome."

Glenaladale brought the Prince into the cave. The seven, starting to their feet, looked at him, and fell on their knees in homage. They knew him at once.

After a forty-eight hour fast the mutton tasted good,

and Charles did full justice to the meal. When he was finished, the seven broken men led him proudly to a bed they had prepared, of ferns and heather-tips, springy and soft and fragrant. A tiny brook purled through the grotto, and with the scent of the heather and ferns in his nostrils, and the soft murmur of the stream in his ears the Prince fell asleep.

While he slept the seven eyed him with compassion, noting his coat of coarse dark cloth, the badly worn tartan vest, the ragged, dirty shirt, and the Highland brogues so battered and worn that they would hardly cling to his feet. His yellow wig was bedraggled and dirty, and he had only an old handkerchief bound round his neck. Only his kilt had survived the wear and tear of his adventurous wanderings.

" The Prince must be properly clad ! " they declared, and sallied out. They had had word that Lord George Sackville was marching from Fort Augustus to Strath-glass, and they had a mind to levy toll of him. They hid between two hills near the Strathglass road, and waited for what might come. Soon my lord and his detachment went marching past, and the Highlanders waited until they had gone a short way, then fired on the servants who brought up the rear with the baggage. One volley, then they charged, rushing down the hillside with the fleetness of stags to fall upon the baggage. The servants took to their heels. The seven broken men laid hold of the portmanteaus and ran nimbly back among the rocks. My lord George Sackville, galloping back in a rage, was left to curse—and do without his changes of linen and his finery.

But it did not occur to him that the man who was destined to enjoy his fine clothes was the one man every redcoat in Britain longed to catch. For the rumour was going around that the £30,000 had already been won. The Prince was dead.

It happened that among the Prince's life-guards there had been a young Highlander of good family, Roderick

MacKenzie, and people had often remarked on his striking resemblance to the Prince. He was of the same age and build, tall and slender, and his features were somewhat similar. After Culloden, he would have made for Edinburgh, where he had two unmarried sisters, but it seemed too dangerous, so he had taken to the hills.

One day, hearing a rumour that the Prince was concealed nearby, he conceived an idea. There were troops everywhere, scouring the district, and to these troops he showed himself, in broad daylight. Then he took to his heels. Like most Highlanders, he was swift footed, and could easily outdistance his pursuers. The hue and cry went up, and for several days he kept the military occupied, chasing him fruitlessly.

He repeated these tactics a number of times, drawing the hounds off whenever he heard that the Prince was in danger ; but that game can be played once too often.

One day he was surprised by a large body of troops, and turned to run. But he was hemmed in. He drew his sword, and for a few minutes defended himself with desperate courage. Then a soldier, waiting his chance, shot him at close range.

Mortally wounded, Roderick fell to the ground ; and as the soldiers, clubbing their muskets, came rushing at him, he cried out, in a strong clear voice :

" Villains, you have killed your Prince ! "

He died a moment later ; and the elated soldiers gathered round the corpse. They hacked off his head and carried it in triumph to their camp, to claim the reward. Then, not trusting their superior officers, they took it direct to Fort Augustus, and handed it over to the Duke of Cumberland.

Gazing on the pale, still face, the Duke felt a savage joy. He was completely convinced, and lost no time in making a parcel of the head, and ordering a post-chaise to take him to London. With his prize in his lap he hurried south, gloating upon his triumph . . . and discovered, too late, that he had been completely fooled.

CHAPTER EIGHTEEN

ESCAPE TO FRANCE

My heart is sair, I daurna tell,
My heart is sair for Somebody.
I could wake a winter nicht
For the sake o'—Somebody !

Ochone for Somebody !
Ochey, for Somebody !
I could range the warld around
For the sake o'—Somebody !

THE SEVEN broken men of Glenmoriston trooped out.
Charles had been their guest three days, sleeping,
eating, recovering from the privations and rigours of
his wanderings. Now he was moving to another hide-out,
and the seven, well armed and desperate, indicated their
intentions. Their Prince should have his bodyguard.
For other four days they hid in a cave about two miles
away, until one of the seven came back from
reconnoitring to report that Captain Campbell, one of
Seaforth's stewards, had pitched camp a short distance
away with his militia company, to graze a large herd
of cattle they had lifted. It was time to move again.
They made for the heights above Strathglass, where
the seven found a little sheep-cot and prepared a bed
and pillow of turf for their royal guest. They had
picked up a report that some French ships had been in
Wester Ross, and Charles sent one of them off to look
for news. It would be a long hard journey, so after
waiting for three days the Prince set out after him,
expecting the news to be good. With large bodies of
troops still roaming the country, he dared not ever
linger long in one place.

On the 10th of August they reached Glencannaidh, and after hiding all day in a wood they made their way into the little village, which was free of soldiers. At two o'clock in the morning they set out to scramble up the hill on the north side of the glen, finding shelter in a shieling for two days while a party went foraging. There the messenger found them on his way back, to report that two French officers had landed from a French ship and gone off to Lochiel's country in search of the Prince.

" We must double back, then," Charles decided, and on the 13th they crossed the water of Casina, passing near the home of young Hugh Chisholm and reaching Fassnakyle in Strathglass at two in the morning.

A wood offered sanctuary, and for three days they lived there while scouts went out. They came back with word that the soldiers had all been recalled to the camp at Fort Augustus. The road was almost clear. Roderick MacKenzie's death had not been in vain.

On the 17th they toiled by unfrequented paths to Glenmoriston, spending the day on top of a hill and travelling by night ; but soon one of the seven men, scouting ahead, brought word of a large body of troops searching the Glengarry district for the Prince.

Next day Charles sent a messenger to Cameron of Clunes, asking him to meet Glenaladale at Achnasalt, and on the evening of the 19th he and his party set out on the perilous journey. A thick mist came to their help, and they slipped through Glenmoriston and Glen-lyne in safety, and reached Glengarry. The river was in spate following heavy rain, but they waded across and clambered up the steep hillside in a drenching down-pour and pitch darkness. There was no shelter to be had, so they lay down on the sodden ground and slept.

Next morning they reached the rendezvous.

There was no one there, and they had perforce to sit down in the rain and wait. There was no food left, and when Peter Grant returned to say that Clunes could

not join them until next day the situation seemed
desperate. Clunes, however, had recommended a thick
forest about two miles away as the safest place, and,
staggering to their feet, the party set off down the hill.

" Lochgarry is hiding nearby, sir," Glenaladale told
the Prince. " May I invite him to join us? "

" By all means," Charles replied readily, " I'll be glad
to see him." Glenaladale sent off a messenger, and
presently they reached the wood. As they entered it,
one of the seven raised a warning hand. Quietly, while
they waited in tense excitement, he loaded his musket
and crept forward. The musket cracked once, and he
beckoned to them. They ran forward to find him kneeling
beside a fine buck, his face transformed with joy.

They gralloched it and carried it into the heart of the
forest, where they soon had a fire blazing, and the odour
of roasting venison in their nostrils. Without salt or
seasoning, without bread or oatmeal they feasted, washing
the meat down with water from a stream; and Lochgarry
joined them in time to take his share.

At ten o'clock next morning Cameron of Clunes
appeared. He had expected to find only Glenaladale, and
the sight of the royal fugitive affected him deeply.

" There is a safer retreat in a forest at the foot of
Loch Arkaig, sir," he declared, and they repaired thither,
sending a messenger to Lochiel. Here all of the seven
men of Glenmoriston, except Peter Grant and Hugh
Chisholm, took their leave ; the Prince would be safe
in Cameron country. But the messenger came back
from Lochiel to say that the chief was still unable to
walk. He had been wounded in both ankles at Culloden;
since then, with Achnacarry in ashes, he had been in
hiding, attended by an Edinburgh snrgeon, Sir Stewart
Thriepland, and had recently joined forces with that
staunch old warrior, MacPherson of Cluny. He sent
his brother, Dr. Cameron, with his apologies, and the
news that two French officers were with him.

There was very nearly a tragic incident when Dr.

Cameron arrived, for Clunes had gone to seek him, and the Prince, with Peter Grant and one of Clunes's sons, had sought a safe hiding place to sleep. Grant was keeping watch, but, worn out and overcome with fatigue, as he watched he nodded, so that Clunes and the doctor and his two servants were almost upon them before he roused himself. Imagining the enemy was at hand, he woke the Prince and young Cameron, and they prepared to defend themselves. However, as they were about to open fire, young Cameron recognised his father and called out.

The good doctor was deeply distressed at sight of Charles, barely recognisable now. He was barefooted, clad in a dirty shirt, an old black tartan coat, a torn and bedraggled plaid and kilt, and his beard had grown to a great length. But he came forward with all the old spring and grace, his health unimpaired by his sufferings and his spirits undamped by all that he had been through.

Grant had killed a cow, and they had also got a small supply of bread and newspapers from Fort Augustus. These were rare luxuries, and the Prince, acting host, enjoyed his dinner and made light of his misfortunes. The doctor reported that Lochiel was suspicious of the two Frenchmen, as it seemed hard to believe that without any knowledge of the language they had succeeded in coming so far and avoiding capture. Their ship had brought a party of sixty volunteers from France, bent on rescuing the Prince, and two of these had landed with the officers, but had been taken. One, Fitzgerald, a Spanish officer, was promptly hanged ; the other, being a French officer, M. de Berard, was sent south and exchanged for an English prisoner in French hands.

§

Charles was eager to see Lochiel, a man whom he rightly regarded as one of his staunchest friends ; so the next move was towards Achnacarry, which had been burnt by Cumberland's troops. The doctor and Lochgarry went off by different routes to watch the movements of the military, and Clunes and his son conducted the Prince safely to a hut near the ruined mansion.

Charles, determined to meet the French officers, decided on a stratagem. He wrote them a letter, stating that he was in hiding at a distance and could not see them personally, but that they were to give all their news to the bearer, Captain Drummond. He sent for them, and in the guise of Captain Drummond handed them the letter.

But, as it transpired, they had little to tell. The despatches they carried for the French ambassador were in cipher, and Charles could make nothing of them. They had no idea where their ship now was, or whether they could reach her again, so for the moment there seemed nothing to be done.

§

Charles woke with a hand on his shoulder, and started up out of a deep sleep to be greeted with alarming news. Lochiel's brother, the Rev. John Cameron, and one of Clunes's sons had gone off to Clunes for intelligence, and had found the old man in a hut near his ruined house. They had not been there half an hour when a little girl came running with word that the soldiers were approaching. A rumour had reached Fort Augustus that the Prince was in the neighbourhood, and they had come hot-foot to pick up the scent. Old Clunes had stayed to watch their movements while the other two hastened to warn the Prince. They had crossed the river under cover of the woods, slipped past the soldiers within pistol shot and got clear away.

Charles remained perfectly calm.

" My gun, Peter," he ordered, and slipped out of the hut. From a vantage point they looked down and saw the soldiers in the act of burning Clunes's hut and searching the woods. A quick glance showed a way of escape, and the Prince did not hesitate. He threw himself into a torrent that poured down the mountain, and scrambled up it, under cover of its deep banks. The others followed, and so they reached the rocky summit of Meall an Tagraidh, a height of well over 2,000 feet.

All day they lay among the rocks without food or shelter, and at midnight another of Clunes's sons arrived, bringing whisky and bread and cheese.

" My father got away," he told them. " He'll meet you later on with more food."

Fortified, they set off for the new rendezvous, and now they faced the severest test of all the Prince's wanderings. There was no track—only the gigantic mountains, a wilderness of rock and precipice and torrents, with here and there the stumps of trees of old plantations which tore their clothes and scratched their arms and legs savagely.

Hour after hour they toiled on, slipping, falling head-long, dragging themselves up sheer cliff faces, until his guides begged the Prince to rest.

He shook his head stubbornly.

" We cannot keep the old gentleman waiting," he replied simply. " We must go on."

He was almost completely exhausted. For days he had had little food, had lain at night exposed to the weather among these bleak craggy heights, and this terrible journey might well have killed a weaker man. His companions were in equally bad straits, but they summoned their remaining strength and two of them supported him over the last few miles.

When finally they reached the meeting-place that old Clunes appointed they found him busy preparing a meal. He had slaughtered a cow in readiness for them.

Lochgarry and Dr. Cameron found them there, and brought word from Lochiel. He and Cluny wanted the Prince to seek sanctuary with them in Badenoch. The passes were not so strictly guarded now, and after a short rest Charles got to his feet prepared to carry on. His vitality was unimpaired, his spirit unquenchable, and

the party set off with all the old speed and endurance
for Loch Arkaig. They crossed over to a fir wood
belonging to Lochiel, where they meant to wait for
Cluny to join them ; but now the Prince was consumed
with impatience. Lochiel he counted the sincerest of
friends, and he longed to see him again and hear all his
news. So on the 30th of August he went on, with Lochgarry and Dr. Cameron and two of the doctor's servants,
to the rendezvous at Meallan Odhar.

As they approached the hut Lochiel and his men,
mistaking them for militia, made ready to receive them
with a volley ; but at the last moment they were
recognised and the chief, limping out, went eagerly
towards the Prince.

As he was about to kneel, Charles clapped him on the
shoulder.

" Oh no, my dear Lochiel ! " he cried. " We do not
know who may be looking from the top of yonder
hills."

They shook hands instead, and Lochiel led the Prince
into his hut. Charles stared about with wondering eyes,
amazed at the sight of such stores of food—abundance
of mutton, some good beef sausages, a large and well-
cured ham, plenty of cheese and butter, and an anchor
of whisky. He drank a dram to the health of his friends,
and Lochiel placed before him a pan full of mince collops,
and a silver spoon to eat with.

The Prince received these luxuries with undisguised
joy, and ate heartily.

" Now, gentlemen," he cried gaily, " I live like a
prince ! "

When he had finished, and the others too had dined,
he spoke to Lochiel.

" Do you always fare so well ? " he asked.

The chief smiled.

" Yes, sir, for near three months past I have been
hereabouts with my cousin Cluny. He has provided for
me so well that I have had plenty of such as you see,

and I thank heaven your royal highness has got through so many dangers to take a part."

Two days later Cluny arrived, and would have kneeled, but Charles prevented him, embraced him instead, and said : " I am sorry, Cluny, you and your regiment were not at Culloden. I did not know till very lately that you were so near us that day."

Later, when they discussed their situation, Cluny thought it wise to move again, and next day he conducted the Prince to a little shieling two miles farther into Ben Alder. The hut was small and rough, and full of smoke, but to the Prince it seemed a handsome dwelling, and he stayed there well content for two further nights. Then they went on to a place that Cluny's people had prepared for their chief, on the precipitous south side of the Ben where it pitches to the water near the south end of Loch Ericht. " Cluny's Cage," they called it, and the Prince, clambering up into it, looked round in astonishment to see how well it had been made.

It was a wild and inaccessible spot among a wilderness of rock and stunted trees, and the entrance to the cave was hidden by the thick bush of a little wood. A floor had been made of logs supported against the steep face of the mountain and levelled with mud and gravel. Between the logs were stakes fixed in the earth which, like the trees, were interwoven with ropes of heather and birch twigs to make the walls. It was roofed over in the same way, and the whole fabric hung by a large tree which sloped up along the roof.

Two stones formed a natural hearth for the fire, and the smoke, escaping through the roof, spread itself over the sheer face of rock above, which was exactly the colour of smoke. Thus on the clearest day it was quite impossible to detect the smoke, or to guess that the bushes hid this strange dwelling that clung to the cliff face.

There was room only for six or seven in the Cage ; but Charles was used well enough to cramped quarters, and he settled down to enjoy, a spell of rest and security.

He could never be idle, however, and there was immediate work to do. The greatest difficulty in his wanderings had been the need for secrecy, for constant movement. Several times French ships had risked the perilous passage to the Western Highlands in search of him, and each time they had failed to find him before they were forced to leave. So now he set about organising a regular system of communications.

He was farther from the sea than he had yet been in his wanderings, but even so the chances seemed better than they had ever been. Arrangements were made for messages to be passed swiftly, and he and his companions settled down to wait.

Cluny had been hiding in his own country ever since the disaster. A large force was permanently quartered on his estate, hunting for him without respite, spurred on by an offer of £1,000 reward for his capture, alive or dead. He had been quite secure, for his people had only one thought—to protect their chief. So he lived his strange life, sallying out only at night to visit friends, but determined not to quit his own country.

Here, for a while at least, Charles should be safe.

§

The days passed. They whiled the time away playing cards, smoking a companionable pipe, talking endlessly ; and then, on the 13th of September, a messenger arrived. He came from Cameron of Clunes. Colonel Warren, of Dillon's Regiment, had been pestering the French government to send some warships to rescue the Prince, and at last he had won his way. Two ships, *l'Heureux* and *La Princess de Conti*, had sailed from St. Malo at the end of August and had reached Loch nan Uamh after a swift and uneventful voyage. Captain Sheridan, Sir Thomas's son, had come ashore with M. O'Beirne, a lieutenant in the French service, and had met Glenaladale, who had set off at once in search of Charles.

He had gone first to find Clunes ; but the old chief had moved to a distance after taking farewell of the Prince. While Glenaladale was standing disconsolate and uncertain of his next move, an old woman had come along, and from her he had learnt Clunes's new hiding-place. He had given him his message and gone back to report to Colonel Warren.

" We shall leave at once," the Prince decided, and took farewell of his cheerful host. But the journey could not be swift, for Lochiel was very lame still, and besides they had to travel only by night. It was not until the 19th that Charles saw the familiar shores of Borrodale, and the ship that waited in the Loch to carry him back to France.

Lochgarry and John Roy Stewart and Dr. Cameron and others had joined the party on the journey, for Charles had sent messages right and left to warn his loyal friends and invite them to accompany him if they desired ; and now the final moment came, to take farewell of Scotland and of the men who had so generously risked everything on his behalf.

Upwards of two hundred people had helped him on his wanderings, or had known where he was ; yet none had dreamt of giving him away. In the Highlands at least he had found that spirit of chivalry and loyalty and integrity that matched his own ideals.

He waited until all his friends had safely embarked ; then he took leave of the country which had been the cradle and the grave of his highest hopes, and going on board ship stood gazing back at the mountains that had grown so familiar until they, like the fortunes of the house of Stuart, faded into the mist and were lost to sight.

CHAPTER NINETEEN

ANE END TO ANE AULD SANG

I hae been in crookie den,*
　　Bonnie laddie, Hieland laddie!
Seeing Willie and his men,
　　Bonnie laddie, Hieland laddie!

Satan sat in a black neuk,
　　Bonnie laddie, Hieland laddie.
Breaking sticks to roast the Duke!
　　Bonnie laddie, Hieland laddie!

WILLIAM, Duke of Cumberland, nicknamed The Butcher, went on methodically with his work. He did it so well that when he returned to London—whither his fame (or infamy) had travelled before him—his own little nephews ran screaming in terror at sight of him.

Twelve hundred men had died at Culloden—on the battlefield, and during the few days after the battle, when hundreds had been murdered in cold blood. Hundreds more were slaughtered by the soldiers marching through the glens, looting and rebel hunting. The "booty" was immense, enough to ensure the highest zeal on the part of the military. The two hundred officers and men who plundered Glengarry's mansion

*The nethermost pit of Hell.

378

received for their share payment at the rate of £11 5s. for captains, £5 18s. for subalterns, thirty shillings for sergeants, one pound for corporals, and fifteen shillings for each common soldier. There were other pickings. Thirty thousand head of black cattle were rounded up and driven off in Strathmore alone.

Moy Castle was destroyed, any fugitives discovered there shot, and the old men and women and children who had not got away were hunted down and killed. Lady Mackintosh was carried off to Inverness and thrown into the common gaol among many other Jacobite ladies.

Lord Lovat's seat, Castle Dounie, was plundered and burnt to the ground. The old chief of the Frasers hid for many weeks in a hollow tree on his estate, but was eventually discovered and sent south for trial. The Earls of Kilmarnock and Cromarty and Lord Balmerino were tried, convicted, and condemned in the following words:

" The judgment of the law is, and this high court doth award, that you, William, Earl of Kilmarnock, George, Earl of Cromarty, and Arthur, Lord Balmerino and every one of you return to the prison of the Tower from whence you came, from thence you must be drawn to the place of execution ; when you come there, you must be hanged by the neck, but not till you are dead, for you must be cut down alive ; then your bowels must be taken out and burnt before your faces ; then your heads must be severed from your bodies ; and your bodies must be divided each into four quarters, and these must be at the king's disposal."

Cromarty was subsequently granted a pardon. Kilmarnock, losing his nerve, recanted his Jacobite principles, but Balmerino remained calm and dignified and stubborn to the end, persistently declaring that he acknowledged only James VIII and III as his king, and Charles as his Regent in Britain. The grand old man by his steadfastness and his complete contempt for his judges and executioners, created a wave of sympathy which caused the government considerable alarm.

Of three hundred and eight-two persons arrested, only a portion stood their trial. The government, alarmed at the effect of such mass trials, decided to draw lots, the unlucky ones standing trial, the others being quietly transported for life. So altogether a hundred and thirty-four death sentences were carried out ; and it is significant that of them all the Earl of Kilmarnock alone recanted. All the rest persisted in proclaiming their staunch adherence to the House of Stuart.

Ratcliffe, a younger brother of the Earl of Derwent-water, and Lord Lovat provided Londoners with their next big sensation. Both were tried, condemned, and executed. Lord Lovat, who had been a cripple for the past three years, was treated with shocking lack of consideration for his age and infirmity throughout his trial, but bore it nobly and went to his death calm and nonchalant as he had been through the long proceedings.

Mr. Secretary Murray of Broughton bought his freedom by turning king's evidence, and so gained the approbrium of honest men everywhere ; but was in keeping with the character he had shown since the moment of the Prince's landing, and was no great surprise to some at least of those who knew him well.

Many parts of the Central and Western Highlands were completely devastated, so that not a living thing remained in any of the glens. Lord President Forbes, whose great exertions had been responsible for preventing the whole of the Highlands from rising—he had, in fact, brought more Highlanders over to the Hanoverian side than rose on the Jacobite—saw Cumberland at Inverness shortly after Culloden, and hinted plainly that the laws of the country should be observed even by the Duke's army, to which Cumberland retorted : " The laws of the country, my lord ! I'll make a brigade give laws, by God ! " And he went about it with a will.

At the end of the year the Lord President went to London, to present his accounts, and was immediately summoned by George II, who knew full well how near he had been to losing the throne, and how much he owed to Forbes.

"My lord president," he cried, "you are the person I most wished to see. Shocking reports have been circulated of the barbarities committed by my army in the north. Your lordship is the best able to satisfy me."

But Forbes, a man of strict rectitude, received this royal command with the quiet contempt it deserved.

"I wish to God that I could, consistently with truth, assure your Majesty that such reports are destitute of foundation," he replied sadly, and the king turned furiously away and refused to speak to him further. Next day he presented his accounts. They were passed only with the greatest difficulty—and they were never paid. The only reward he had for his strict adherence to his duty, for the zeal with which he had supported the Hanoverian cause, was the loss of a great part of his personal fortune. He may have gone home to Culloden to reflect, bitterly, how differently the Young Pretender had regarded his obligations.

The enormities committed by Cumberland's forces were not confined to the Highlands. Many parts of the Lowlands suffered also, and chapels and churches as well as mansions were destroyed all over the country. Sentence of death by hanging was imposed upon anyone harbouring fugitives, and the clergy were ordered to read from the pulpit a document commanding their parishioners to give up all fugitives and to denounce any who were known to have aided those in hiding. The clergy were further ordered to submit lists of their own parishioners who had taken part in the rising. To the lasting honour of the Church in Scotland, the vast majority refused to read these edicts or to obey them, and in particular all the clergy of Edinburgh, making retribution for their pusillanimous behaviour on a former occasion, stubbornly rejected the order.

Apart from the barbarous excesses committed, at his orders, by the Duke's soldiers, there were other causes for reviling the Duke in Scotland. When rebel hunting as an amusement became stale, he and his generals incited their men to all manner of licentious behaviour calculated to offend the deeply religious inhabitants of the East of Scotland, and the swarms of women camp followers took part in spectacles which shocked the country.

The news travelled. A wave of horror and shame gradually swept the whole of Britain as the facts of the devastation of the Highlands became known, and the nickname Butcher clung to the man who was primarily responsible for what had happened. At first, of course, there was only rejoicing in the south, and a grateful people, attributing to his generalship a victory for which he could claim no merit, voted the Duke an addition of £25,000 a year to his pension ; but gradually decenter feelings prevailed, and the government, alarmed at the horror created all over Europe, felt the necessity of making a gesture. A general amnesty was proclaimed in July, 1747 ; but more than eighty men were excluded by name from it, so that in point of fact the amnesty was no more than a gesture. A few notables, however, profited from it, and were set free.

How closely Charles had been pursued was shown by the arrest of many of those who helped him on his wanderings, generally within a day or so of his moving on. Donald MacLeod was taken almost immediately in Benbecula, and brought before Campbell of Argyll, who interrogated him closely.

" Yes," he answered boldly, " I was along with the young gentleman, and won't deny it."

" Do you know what money was upon that gentleman's head ? " Campbell asked. " No less than thirty thousand pounds sterling."

" What then ? " cried Donald. " What though I had gotten it ? I could not have enjoyed it two days. Conscience would have gotten the better of me, and although I could have gotten all England and Scotland for my pains I would not have allowed a hair of his body to be touched if I could hinder it, since he threw himself upon my care."

Campbell, knowing his Highlanders, looked away.

"I can't much blame you for that," he said.

Donald was sent to London to await his trial. But there was to be no trial yet—not until the government was satisfied that there was no danger of another rising and no chance of a reversal of fortune. They were not going to take too much risk!

Ned Burke hid for seven weeks, living on seaweed and limpets, after he left the Prince, and finally he made his way to Edinburgh and found work as a chairman or sedan carrier, which occupied him peaceably for the remainder of his life. But others were not so fortunate.

Lady Clanranald was seized and sent to London, and on the 1st of November Clanranald and his brother Boisdale were also sent south.

Captain O'Neil had the ill-luck to run into a supporter of Hanover whom he mistook for a good Jacobite, and so fell into the hands of Captain Ferguson, R.N. He refused to talk, so he was stripped and put on the rack. He still refused to give the Prince away, and the Captain ordered him to be whipped. This was too much for an officer of the Scots Fusiliers who was on board, and who, drawing his sword, rushed at the naval man.

"By God!" he cried, "I won't see an officer used in this way!"

The Captain, thoroughly scared, climbed down, and O'Neil was saved from the torture. He was subsequently exchanged, since he was technically an officer in the service of France and could claim proper treatment as a prisoner of war. Campbell sent word that if he had any valuables they would be safe in his keeping, and O'Neil therefore was permitted to go and fetch his watch, a purse of four hundred and fifty guineas, and other valuables which he had hidden. He sent them to Campbell; but that was the last he saw of them.

Malcolm MacLeod was taken two days after the Prince left Skye for the mainland, and the good Kingsburgh was also arrested and plundered of his shoe buckles, watch and money. Both were subsequently set free.

As for Flora MacDonald, she was arrested and kept prisoner in various ships and prisons until sent to London on December 6th. Released the following July, she returned to Skye and married young MacDonald of Kingsburgh in 1750. They emigrated to North Carolina in 1774, but Kingsburgh joined the Royal Highland Emigrant Regiment in 1775, and at the end of the war returned to Scotland on half pay. Flora died on the 4th of March, 1790, and her husband on the 20th of September, 1795. Of their children, all five sons became army officers, and both daughters married officers. In 1773 Dr. Samuel Johnson and Boswell visited Flora and her husband, Johnson sleeping in the bed the Prince had occupied in their house. He described Flora, at fifty-one, as a woman of soft features, gentle manners, and elegant presence ; Boswell said of her that she was a little woman of genteel appearance, and uncommonly mild and well-bred.

John MacKinnon of Ellagol was arrested immediately after leaving the Prince, and sent south with his aged chief and confined until the amnesty.

The aged Marquis of Tullibardine, who was also captured, died in the Tower of the lingering illness which had afflicted him throughout the campaign, and so escaped the executioner.

Of those who escaped, the Duke of Perth, Lord John Drummond, Lords Elcho and Nairne, and Maxwell of Kirkconnel got away from Loch nan Uamh in the ships that Charles and his companions saw from the Long Isle in April, 1746 ; but the Duke of Perth died on the voyage to France.

Lords Pitsligo and Ogilvy and about ten others got away to Bergen, where the British ambassador demanded they should be handed over ; the Norwegian government ignored this request, and they were allowed to go to Sweden. Stewart of Ardshiel and O'Sullivan reached France safely, and old Glenbucket, letting his beard grow, wandered about the country disguised as a beggar until, in November, he too escaped to Norway.

Lord George Murray hid in his own country for some time, then went privately to Edinburgh to see his friends there, and sailed from the Forth to Holland.

But the common people, for whom there could be no such escape, could only seek refuge from the soldiers among the most inaccessible mountains, where large numbers of them perished of exposure and starvation, since their whole means of subsistence, the great herds of cattle and sheep that had been their wealth, were slaughtered or driven south to be sold in the English markets.

A great silence, the silence of death, fell upon the Highlands ; and when the persecution was at last removed a new form of persecution took its place, and for more than a century thereafter the clearance of the Highlands went on, whole villages and glens being rounded up and driven on board the emigrant ships, their houses burnt behind them and themselves transported to Canada and other colonies, where they were dumped without any preparation being made for them, and left to fend for themselves in a savage and unknown land.

The tragedy, begun that day on Culloden Moor, was to be played out to the bitter end.

§

So deep was the horror felt throughout Scotland at Murray of Broughton's treachery and at the appalling cruelties of the British army in the Highlands that it inspired the bitterest and most terrible poem ever written in Lowland Scots—

Cumberland's Descent into Hell

Ken ye whare Cleekie Murray's gane?*
He's gane to dwall in his lang hame,
The Beddle clapp'd him on the doup,
" Oh, hard I've earned my grey groat ;
Lie thou there and sleep thou soun',
God winna wauken sic' a loon ! "

*　　　*　　　*　　　*

He's in a' Satan's frying pans,
Smouthring the blude frae aff his han's ;
He's washing them in brimstane lowe ;
His countra's blude it winna thow ;
The hettest soap suds o' perdition
Canna oot thae stains be washin'.

Ae devil roared, till hoarse and roupit,
" He's pykin' the gowd frae Satan's pu'pit ! "
Anither roared, wi' eldritch yell,
" He's howking the keystane out o' hell,
To dam us mare wi' God's daylight ! "
And he dookit i' the cauldrons out o' sight.

He stole auld Satan's brimstane leister,
Till his waukit loofs were in a blister ;
He stole his Whig spunks, tipp'd wi' brimstane
And stole his scalping whittle's whunstane ;
And out o' its red hot kist he stole
The very charter rights o' hell !

Satan, tent weel the pilfering villain ;
He'll scrimp your revenue by stealing.
Th' infernal boots in which you stand in,
With which your worship tramps the damn'd in,
He'll wile them aff your cloven cloots,
And wade through hellfire in your boots.

* Secretary Murray of Broughton.

Auld Satan cleekit him by the spaul,
And clappit him in the dub o' hell.
The foulest fiend there doughtna bide him,
The damn'd they wadna fry beside him,
Till the bluidy duke came trysting hither,
And the ae fat butcher tried the t'ither.

Ane devil sat splitting brimstane matches,
Ane roasting the Whigs like baker's batches ;
Ane wi' fat a Whig was basting,
Spent wi' frequent prayer and fasting.
A' ceased when thae twin butchers roared
And hell's grim hangman stopp'd and glower'd.

" Fie, gar bake a pie in haste,
Knead it of infernal paste,"
Quo' Satan ; and in his mitten'd hand
He hynt up bluidy Cumberland.
He whittled him doun like bow-kail castock,
And in his hettest furnace roasted.

Now hell's black tablecloth was spread,
Th' infernal grace was reverend said ;
Yap stood the hungry fiends a' ower it,
Their grim jaws gaping to devour it,
When Satan cried oot, fit to scunner :
" Ower rank a judgment's sic a dinner ! "

CHAPTER TWENTY

YEARS OF FRUSTRATION

Bonnie Charlie's noo awa',
   Safely o'er the friendly main ;
Mony a he'rt will brak in twa,
   Should he ne'er come back again.

PRINCE HENRY, accompanied by a large gathering of the nobility of France, hastened out of Paris. Somewhere on the road from Morlaix the great cavalcade encountered a party making post-haste for the capital, and the brothers met again, after an interval of nearly three years.

Charles at first did not know his brother ; but Henry knew Charles at once, and ran forward to embrace him. He was, he wrote to his father, still the same Charles, only " grown somewhat broader and fatter." In view of his experiences over the previous five months, this fat must have been all solid muscle.

So the Prince was conducted in state to the residence that had been prepared for him by the French court, the Castle of St. Antoine ; and he immediately set to work.

He had never despaired. He had landed in France with

388

one fixed resolution—not to rest until he had renewed his campaign. And the sense of urgency drove him on.

He asked for an audience of the King at Fontainebleau, and was furious when Louis, overborne by his ministers, had to request him to come incognito. The French cabinet was determined to do nothing now to exacerbate the English government.

James, learning of this, wrote mildly to his son:

" I am far from saying but that the king of France might have done a great deal more for you ; but after all, we must consider the vast expenses he is at during the war, and the system he has certainly laid down to himself of not treating you and your brother as princes of England, which system I own shocked me at first, and seems preposterous in the present situation of affairs ; but when one considers the uncertainty of the events of war, and that if we are not restored before a peace, the king of France cannot but continue to acknowledge the Elector of Hanover as king of England, and by consequence treat us no more as princes of England ; we cannot but own that it is wise in him, and in a certain sense even kind to us, not to expose himself and us to a possibility and necessity of ceasing to treat us according to our birth, after having once done it."

Charles did not share this charitable view of Louis's intentions. By the Treaty of Fontainebleau, negotiated immediately after he had raised his standard at Glenfinnan, France had recognised him as Prince Regent of Scotland ; that treaty still stood, and Charles felt that he should force the king to honour it. In the circumstances, he could see only one thing to do. He would go in state to the French court.

He travelled with a great equipage of coaches and riders, all superbly dressed, and his own dress outshone them all. Rose-coloured velvet coat embroidered with silver and lined with silver tissue, waistcoat of rich gold brocade with spangled fringe, the cockade in his hat and the shoe-buckles studded with diamonds, the stars of

George and St. Andrew embellished with large diamonds
—here was a splendid figure of a man to greet the
delighted eyes of the courtiers ; and the king received
him with great affection and embraced him publicly.

" My dearest Charles," he declared, " I thank heaven
for the very great pleasure it gives me to see you returned
in good health after so many fatigues and dangers."

The Queen, too, received him affectionately, for she
had a maternal tenderness towards the elder son of her
girlhood friend, Clementina, and she drew Charles aside
often for long talks, lasting sometimes several hours.

This was the Prince's first appearance at the French
court. He was by now almost a legendary figure, and
the whole court crowded round him after he had taken
leave of the king, and complimented him on his exploits.
But Charles was not impressed. He returned later to sup
with the king and queen and the royal family in private,
and made subsequent private visits ; but the adulation
of the court left him cold.

Louis, indeed, was making a gesture in defiance of his
ministers. He was not only genuinely fond of Charles,
he had the highest admiration for him, and would have
helped him to the limit ; but his ministers had tied his
hands and prevented him from acting as he wanted to.

On October 25th Charles had another private audience
when he handed over a memoir in relation to his affairs ;
but as he received no satisfactory reply he eventually
retired to Clichy to live in his brother's household there.
Throngs of fashionable people came to call, but Charles
had no wish to see them, and kept himself as secluded
as he could, obsessed with his one imperative idea.

He did, however, consent to show himself occasionally,
and appeared at the opera on the 30th of the month, to
be greeted with loud and prolonged cheering from a
crowded house. At the end of the performance he was
cheered again, and whenever he appeared in the streets
of Paris the people rushed to acclaim him. He had
become the popular idol of the city.

Feeling the need of advice and help, he wrote to Sir Thomas Sheridan, who was in Rome, begging him to join him ; but on the 2nd of December his father's secretary, Edgar, wrote to announce Sir Thomas's death. He died of an apoplectic fit after a violent quarrel with Lord Elcho. Whether Sheridan would have been of much use is a matter of conjecture ; certainly, however, his death led to unfortunate consequences, for now there were only O'Sullivan and George Kelly, whom Charles had appointed his secretary, and who assiduously thrust his advice upon the Prince.

It was, in every way, disastrous advice. Charles had shown his weakness before—a fatal weakness, largely responsible for the disasters of his campaign. He clung to old friendships, however unworthy they proved. He had clung strenuously to Sheridan and O'Sullivan and Murray of Broughton, in face of many proofs of their incompetence or personal interest ; and now, in Paris, he refused to be shifted from his friendship with his two remaining Irish favourites.

Lochiel remonstrated. James also remonstrated, pointing out how wrong-headed Kelly had proved himself on so many occasions. Charles refused to listen.

The court moved to Versailles, where Charles and Henry were made very welcome ; but Charles was rapidly losing his temper. After all he had been through he was in no mood for further procrastination, and the terrible stories reaching him from Scotland confirmed him in the need for speedy action, if only to secure terms for his devoted followers there.

James, growing alarmed, wrote more and more often, counselling caution and moderation ; but Kelly, who was cordially disliked at court, undid whatever good these letters might achieve, and out of spite egged him on to defiance. Charles accordingly presented Louis with a new memorial, designed to force him to show his hand. He pointed out bluntly that Scotland was being deliberately destroyed, the innocent as well as the guilty

suffering without discrimination, so that hatred of the
London government and sympathy with the Jacobites
had spread rapidly ; that the country might thus be
united behind him if he landed there again quickly, but
that every delay meant further weakening of the Scottish
nation ; equally bluntly he laid the blame for his failure
at the door of France, which had not supported him in
the critical moments of the campaign.   With timely
French aid he could have marched on swiftly from Derby
and taken London.   He did not mince his words, and he
ended by demanding eighteen or twenty thousand men
with whom to renew the conflict.

Up to this point he had acted with the greatest
moderation ; but since no notice was taken of this last
memorial he lost his temper altogether—and Kelly,
spoiling for a fight with the French court, spurred him
on.   Louis had granted the sum of sixty-two thousand
nine hundred livres for the relief of the Prince's adherents
who had reached France, and now he generously offered
Charles a very handsome pension.   Charles rejected this.

His father was seriously perturbed.   He understood
far better than Charles the anomalous position of exiled
royalty, and had taught himself to curb the fierce Stuart
pride and avoid giving offence as far as he could.   But
Charles, who could be so tactful and had always been
so considerate of others, was changing noticeably.

He had been brought up in the hope of one day
ascending the throne of Britain.   From an early age he
had set out to prepare himself for that—and for the
campaign that would be necessary first.   All his youth
had been devoted to this one great aim.   Now the
campaign was over ; and even if it had been completely
successful the reaction must have set in.

He could not believe that he had failed.   He persisted
in regarding all that had happened as a temporary
setback, and he remained obsessed with the only purpose
of his existence.   Robbed of that, he would have nothing.
He had proved himself a man of action ; enforced

inactivity preyed on his mind and began, by degrees, to ruin his temper ; and there was always George Kelly, with his spiteful dislike of the French court, to goad him.

Yet he waited two whole months before showing any open sign of his growing exasperation. Then, on the 12th of January, 1747, he wrote to Louis, pointing out that all his thoughts were of a new campaign, that he had no personal interests at all and that any suggestions for a pension had been made without his knowledge. If Louis was not yet prepared to do anything for him in the one direction in which he wanted help, then he would retire from Paris and wait quietly until Louis considered the time was ripe. When that happened, he would be ready at a moment's notice.

Lochiel, hearing of this decision, was seriously annoyed with Charles. His mind was fixed upon renewing the attempt in the late spring, and, tortured ceaselessly by the thought of the sufferings of his people, he was burning with impatience to get back to his own country—and with sufficient force to put a stop to the slaughter and persecution and, even if no hope remained of restoring the Stuarts, at least compelling the government to grant proper terms. The Prince's proposed retirement from the court meant the indefinite postponement of a new attempt. Lochiel saw clearly that the government was bent upon depopulating the Highlands—a policy which London persisted in for more than a century thereafter —and delay meant not only the ruin of Charles's hopes but the total destruction of Clan Cameron.

Lord Ogilvy had been given a regiment by the French king ; Lochiel, learning that Charles proposed to secure him a similar appointment, angrily refused. It would be tantamount to declaring publicly that he had no hope of returning to his own country.

" However much Lord Ogilvy may incline to make a figure in France," he told the Prince flatly, " my ambition is to serve my country, or perish with it."

But Charles persisted, and as he raised the matter with

the king, and Louis promptly agreed, Lochiel had no
option, out of respect for them both, but to accept.
All the same, he qualified his acceptance by declaring his
determination to share the fate of his people. " If they
are to be sacrificed to the vengeance of the government
I mean to fall along with them."

For that reason he did his utmost to dissuade the
Prince from leaving Paris. But Charles had made up
his mind. He meant to go to Spain and see what could
be done there—and he had no intention of telling anyone
what his plans were.

Accordingly he quitted Paris at the end of the month ;
but before he went he gave certain instructions to his
brother. If Lord George Murray should appear in Paris,
he was to have him arrested at once. Kelly and O'Sullivan
had succeeded at last in persuading him that Lord George
had been a traitor to him and solely responsible for the
failure of the rebellion. His father was greatly shocked.

" By what Bramston* says, I am sorry to find that
you have not been pleased with him (Lord George
Murray), but tho' I questioned Bramston much about
him, yet I own I don't see any motive to suspect his
fidelity and loyalty . . . considering his birth, and
the figure he made in your service, and that you had
never writ to me about him yourself, I thought it would
be very wrong in me not to receive him with all kindness,
and even distinction. . . . I must do him the justice
to say that he never speaks of you but with great respect
and even eulogy."

There is something vaguely apologetic in James's
letters to his son, as if he stood much in awe of that
stirring young man ; but could still, when occasion
demanded, be very much of a severe father, issuing orders
that his son more often than not entirely ignored.

One day a letter came from Henry, enclosing one from
his father in which James told him that he proposed to
send him to Spain. Charles read it angrily, for it cut

* The name by which O'Sullivan was known in correspondence.

right across his own plans. He brushed aside Henry's affectionate note, regretting that he would thus be so far away from him, and he wrote back petulantly that he meant to go to Spain himself, and had not told his father for fear of being refused permission. Henry must not on any account leave Paris until they saw how Charles's visit to Madrid fared.

Henry wrote back dutifully. Of course he would do as his brother asked, and he was sure, he added mildly, that their father would agree this was best when he heard of Charles's trip. Henry had not yet realised that his brother, who had been so fond of him once, had lost all patience with him and had begun positively to dislike him, largely because of his docility and mildness.

Kelly and the good Dr. Cameron accompanied the Prince from Avignon to Madrid ; but it proved a wasted journey. Their reception was cold and formal. On the 6th of March Charles asked the minister, Caravajal, for ships, arms and food, and commissions for three Scots regiments to be raised, but the reply was not encouraging. His master, said Caravajal, had no ships to spare, but he would give orders for thirty thousand fusils and ten thousand sabres to be manufactured immediately, and a supply of grain got ready ; also, he would speak to the king about the regiments. Charles retired to Guadalajara to await developments—and learned that the king had at last agreed, provided that only Scots were recruited in the Scots regiments. It was an impossible condition, since there were few Scotsmen in Spain at the time—and Charles was forced to take the hint.

He reported to his father, and received a reply by no means cordial :

" I am much more concerned than surprised you had not a better reception in Spain ; but I am in hopes your going thither will be of no ill consequence, provided you manage your matters in a proper manner on your return to Paris."

With this rebuke in his pocket, Charles returned to

France. Lochiel had written to Avignon remonstrating with him for remaining away from the capital. Peace was in the air and France eager for it. Charles ought to be in Paris to protect his interests, and Lochiel, knowing what peace in Europe would mean, proposed an immediate return to Scotland to renew the campaign, if France would agree to supply even a few battalions of foot and some artillery.

Charles, hastening back to Paris by the 24th of March, renewed his application for help. He got only the customary evasive reply.

He refused to be discouraged. But he was soon to be faced with a new exasperation—this time from his own family.

He had treated the gentle and kindly young Henry very badly indeed, neglecting him for weeks on end ; and suddenly he discovered in April, 1747, that Henry was no longer in Paris. He had gone off—without so much as a " by your leave." Charles was furious. Had Henry no sense of the obligations of a Prince towards his elder brother? Charles had several times made peevish references to Henry in his letters to his father, and now he wrote very angrily indeed. James wrote back, with the pawky humour he often displayed, that certainly it was wrong of Henry to go away without taking leave of his brother, but that he could not blame him in the circumstances !

Charles, still stubbornly refusing to accept the pension Louis offered him, had got into financial difficulties. James had sent him an order for fifteen thousand livres on Waters, his Paris banker, but had hinted that he presumed Charles had some private means since he despised Louis's offer ; he also instructed O'Bryan to draw the pension and apply a third of it to Henry's interest and pay the rest, from time to time, into O'Sullivan's hands. Charles, seeing through this simple deception, would not touch a penny piece of it.

James was by no means a rich man ; but he had always

been a strictly honourable one, and he made shift to repay every debt his son had contracted, beginning with the money advanced by those two generous privateers, Walsh and Ratcliffe, who had furnished the ships for the voyage to Scotland. All the sums advanced during the campaign, as well as certain sums that had been intended as gifts, were dutifully repaid out of the Old Pretender's rather meagre coffers.

But Charles had his own reasons apart from pride for refusing the King of France's bounty. He believed it would injure him with his English friends—and he was becoming more and more aggressively British. In this attitude Kelly supported him, and as more and more open offence was being given to the French court, Lochiel and Drummond of Bochaldy, seriously perturbed, got Sempil to write to James protesting against the pernicious influences surrounding the Prince. James, growing more and more annoyed with this impetuous son of his, seized upon the quarrel with Henry, and referring to some more complaints Charles had made against his brother, wrote : " What you now write to me is manifestly the product of Kelly's malice. . . . As long as you are directed or influenced by him, depend upon it nothing will go well with you, and you will never have a moment's quiet yourself."

As if to point the object lesson, new negotiations which Charles had started, following a proposal by the Marquis de Puyzieux to embark a force for Scotland on the dissolution of the British parliament, fell through entirely—because, it was bluntly hinted, the persons in whom Charles reposed his confidence, that is, Kelly and O'Sullivan, were considered unworthy of trust.

Even this was not enough to disabuse the Prince's mind, and he only clung all the more stubbornly to the men against whom everyone seemed to turn. His father's protests were in vain. Then, on the 13th of June, James wrote from Albano. Henry had been offered, and had accepted, promotion to a cardinalate.

Charles was stunned. He shut himself up in his own room in a storm of grief and rage, for he saw, beyond any possibility of equivocation, that all hope was lost now. England would never accept a royal family thus closely bound to Rome.

So this was why Henry had slipped away from Paris without a word ! He had gone to Rome to discuss the matter with his father, and the pair of them had made their decisions without consulting him ! It seemed the last straw, and Charles, emerging from his room, gave orders that his brother's name should never again be mentioned in his hearing. As for his father . . . he had paid little heed to him for some years past ; he would play less heed in future.

The fact was that neither James nor Henry had any great desire for a throne. The Old Pretender had had his day ; he no longer cherished any ambition for himself. As for Henry, affairs of state were not for him. Gentle, kindly, scholarly, and deeply religious, he had little interest in worldly advancement and was happy to devote all his energy to his chosen vocation.

It was at this particular juncture, while Charles was still seething over what he considered his brother's duplicity, that Lord George Murray arrived in Paris.

Charles was at St. Ouen, and thither Lord George proposed to go, to seek a reconciliation with the Prince. This was on the 10th of July, by which time Charles had received several exhortations from his father to treat Lord George well ; but, his mind wholly poisoned by the insinuations of Kelly and O'Sullivan, he had turned a deaf ear to these entreaties ; and now Lord George, before he could set out for St. Ouen, received a visitor.

Stafford, a member of the Prince's household, called upon him and told him bluntly that it was the Prince's wish that he should not appear at St. Ouen, but should leave Paris as soon as possible.

Lord George, saddened by this further proof of the complete ascendancy over the Prince's mind gained by his unworthy favourites, quitted Paris immediately, and made no further effort to renew the old association.

It was being gradually borne in upon Charles that diplomacy was not his *forte*. The French king and queen were genuinely fond of him, but the French ministers were far too adept and adroit to allow him to benefit from that fact. They had used him all along as a goad with which to prick England in the flank; had it suited their book they might have used him as the spearhead of a direct attack, but the restoration of the Stuarts was a matter of complete indifference to them.

So Charles appealed to the aged Earl Mareschal. No man, he wrote, could help him so effectively as his old and tried friend who had spent a lifetime in diplomacy ; but the old and tried friend wrote back positively refusing to abandon his retirement and return to the court of France. He was, he declared, done with all that ; Charles would have to find someone else.

He was thrown back upon Kelly and O'Sullivan, and the consequences were disastrous.

While the war lasted, the French court kept up appearances with the exiled family, and reaped great benefit thereby, for the government in London was kept in constant fear of invasion and dared not send enough troops to the Continent to prosecute the war effectively. But the war had dragged on long enough. The French navy had been almost obliterated, the French exchequer drained, and early in 1748 the French government proposed negotiations for peace. The congress opened in due course at Aix-la-Chapelle in March.

Charles gave orders to the Sieur Roettier to strike a medal bearing his head, with the inscription : *Carolus Walliae Princeps* (Charles Prince of Wales) and on the reverse Britannia and a fleet of warships with the motto: *Amor et Spes Britanniae*—" the love and hope of Britain."

The sensation it created was tremendous. Charles was still the idol of the Parisian populace, acclaimed wherever he went ; but the medal gave deep offence. The Prince of Conti, encountering Charles one day in the Luxembourg Gardens, stopped politely to chat and then, with a sneer in his pleasantry, remarked :

" The device of that medal of yours is not just so applicable as some people might at first suppose. The British navy has not shown any particular friendship for your royal highness."

"That is true," Charles retorted. "But nevertheless I am the friend of the navy against all its enemies, as I shall always look upon the glory of England as my own—and her glory is in her navy."

During the negotiations Charles continued to go to court now and then, but suddenly, learning that the preliminaries had been signed some time ago, he gave up attendance altogether. Everyone expected that he would leave the country, since France was once more about to sacrifice the interests of the Stuarts to her own ; but Charles thought differently.

He took a lease of a splendid mansion on the Quai de Theatre—to be handy, he said, for the Opera, the playhouse, and other centres. He appeared gayer than ever before, and when the congress was mentioned in his hearing he affected not to notice. The stubborn streak had come uppermost.

All the same he drew up a protest against any clauses in the forthcoming treaty that might be prejudicial to his own rights, and he issued this without waiting to consult his father, who meantime had drawn up and issued a similar document on behalf of the family.

The terms of the treaty soon became known. Louis had been compelled to agree to expelling Charles from France. He hinted as much, as delicately as he could, to the Prince ; but Charles blandly ignored the warning and remained in Paris. The Marquis de Puyzieux wrote more bluntly to the Prince, and demanded a reply. Charles, growing more stubborn, sent back an evasive answer the same day—and stayed.

Nothing more happened until October, when the

Treaty of Aix-la-Chapelle was signed. Louis had been actively looking out for a suitable refuge for his beloved Charles, and, knowing he had sworn not to return to Italy, directed his envoy in Switzerland to ask for a residence for Charles in Fribourg. The regency complied, whereupon Mr. Barnaby, the British minister, lodged a protest so violently worded that he was very nearly expelled from Switzerland. Charles would be welcome in Fribourg.

Cardinal de Tencin was the next person to whom was entrusted the delicate task of shifting Charles from Paris. He set about it with the greatest diplomacy and kindness —and came away without the slightest satisfaction. Charles, having suffered sufficient disasters through France, was not at all disposed to make things easy for the French ministers now !

Louis waited patiently a further fortnight ; then, as there was still no sign of Charles relenting, he sent the Duc de Gesvres, governor of Paris, to see what he could do with the obstinate young man. The Duc, not so diplomatic as the cardinal, spoke more bluntly—and got a blunt reply.

" I have no intention of quitting Paris," Charles told him. " There is a treaty between myself and the French king prior to this Treaty of Aix-la-Chapelle, and neither he nor I can depart from that with honour."

Thereafter he made a point of appearing in public on every possible occasion, to the utter fury of the two hostages whom England had given as security for the return to France of Cape Breton—hostages whose mere presence showed how little the word of England was trusted. They complained of the insult to their sovereign that Charles's presence implied, and they demanded his immediate removal under the terms of the treaty.

The Duc de Gesvres went a second and a third time to remonstrate with Charles without result, except that Charles sent him a very explicit statement of his intention to stay, since the Treaty of Fontainebleau was still binding.

Louis found his patience wearing thin. He hated the idea of having to take violent measures, especially in view of the solemn contract he had entered into when Charles was in Scotland, so he sent a courier off to Rome. Perhaps Charles's father would be able to do something ! James promptly wrote to Louis, enclosing a letter from the Prince which Louis was to read and pass on.

James, always able to wield an effective pen, complained briefly of his son's conduct towards himself, and went on to say that he saw him standing on the brink of a precipice from which it was his duty to pull him back, and there he therefore felt obliged to order him as his father and king to conform himself without delay to the wishes of the French king, by leaving his dominions with a good grace.

Louis sent the Duc de Gesvres to deliver this letter, along with one from himself containing a blank order to be filled up by the Prince himself for a yearly allowance.

" I want no pecuniary favours from his majesty," Charles retorted roundly, " and it is not consistent with honour to comply with his demand to leave France."

The Duc, disturbed, begged him to reconsider.

" My mind is made up," Charles replied impatiently. " In future I shall decline to receive any communications except from the king himself."

" What," cried the Duc, scandalised and sarcastic, " do you suppose, sir, that his majesty will come in person to the Quai de Theatre ? "

" In short, sir," Charles flung back at him, " I have nothing further to say than what I have said already. Pardon me—I have some business."

And he left the astounded duke to make his way out.

The whole of Paris was talking. Gleefully people exchanged the latest news of this bold young man who defied the king in his own capital ; and as he was the idol of the mob, his appearance at the theatre practically put an end to any performance. The audience rose and cheered him to the echo.

The controversy raged with increasing acerbity, and Charles alone seemed unmoved, treating the whole business lightly. But this state of affairs could not go on. The government must carry out its obligations, and Louis reluctantly signed an order for his arrest.

" Poor prince ! " he declared, as he took up his pen. " How difficult it is for a king to be a true friend ! "

That was at three o'clock in the afternoon. By evening all Paris knew about it, and it was brought to Charles's ears. He refused to believe it.

" An idle romance," he said contemptuously. " They know I will obey my father."

But when? He showed no signs of making preparations, and on the morning of the 10th of December, as he was walking in the Tuileries, a nobleman of his acquaintance came up to him.

" You will certainly be seized to-day if you do not make an immediate departure," he warned.

Charles waved the alarming news away, and turned to one of his attendants.

" Hire me a box at the opera for this evening," he ordered, and strolled on.

The government felt forced to act. But it would take no risks, knowing well how Paris felt. The least to be expected was a serious riot if Charles was touched. So twelve hundred of the guards were drawn out during the day and posted in the court of the Palais Royal ; grenadiers in cuirasses and helmets filled the corridors of the opera house ; cordons of police were thrown all round it, in all the streets leading to it, with orders to stop every coach.

Six sergeants of grenadiers were given orders to seize the Prince. Two companies of grenadiers were posted in the courtyard of the kitchens, where the Duc de Biron, colonel of the French Guards, waited in disguise in a coach to watch the issue. The famous horse-guards, the Musketeers, were ordered to be ready to mount instantly, and troops were posted along the road from the Palais

Royal to Vincennes.   Hatchets and scaling-ladders were
prepared for breaking into the Prince's residence, lock-
smiths were ordered to be in attendance, and a physician
and three surgeons were brought on the scene to deal
with the casualties.   There was no saying what would
happen when they tried to capture the man who had
eluded the whole British army for five months !

In point of fact, the government assumed that the
Parisians themselves would get out of hand and rescue
the Prince.

Charles remained serene.   Notes showered upon him
from all his friends warning him of the preparations ;
he enjoyed them thoroughly, and, punctually to the
minute, set out in his coach at a quarter past five for the
opera house.

In the Rue St. Honore a friendly voice called out a
warning that the streets were blocked ; but Charles told
his coachman to drive on.   The coach entered the
cul-de-sac, and immediately a barrier was thrown across
behind it, the doors of the opera house were closed, and
as he descended from the coach Charles was seized by
the six grenadier sergeants, who had disguised themselves
as tradesmen.

They swept him off his feet, hustled him through the
porte cochere into the courtyard of the Palais Royal, and
there M. de Vaudreuil, major of the Blue Guards,
approached him.

" Monseigneur, I arrest you in the name of the king,
my master."

Charles looked at him coolly.

" The manner," he said quietly, " seems a little too
violent."

He was carried indoors, where he mildly presented
his sword, and was searched for weapons—two pocket
pistols and a penknife.   Then he was bound with silk
cord.   On seeing the cord, he offered his parole, but the
Duc de Biron would take no chances and, securely bound,
he was carried out to a hired coach and driven under a

very strong escort to the castle of Vincennes, where he was confined in a small apartment in the tower.

His only companion here was Neil MacEachan, who had been with him on the perilous journey from Uist to Skye, and had come to France with him.

" We have known poorer quarters," he remarked to Neil, with a rueful smile ; but as for the indignity offered him he remained completely composed. The disgrace attending it, he pointed out to Vaudreuil, could only affect not himself but the king of France.

Parisians were furious. By morning, the whole city was plastered with lampoons castigating king and ministers for their treatment of the Prince. One particularly furious one took the form of an order from King George to his " viceroy," Louis de Bourbon, commanding him to seize, and if necessary to bind, Charles Edward Stuart and conduct him out of France ; and if Louis continued to please his master, the King of England would allow him to go on ruling as viceroy in France !

Charles, however, remained unruffled, although he wrote to Louis protesting about being closely confined, and on the 14th of December was allowed out for a few hours to walk in the gardens. He then gave his parole to leave France without guards, and was released at seven o'clock on Sunday morning, the 15th.

He drove by chaise to Fontainebleau, whence he sent off a facetious note to M. de Boile at Paris, reporting his head still safely on his shoulders ; then he travelled by easy stages to Avignon, which, since it belonged to the Papal See, was not part of the royal domains of France.

He had chosen this destination deliberately, for Avignon was in reality in the heart of France. It was one more gesture of defiance, but one which Louis could not counter ; and before any move could be made to induce the Pope to order him to leave he startled the whole of Europe by disappearing for several years.

He was next heard of, authentically, in London.

CHAPTER TWENTY-ONE

POOR VISION OF A MAN

THE CHAISE bowled along the Lyons road. Charles and his friend, Colonel Henry Goring, disguised as French officers just released from service, sat back enjoying the swift motion, and the feeling of playing truant, and characteristically the name appearing on the Prince's papers was M. le Comte d'Espoir. It is said that the hope he cherished at the moment was of a matrimonial alliance with the Landgrave of Hess Dermstadt, who had a charming daughter, the Princess Charlotte Louisa ; but if this were the case the Prince's father certainly knew nothing about it. He had once tried to exert parental authority and induce his son to make a suitable match, but the lady proposed, a daughter of the Duke of Modena, was not Charles's idea of a wife and he managed to avoid the issue.

Now, quitting Avignon on the 28th of February, 1749, he may have gone in search of a wife—or he may have gone simply because he was too restless to settle down.

After reaching Lyons he drove to Strasbourg ; but he was back in Paris in May. He had behaved composedly enough when he was arrested, but he never forgot the insult, and it may have given him some satisfaction to move about at will and in complete defiance of the French.

Where he went was never known, except that he spent a good deal of time on the estates of his old friend, the Duc de Bouillon, roaming the wide and solitary forest of Ardennes and solacing his energetic spirit by hunting wolves and bears—the most dangerous pursuit he could find. He rarely bothered to write to his father, but James's secretary, Edgar, kept up a persistent correspondence with him. Edgar referred to him, with facetious affection, as " the dear wild man."

Then, in September, 1750, Lady Primrose, an ardent Jacobite and popular hostess, had a shock. One day, at her house in Essex Street, Strand, a servant announced a visitor whose name was unfamiliar, and a tall youngish man walked into the room. Her other guests glanced up from their game of cards with quick interest, and the stranger, after greeting his hostess with complete ease and charm, took up his position almost directly in front of a large portrait of Prince Charles Edward Stuart that hung upon the wall.

Lady Primrose, frightened out of her wits, could do nothing about it. Her visitor behaved in the most natural manner, while startling suspicions crowded into the minds of her guests.

She sent an urgent message to another Jacobite, Dr. King, Principal of St. Mary's Hall, Oxford, and he hurried round immediately. She had got rid of her guests, and led him, when he arrived, to a dressing-room, where she presented him to her visitor, who smiled charmingly and promptly got down to business.

He had come over to sound his friends, to investigate the possibility of another rising, and to select suitable spots for landing arms and ammunition ! Dr. King, flabbergasted, felt terrified—and indignant. It appeared that the Prince's friends on the Continent, wearying of exile, had concocted a scatter-brained idea of making a new attempt to restore the Stuarts—and themselves—to Britain. Dr. King hastily set about disabusing him.

Charles, realising that he had been completely

deceived, stayed only five days. He visited Dr. King at his lodgings, and drank tea with him, the doctor having almost a heart attack afterwards when his servant remarked how wonderfully his guest resembled the exiled Prince !

He wandered openly about London, took a turn in Pall Mall and strolled around St. James's, which he was seeing for the first time. He even inspected the defences of the Tower of London. Then he went back to France.

Oddly enough, he was in no way disheartened. He decided to look for help elsewhere, and pitched on Berlin and Stockholm as the likeliest places. So in June, 1751, Colonel Goring was sent to Berlin, where the Earl Mareschal had been living for some years past and through his brother, Field-Marshal Keith, was on excellent terms at the Prussian court. But Goring was back in Paris in September to report a negative result of his visits.

The pair started their wanderings again, and on the 5th of April, 1752, Charles was seen by Donald Mackintosh at Middelburg, where he stayed four days. The same year he formally renounced the Roman Catholic religion and got rid of those of his followers who were not Protestants. The story, not, however, sufficiently authenticated, is that he made the formal declaration in a little church in Gray's Inn Lane or in the Strand, under his own name of Charles Edward Stuart—which would at least be in keeping with his character.

Characteristically, too, he sent orders in November, 1753, for the dismissal of all his servants at Avignon who were Papists ! It was a gesture whose significance could not escape His Holiness, or those devout Catholics, James and Henry ; but Charles was fixed in a mood of defiance to the whole world.

§

In 1749 Dr. Cameron had made the perilous journey to

Scotland in order to bring away a large sum of money which Charles had left in the care of MacPherson of Cluny. In 1753 he went back, for more obscure motives, although there seems to have been some design to bring about another insurrection. Unhappily he was discovered, arrested, and sent to London for trial. Being convicted, he was executed at Tyburn, a piece of characteristic harshness which even the most zealous Whigs felt was nursing old scores a little too long. His fortitude and calmness were greatly admired, and Louis gave his widow a pension of twelve hundred livres, and his two sons, who were officers in his service, pensions of four hundred livres each in addition to their pay.

This was a serious loss to Charles, for Lochiel, too, was dead—he had lived less than three years in exile ; but until 1754 Charles maintained a regular correspondence with the Jacobite faction in England.

He was lonely, embittered, and no longer in the best of health. Perhaps he felt the need of someone to look after him. At any rate, he wrote to Clementina Walkinshaw, reminding her of her promise ; and Clementina packed up at once and hastened to join him.

Charles had never been much of a success as a diplomatist ; he was even less successful as a lover. He had no experience of women, no notion of how to treat them in any but formal relationships, and no patience whatever. Men he understood, better and better, and among men he had always been amazingly popular ; but women were beyond him, and it was not long before the good Clementina repented of her bargain.

Others repented of it too ; for Clementina had a sister who had become a lady-in-waiting in the household of Frederick, Prince of Wales. When word got about that Charles had taken a mistress, and that that mistress was Clementina Walkinshaw, there was panic among the English Jacobites. They sent a Mr. MacNamara, a gentleman of considerable tact and sense, to reason with him, and Mr. MacNamara did all he could.

Clementina, he pointed out, might well be a spy. In fact, he was convinced she must be ; and Charles was completely under her thumb. He told her everything. It was highly improper that anyone so suspect should be admitted to his household.

Charles saw red—just as his father James had done over Mrs. Hay.

" I have no violent passion for Miss Walkinshaw," he retorted angrily. " Not even any particular regard for her. I could see her removed without any concern. But I will *not* receive directions for the regulation of my private conduct from any man alive ! "

MacNamara tried to calm him down, but Charles had stood more than enough, and told him so bluntly ; whereupon the unhappy envoy exclaimed :

" What has your family done, sir, thus to draw down the vengeance of heaven on every branch of it through so many ages ? "

He went back to London and reported ; and the Jacobite gentlemen, many of them men of fortune and high position, decided to break with Charles forthwith. The Earl Mareschal, who had come to Paris as ambassador of the King of Prussia, heard from MacNamara the results of his interviews with the Prince, and made up his own mind. Had MacNamara succeeded in persuading Charles to dismiss Clementina, he was prepared to enter his household and work again on his behalf. Now, however, he was disgusted, made up his mind to have nothing more to do with him, and wrote him a stern letter.

" My heart is broke enough," wrote Charles in reply, " without that you should finish it."

But indeed he was fast losing all his friends.

§

The following year he was back in France again, full of plans and energy. War between England and France

seemed inevitable, and here surely was his chance ! But
it petered out. Months of weary negotiations, of half-
promises that meant nothing—all the old frustration and
misery of diplomacy and duplicity ; they led him
nowhere except to further heartbreak.

On the 15th of August, 1755, a conference was held at
Paris, in which the emissaries of the English Jacobites
did not mince their words. They roundly condemned
the Prince's way of life, disapproved of his conduct in
a hundred particulars, and told him so to his face. He
told them, equally bluntly, that reason, he hoped, would
always prevail with him, but that threats never would ;
and the conference came to nothing.

He still wrote very occasionally to his father, whom
he addressed, with more understanding of him than he
had shown before, as " honest man," a term which gave
that old unhappy exile a moment of rare pleasure ; but
James had never outgrown his stern sense of duty, and
wrote back, earnestly :

" Do you rightly understand the extensive sense of
honour and duty from which you say you will never go
astray? If you can keep up to that rule, you will then
be really an honest man, which is the new name you give
me, and with which I am much pleased, since it is a title
I value more than all those which vanity can desire, or
flattery invent. It is a title we are all obliged to pretend
to, and which we may all, without vanity, think we
deserve, and unless we deserve it, we, in reality, can
neither be happy in the next world, nor even in this,
because peace and tranquillity of mind is only the share
of honest men. The best I can therefore make you, is
that you may yourself long deserve and enjoy that title.
It would be the most effectual means of drawing down
God's blessing upon you."

Now, with one more failure to add to the long
melancholy tale of failures, Charles went back to Italy,
soured and embittered and growing ever more touchy.
He was very much alone, for he had lost even his friend

Goring, who could not abide Clementina and told him so very bluntly. They quarrelled over her, and Goring left. Life was growing daily harsher for the Prince.

Two years later the French court offered him a military command for the projected attack on English-held Minorca, a subtle insult which he resented bitterly. " I will no longer serve as a mere bugbear," he retorted angrily, and so added one more black mark against himself at the French court.

In 1760 the monotony and wretchedness of his life was relieved a little by the birth of his daughter Charlotte; but even this could not save the wreck of his domestic existence. Clementina, who had stood all she could bear of his strange temper, left him and took refuge with her little daughter in a convent.

" I am always in dread of my life from your violent passions," she wrote to him, excusing her conduct, and it seems that at this period Charles's mind had indeed grown somewhat unhinged. The eagle was beating his wings in vain inside the cage in which life had imprisoned him. He had known only one brief spell of liberty, and all the rest could only be unhappiness.

During his campaign he had rarely touched liquor ; during his wanderings in the Isles and the Highlands he had drunk a great deal, often because there was no food to be had and some stimulant was necessary. But it is one thing to drink a bottle of brandy or whisky out on the hillside, in the midst of tremendous exertions and exposure ; quite another to take even half that amount while leading an ordinary sedentary life. And although there is no evidence that he ever drank to excess in an age when to be drunk was to be fashionable, he certainly injured his health by this customary indulgence of the times—and injured his reputation still more ; for the English agents, Walton and the rest, were assiduous as ever in spreading all manner of stories to his detriment, and a legend of debauchery was easy to create. The proof of its falseness lies simply in the fact that he went on living, and remained remarkably active almost to the end.

His father, however, was ailing, and for the last two years of his life was bedridden. He died on the 31st of December, 1766, and, after lying in state for three days, was interred in St. Peter's. He left his real estate, which yielded fifty thousand crowns annually, to Charles, exclusive of pensions, and a box containing the Sobieski crown jewels ; the Stuart family jewels were divided equally between the two brothers.

From the many acts of individual kindness done by James towards his adherents and those around him, from his invincible honesty and sense of decency and right behaviour, he had shown himself a man of benevolent and estimable character, in spite of a lifetime of adversity. Although overshadowed always by his energetic and brilliant son, so that his private life and character received little attention, he was, undoubtedly, the better man, and his kindliness and sense of high duty shone in the character of his younger son, who was always ready at any time to forgive his brother and be reconciled.

Charles was now the direct claimant to the throne of Britain ; but by this time he had entirely abandoned any thought of a restoration. After his father's death he returned to Rome, where he was hailed by both the aristocracy and the populace as Charles III, and made much of. His old friend Lumisden reported : " He charms everyone that approaches him "—something of the old lovable Prince Charles still lingered in the soured and embittered man.

Henry sought a reconciliation, and the pair, finding perhaps some points of contact as they aged, were to be seen together once more. They drove in Henry's carriage, and the gentle, kindly churchman gave him the right-hand place, thus bringing down upon himself the reproach of the Pope, who pointed out punctiliously that a cardinal should not yield the right-hand place to any but reigning monarchs.

Charles appeared more often now in public, dined out, went to the opera and the theatre ; then he revisited his old friend the Grand Duke of Tuscany, near Florence, and went next to Albano, where, among the familiar scenes of his stirring boyhood, he recaptured some of the joy of life.

The shooting season opened, and the old energetic, tireless hunter reappeared. Once more the crack shot was " papping them down " as he had done, to the amazement of all, in Scotland. Once more he savoured the keen joy of the mountain air, the long hard days with his gun, the freedom and the sense of release of those arduous expeditions.

In 1770 he was seen in Rome by an interested English lady, who wrote of him that he was a man " naturally above middle size, but stoops excessively ; he appears bloated and red in the face, his countenance heavy and sleepy. . . . His complexion is of the fair tint, his eyes blue " (but some observers said brown ; the matter has never been decided), " his hair light brown, and the contour of his face a long oval ; he is by no means thin, has a noble person and a graceful manner. . . . Upon the whole he has a melancholy, mortified appearance."

Poor Charles, it would have been a miracle if he could have looked otherwise. The man of action had had a quarter of a century in which to run to seed.

In 1772 the court of Versailles did him the worst turn they had yet achieved. They conceived the notion of marrying him off. It would scarcely suit France's book to allow the Stuart line to die out ; Charles must take a wife and have a son and heir. The lady chosen for this purpose was the Princess Louise Maximiliana Caroline of Stolberg Gedern, a sprightly young woman with a mind of her own. Versailles could not have made a more unsuitable choice.

The lady, young and lovely, was a blonde, with " deep blue eyes, a nose slightly turned up, and a complexion dazzling fair " ; her family might be impoverished, but there was no lack of looks or pride about Louise.

Charles, now living as the Count of Albany, the title by which he had been known as a youth, spent the few months before his marriage with his friend, the Grand Duke of Tuscany. There had been a wedding by proxy in Paris, and Louise, like Clementina before her, set out on the long journey through the Austrian dominions to Italy. On Good Friday, 1772, she and her husband were formally united at Macerata ; but the Pope refused them royal honours ; Clementina and her daughter were living in Rome, and in 1774 the pair removed to Florence.

Charles had been too long a bachelor to make a satisfactory husband now. He had never felt drawn to women, had always preferred the company of men, and had lately developed a strong aversion to women in general, of whom, at the very time of his marriage, he wrote some harsh and unkind things. There was no possibility that the match could turn out well, and Charles and his bride soon both repented of their rashness.

The marriage dragged on for a number of years, however, during which Charles treated his beautiful and accomplished young wife with scant consideration—and received even less in return. Inevitably Louise turned away from her middle-aged spouse and found consolation elsewhere. In 1777 she met the great Italian dramatist Alfieri, and the pair promptly fell in love. Whether she was unfaithful to Charles remains a matter of pure speculation ; but she certainly appealed to the Pope against her husband, and the Pope, who had no reason to love the soured and sharp-tempered heretic, believed everything she liked to say against him and took her part—even when Alfieri openly accompanied her to Rome.

Finally, in 1780, she left Charles and took up her residence with brother Henry before proceeding to Paris, where Alfieri ultimately joined her. Charles had to pay over to her half his pension, so once more he was financially in difficulties.

Now, all alone, ageing and unhappy, Charles looked

round in desperation for a friend. He found one who was to make his last declining years at least bearable— his daughter Charlotte.

She was a gentle, kindly creature, who bore her father no illwill, and at twenty-five she was ready to devote her life to him. They went to live in Rome, and visitors came occasionally to call upon them. Charlotte was studious of his health and set herself always to lead the conversation away from the one subject that was sure to upset him —the mention of the Highlands.

Always it roused him, and for days after he would be restless and deeply saddened, for the sufferings of the Highlands, the terrible consequences of the Forty-Five, were abundantly clear. Gently Charlotte warned his visitors to avoid the subject, and when they did not she quickly intervened.

So the end approached for this " poor vision of a man," as the English agent called the ageing Prince.

Through his settled melancholy there ran now some sense of peace at last, a cherished companionship that relieved his misanthropy and the terrible burden of his disappointed life ; but it was not to last for long. His health had deteriorated, he suffered much from dropsy, and in January, 1788, he was stricken with paralysis. The splendid virile body that had carried him through such desperate adventures and had known such privations and had triumphed over them all was reduced at last to impotence.

For three weeks he lingered on, helpless and prostrate ; then, still with a box of money—twelve thousand sequins —under his bed in readiness against the time when he should be called to St. James's, he died ; and the faithful Charlotte, whom he had legitimised, followed him to the grave within a year.

Henry lived on into a gentle old age, dying at the age of eighty-two ; and the race of Stuart was extinct.

THE END